Alfred Russel Wallace:

The Journey of a Lifetime

Alfred Russel Wallace soon after his
return from The East

Denise Carrington-Smith

Alfred Russel Wallace:

The Journey of a Lifetime

Storixus

First published 2022 by
Storixus Independent Publishing
Canberra, Australia

www.storixus.com

ISBN 978-0-6454958-0-5 (Paperback Edition)
ISBN 978-0-6454958-1-2 (eBook Edition)

Acknowledgment

This book would not have been possible without the help of my good friend, Elizabeth (Liz) Meth, who used her computer skills to track down the reprints of Wallace's writings which are the subject of this study. Some were not easy to find and I thank her, most sincerely, for all her patient efforts.

Preface

Alfred Russel Wallace needed two volumes when he wrote his autobiography. Here, those two volumes have been condensed to one chapter each, the first for his childhood and his early life of physical exploration, the second for his mature manhood and mental exploration, not only of the world around him, but of the Universe.

Much has been written about the first of these 'explorations', which brought him to the theory of Natural Selection at the same time as Darwin. Little has been written of his later life, which, in many ways, is more relevant today.

It is acknowledged that no two humans are the same and yet, in some ways, we are all so alike. It is the same with societies. No two are precisely the same and yet, in many ways, all are so alike. They have to be. They all consist of human beings. Many of the issues about which Wallace wrote still exist today. Some have changed for the better, some are much the same, and some are worse. Much of that which Wallace wrote then is still relevant now, still worth pondering.

Wallace's interests were so broad and so deep that it would be impossible to do them all justice in just one volume. I have tried to cover only the second half of the life of this incredible man - one of England's greatest ever. I have done my best. I hope he is pleased.

Denise Carrington-Smith.

Port Douglas.

2020

Content

Chapter 1

Outward Bound

In 1905, at the age of 82, Alfred Russel Wallace published his autobiography - *My Life: A Record of Events and Opinions.* It was published in two volumes. The first half of Wallace's life was devoted to exploring. Initially, the exploring was carried out on British soil, collecting and studying plants and small animals, comparing them, trying to establish relationships and differences, a task which turned out to be far more complicated than the young lad had anticipated. Wallace was twenty-five when he and a friend set out for South America, where they spent four years in the Amazon. After returning home for two years, in 1854 he set out again, this time to spend eight years in the Malay Archipelago, returning early 1862. There were plenty of events to be remembered from that time - including being ship-wrecked.

The second half of Wallace's life was spent at home, in England, with his wife and family. His interest in living things had extended to humans, especially the ways in which they were superior to animals - and the ways in which they were not! He wrote many papers and books (Appendix II) and expressed many opinions.

While Wallace's association with Charles Darwin, and the establishment of the theory that evolution had occurred by a process of 'Natural Selection', is well-known and has been written about quite extensively, very little attention seems to have been given to Wallace's later work, much of it on the subject of social reform. Some of the changes Wallace urged have been adopted; many were not, yet the issues they addressed are as pertinent today as they were then. Others of Wallace's writings are merely musings of interest - his paper on the importance of dust, for instance, and of mosquitoes! It is the purpose of this book to bring Wallace's thoughts back to attention. I have not agreed with everything Wallace said, and I am sure you will not either, but simply thinking over the points he raised, if only to marshal objections, is a worthwhile exercise.

Before studying the work, it is time to study the man.

Wallace was born on 8th January, 1823, at Usk, in Monmouthshire, Wales. Outside his immediate family, he had few relations. All four grandparents had died before he was born. His father appears to have been an only child, his mother having one sister, who had eight or nine children, all but two of whom migrated to South Australia in 1838. He never met the two who remained behind. However, his childhood was not a solitary one. Although his mother gave birth to nine children, three of his five sisters had died before he was born. All three brothers, William, John and Herbert, who preferred to be known by his second name, Edward, grew to adulthood. Wallace's only knowledge of his family came from notes made in an old family Prayer Book, in which had been recorded dates of births and baptisms, and an examination of Parish registers and tombstones.

The Wallace family came from Hanworth, Middlesex. Wallace does not seem to have been able to trace his family beyond the early 1700s, leading me to wonder whether they had left Scotland, along with many others, migrating to England with James VI of Scotland, who, having inherited the

English throne, became James I of England. At that time, Britain being in the grip of the Little Ice Age, much of Scotland was uninhabitable and many took the opportunity to travel south. Of most interest to Wallace was the tomb of Admiral Sir James Wallace, although he does not state the exact relationship. However, since Hanworth was but a village, with a population in 1840 of only 750 persons, all the Wallaces resident in Hanworth could be presumed to have been related.

The village lay on land owned by the Dukes of St. Albans. A younger son of one of the Dukes had been created Baron Vere of Hanworth. He eventually inherited the Dukedom. Wallace's father's name was Thomas Vere Wallace and Wallace, rather naïvely, suggested his father's father may have been a tenant of Baron Vere. Wallace must have known that tenants do not take the family name of the local aristocrat! It was not unusual for a wife from an established family to give her family name to one, at least, of her children, as a middle name. This was how Wallace acquired his own middle name, Russel, spelt incorrectly, he assumed, due to a mistake by the clerk at the time the birth was registered, although Wallace was uncertain whether the Russell's were relatives, or merely close friends, of his mother's family, the Greenells. (I suspect his mother's mother was 'Russell'.) Almost certainly, the Wallace family had aristocratic connections. I mention this because, so often, Wallace is portrayed as being of a poor family and as having received but little education, which was not the case. The Wallace family had their origins in Sterling and were descendants of the Scottish hero, Sir William Wallace, a claim supported by his family crest. The tombstone of one, William Greenell, who died in 1791, was inscribed with the words "he acquired an ample fortune" and his mother's grandfather, who died in 1797, was an alderman for many years and twice Mayor of Hertford. Wallace believed the

Greenell family originally came from France as refugees after the massacre of St. Bartholomew in 1572.

After leaving school, his father had studied Law, records showing that, at the age of twenty-one, he had been sworn in as an Attorney-at-Law of the Court of the King's Bench. However, being a gentleman of independent means, he never practised. Until his marriage, at the age of thirty-five, his father had lived an 'idle' life, living up to his income (i.e., not saving anything). He travelled extensively, but only within England. As he became the father of a growing family, there was need for additional income, which his father tried to provide by means of publishing an illustrated magazine. The problem was 'illustrated'. This was before the days of photography and each illustration needed to be individually produced, not only on paper, but as an engraving suitable for printing. Not surprisingly, despite (or because?) of its high quality, the magazine enjoyed but brief publication. His father bore the brunt of the loss. The family moved from Marylebone (London), to St. George's, Southwark (still London), then to Usk, in Monmouthshire where Wallace was born. They kept but one servant, his father undertaking the garden work himself. This entailed cultivating fruits and vegetables for the family, meat and dairy products being locally available – plentifully and cheaply. Beautiful surroundings, clean country air, fresh food – Wallace believed this to have been the happiest time of his father's life.

The death of a relative improved the family finances, enabling a return to England, to Hoddesdon, Hertfordshire, where his father died in 1843. The Wallace children had received their early schooling at home, being taught by their father; now he taught a few other pupils and received a small salary as librarian to a subscription library. Wallace's older sister, Fanny, established a small boarding school, where his father also lived for the last few years of his life, free from worry about matters of money, Wallace explained, because "these had reached such a pitch that nothing worse was to be expected" (p. 13). There was a reason for this. A solicitor friend had persuaded his father to invest in ground rents. (If this term is unfamiliar to you, do not worry. You will hear plenty about them when we come to consider Wallace's work.) The solicitor, encountering financial difficulties, embezzled the Wallace money, which resulted in legal moves for recovery, some of the money being received in small amounts. The family survived mostly on a small endowment of Mrs. Wallace's, along with the fees paid by the students of his father and sister, Fanny.

Wallace records that the first friendship he formed on moving to Hertford was with the boy next door - George Silk. Over the eight or nine years during which the Wallace family lived in five different houses, the Silk family lived next door to three of them. His friendship with George was to last his life time. Was Hertford chosen because the local miller was related to his mother? Possibly - the miller was described as being 'one of the richest men in town' (p. 33), a further indication that his mother's family were financially 'comfortable'. One did not have to be an industrialist to become wealthy from one's work - at least not during the first half of the nineteenth century.

Wallace's father did not educate his own children beyond the earliest stage. Wallace, with his brother John, attended the local grammar school. At that time, there was no compulsory education; the Church ran Parish Schools, which provided basic education for the children of the workers, concentrating on the 'Three R's' - reading, (w)riting and (a)rithmetic. That Wallace attended the Grammar School is a further indication that, despite the family's somewhat straightened circumstances, their father still embraced the position of country gentleman. During this time, Wallace suffered three severe illnesses, the first being scarlet fever, the other two not identified. On each occasion, he was not expected to survive. His poor mother! She had already lost three children.

The school had been built in 1617 - quite early for a school at a time when most sons of upper class families received their education at home from a resident tutor. The concept of the sons of the emerging middle class receiving joint education at a school was still novel during the seventeenth century. At the time Wallace attended, more than two hundred years later, the school itself consisted of one large room, desks and seats being against the wall. There were also two rows of desks in the centre. Eighty boys were taught by four masters. School started at 7 a.m., and three days a week continued until 5 p.m., by which time, in winter, it was dark. Each child was responsible for bringing his own candles. Wallace endured six years of Latin and remembered history and geography as being nothing but lists of dates and names of places, the memorising of which resembled the learning of the times table.

The boys did not spend all their time tied to their desks. Wallace recalled cricket, baseball, leapfrog, high and long jump and 'turnpikes with hoops' (p. 56). This entailed guiding one's hoop through the turnpikes (bricks or stones) set around the playground, as many as a dozen or more boys playing at the same time: '... the game was not devoid of its little excitements' (p. 57).

After his father's death, the family moved again, this time to Neath in Glamorganshire, Wales.

On leaving school, Wallace worked first as a builder, then as a surveyor, in both cases under the tutelage of his older brother, William. We are so used to seeing builders off-loading pre-prepared planks of floorboard, rapidly securing them in place by the use of nail guns, that it was quite an eye-opening experience to read of the time and trouble taken to ensure that each floorboard was cut to the precise length required and then sanded *by hand*. Patience and thoroughness were necessary qualities in so many ways in times gone by. Wallace's work as a surveyor for the railways, not only instilled in him an appreciation of geography and geology – Charles Lyell's ground-breaking work on the latter subject having been published during the 1830s – but of earlier, now extinct, life-forms, evidenced by the fossils which were being unearthed during the building of the railways and the canals. Miners had previously considered such things 'idle curiosities'. Not any more! These items were indeed exciting curiosity – but it was far from idle! They were being carefully studied. Wallace had been much impressed by his reading of Robert Chambers' book, *Vestiges of the Natural History of Creation*, (published anonymously in 1843) and also by Darwin's *Journal*, which had been republished, greatly amended.

As a budding naturalist, Wallace's primary interest was in the discovery of new varieties, new species, but all naturalists were also acutely aware of similarities, for example that between vertebrates, all of which possessed a spinal column. Some could walk, some could swim, some could fly, some could accomplish two of these things, some all three! How had these similarities/differences come into being? How had they spread and diversified? Stories, drawings, samples (both dead and alive) of flora and fauna previously completely unknown to Europeans, were flooding in from all parts of the world and Wallace longed to see and experience these things for himself.

Wallace was not drawn to the comparatively well-known shores of Africa, Australia or India. His first choice was South America, the jungles of the Amazon, known, but yet unknown, within the reach of civilisation, in many places, still not set foot upon by white man. He and his good friend, Henry Bates, had been inspired by W. H. Edward's book, *A Voyage up the Amazon*, and set about making their preparations, seeking advice from other travellers, obtaining the services of an excellent agent, Samuel Stevens, who remained Wallace's agent for the full fifteen years of his explorations.

When reading the biography of the work of the American naturalist, Asa Gray, published after his death by his wife, Jane Gray, I had been puzzled by a short letter reproduced therein, written by a friend of Wallace's when Wallace was suffering his severe bout of fever in the Amazon, and not expected to recover. This letter had been addressed to Mr. John Smith, Director of London's Kew Gardens, who was my mother's great-uncle. It was a short letter, making no mention of any other matter. I was puzzled because Kew Gardens dealt only with plants and Wallace was sending back samples of animals. While pleased to learn that Wallace and a member of my family had a friendly, if not a working, relationship, I wondered how the two had met. It appears that Wallace had called upon Mr. J. G. Smith, " ... the gentleman who had collected butterflies at Pernambuco and Para ... he invited me to dine with him ... and gave us much information ..." (p. 267). That he (John Smith) should have travelled before taking up his position as Director of Kew Gardens made sense and I was gratified to note that it was the time Wallace and Bates spent with Mr. Smith discussing the Amazon and admiring the samples he had brought back from Para, that helped Wallace and Bates to select the Amazon, the Para district in particular, as their destination. (John Smith's granddaughter, my mother's Auntie Allie (Alice) had a lovely butterfly collection, which I duly admired when visiting as a child. Now I wonder where that collection came from and - more importantly - what happened to it when she died? - which she did in 1968 at the age of 102!) More than twenty years later (1868) Wallace mentions taking 'his friend, Mr. John Smith, the banker' (v.2: p. 292), to a gathering at the home of some friends. Smith had long since handed over the administration of Kew Gardens to the Hooker family, under whose careful watch the work of converting the private gardens of the kings, George

III and George IV, into the well-loved and respected public gardens of today, was completed. The Smith family were goldsmiths; it would seem John Smith had returned to the fold.

Of Wallace's five sisters, the first-born died when five months old; Eliza died of tuberculosis at the age of twenty-two. Mary Ann and Emma died at the ages of eight and six, respectively, before Wallace was born. Only his sister, Frances (Fanny) lived to an old age, dying at the age of eighty-one. Wallace's eldest brother, William, died in his early thirties from congestion of the lungs (pneumonia?) having become sick following the ill-effects of a long, cold, damp railway journey, travelling in an open third-class carriage. Wallace's younger brother, Herbert, joined Wallace in Para, spent a year on the Amazon but did not adjust to the life of a naturalist. He intended to return to England, but on his way back to Para, caught the yellow fever, dying a few days later at the age of twenty-two. Three of the nine Wallace children lived to an old age, Wallace himself, who died at 90, sister Fanny, who lived to 81, and an older brother, John, who died in 1895 at the age of 88, but who had migrated to California in 1849, never returning home for any visit that Wallace mentioned. Life cannot have been easy for Wallace's mother. How hard it must have been for her when Alfred chose to explore the Amazon at the age of twenty-five, even harder when a second son joined him, never to return. With what joy she must have greeted the news that at least one of her two sons was returning home!

The newspapers of that time carried daily reports of shipping activity: those departing, when and where, and those in transit home. Wallace's journey to the Amazon had taken twenty-nine days. The vagaries of wind and weather made accurate prediction difficult but when Wallace, on Monday, 12th July, 1852, boarded the vessel which was to bring him home, he would have expected to arrive mid

August. With him, he had thousands of samples of species of butterfly, beetles, and other insects, possibly the skins of small animals and certainly skins and feathers of many birds, as well as some livestock: "... numerous parrots and parakeets, several uncommon monkeys, a forest wild-dog, etc." (ff. p. 302). On Friday, 6th August, the Captain came to his cabin and said: "I am afraid the ship is on fire." Efforts to put out the fire having proved unsuccessful, there was nothing for it but to abandon ship. Through the thick smoke in his cabin, Wallace was able to retrieve a small tin box, into which he put a few shirts and some drawings, his watch and a few sovereigns. The rest of his samples (and, sadly, the livestock), along with three years' precious journals, had to be abandoned. Everyone was able to fit aboard the two boats, along with provisions. The boats were leaky and constant bailing out was necessary - day and night. They were in the shipping lane and expected soon to be found. Wallace recalls that he felt quite calm, one might almost say resigned, because he stated that "... after a few days I began to have more hope" (p. 305). One would have thought the reverse would be the case. However, his new found optimism proved justified. After ten days they were sighted by a vessel, two hundred miles from Bermuda. As luck would have it, the vessel was bound for London.

The rescued may have been very happy to see the rescuers, but the same could not be said for the reverse. The ship had enough food on board for the crew. Now they were on half rations. There were no spare bunks. The vessel was old, and even with favourable winds rarely exceeded five knots. Her usual speed was closer to two or three. They obtained some extra supplies from an outward-bound ship, which helped - a bit. It was hurricane season, and Wallace's (misplaced) desire to experience the phenomenon was soon gratified. The second storm was worse.

On 1st October, they docked at Deal and by 5th October, he had arrived in London. Wallace's arrival was delayed at least six weeks. Just imagine the mental anguish of his mother, who had already lost three daughters in early childhood, two sons in early manhood, and a third son by migration to California, whom she never saw again. He recalls how, when being tossed about on the stormy sea, he vowed never to venture sailing again, but now, safely ashore and in London, he told a friend, in a letter written that very day, how he was already trying decide whether the Andes or the Philippines would be his next destination. One would like to think that he did not share these thoughts with his mother at that time, but he was only twenty-nine years of age, young enough to be foolish. His sister, Fanny, had married Thomas Sims, a practitioner of the new art of photography. He and his mother moved in with the Sims at their London studio for what Wallace described as 'my stay in England'.

Wallace had been fascinated, not only by the wondrous new plant and animal life he had been privileged to witness, but also by his first sight of human beings in their natural state. He made two voyages up the Rio Negro, on the first venturing beyond the boundary of Brazil, crossing by a road in the forest to one of the tributaries of the Orinoko. He also travelled up the Uaupés River and it was here that he had his first meeting with "absolute uncontaminated savages!" (p. 288):

> They had nothing that we call clothes; they had peculiar ornaments, tribal marks, etc.; they all carried weapons or tools of their own manufacture; they were living in a large house, many families together, quite unlike the hut of the tame Indians; but, more than all, their whole aspect and manner were different – they were all going about their own work or pleasure which had nothing to do with white man or their ways; they walked with the free step of the independent forest-dweller, and, except the few

that were known to my companion, paid no attention whatever to us, mere strangers of an alien race. In every detail they were original and self-sustaining ... I could not have believed that there would be so much difference in the aspect of the same people in their native state and when living under European supervision. The true denizen of the Amazonian forests, like the forest itself, is unique and not to be forgotten.

Fortunately, Wallace's agent had taken out insurance on his behalf and he received £150, although Wallace estimated the actual value of his samples to have been closer to £200. This amount enabled him to live a year in London, buy a good outfit of clothes, with sufficient left over to fund his Malay journey – helped by the free passage he received. No money could adequately recompense Wallace for his loss, but some compensation was offered by family and friends, to whom he had written letters, many quite lengthy. The Victorian era was one of personal letter writing, such as had never before been seen and which has not since been equalled. They not only wrote letters, long letters, they kept those they received, along with their diaries, and Wallace was able to access many he had written, using them to replace his lost notes, writing accounts of his voyage and explorations for publication, either as books or papers, and to assist in the preparation of the talks he was asked to give. Wallace mentioned attending the Linnean Society, a group which was to play an historic role in establishing his work along with that of Charles Darwin. Wallace became quite well known, sufficiently so for him to be offered free passage when he set out, two years later, for the Malay Archipelago, where he was to stay for eight years. Sir Richard Murchison, President of the Royal Geographical Society, made representations on his behalf, obtaining free passage for him aboard the *Frolic*. (Even while at anchor, the ship pitched and rolled. Wallace felt sea-sick. The sailors teased him about what was to come. Clearly, the ship had received its name for a reason!) There was no spare cabin; Wallace slept in a cot slung in the captain's cabin. The interest in people which had been sparked by the natives of the Amazon was fed by the differences in manners and characters of those on board, which he studied, day after day, while waiting to leave. It was a long wait - weeks! Eventually, orders came - to sail, not to Singapore, but to the Crimea, where war was about to break out.

Wallace disembarked and returned to London. He called on Sir Roderick Murchison, who immediately obtained for him a first-class ticket to Singapore by the next Peninsular and Oriental (P. & O.) steamer, which sailed the following week. It was February, 1854, when Wallace finally set sail for the Archipelago. A short stop at Gibraltar, a day exploring Malta, where he inspected, among other things, the tombs of the knights at the Cathedral of St. John, which Wallace described as 'gorgeous with marbles and gold' (p. 332), then on to Alexandria. He saw the pyramids, before arriving in Cairo at sunset. The Suez canal not yet having been built, Wallace made his way by land to the small town of Suez, where he boarded a boat bound for Singapore. God's time may not be human time, but after the wait, it can be a good time!

In Singapore, Wallace stayed with a French missionary, busying himself with the collection of insects. By the end of May, he had already sent more than a thousand beetles back to his agent, Stevens, and had nearly as many other insects waiting to be dispatched. From there, he moved on to the Dutch city of Malacca, which had once been Portuguese. Wallace was becoming fluent in Portuguese and was able to converse with his servants (helpers), a cook and a hunter. He noted that in neither Singapore nor Malacca was there a single Protestant missionary, even though the Dutch were Protestant. The Chinese residents were most hardworking, cultivating their land with neatness and industry. Wildlife, including monkeys, was abundant, more so than in Brazil. The ground swarmed with leeches, but there were fine new butterflies and hundreds of other new or rare insects. Huge centipedes and scorpions, some about a foot long, were common.

Returning to Singapore, he made the acquaintance of Sir James Brooke, the Raja, who was to become a close friend.

In November, 1854, he arrived in Sarawak, Borneo, which was to be his headquarters for the next eight years, the place from which he embarked upon his travels and to which he returned for respite. The people continued to intrigue him. "The more I see of uncivilized people, the better I think of human nature on the whole, and the essential differences between civilized and savage man seem to disappear" (pp. 342-343). The Chinese inhabitants may have a reputation for being thieves and liars, the Malays for being barbarous and bloodthirsty, but his experience was that they were honest and trustworthy. The occasional squabble was all that he witnessed. He went about unarmed and slept with open doors. The Dyaks had previously been headhunters, and the older men were somewhat put out that this practice was no longer acceptable. Among themselves, crime was rare.

Wallace missed the flowers and the fruit. There were some flowers at the tops of some trees, but at ground level, there was scarcely anything but green vegetation. The only fruits were the mangosteen and durian.

While in Sarawak, during the wet season, Wallace put pen to paper and wrote his first journal article on the subject of evolution: *On the Law which has regulated the Introduction of New Species* which was published in 1855 by *The Annals and Magazine of Natural History*. As had been suggested in *Vestiges*, evolution would seem to have occurred, "each [new] species coming into existence coincident both in space and time with a pre-existing closely allied species" (p. 355). Vestiges had spoken of change/evolution over great

14

expanses of time in a general way. Wallace's contribution was the understanding that this had been a gradual process as one variety/species, mutated into another. All change was gradual and *local*. The Creator had not created similar entities, either plant or animal, in widely separated places, as whim might take Him.

In January of 1858, Wallace had written to his good friend, Henry Bates, regarding a paper he had written: *Succession of Species*. He explained that paper was "... merely the announcement of the theory, not its development. I have prepared the plan and written portions of a work embracing the whole subject ...". While confined to bed with yet another bout of fever, he committed some of his thoughts to paper, sending them to Darwin as soon as he recovered. It was this paper which was read jointly with some unpublished notes of Darwin's, before the Linnean Society on 1st July, 1858, neither author being present in person.

On pp. 360-363 of the first volume of his autobiography, Wallace further extrapolated upon his line of thought over the years he had been pondering 'the origin of species', what troubled him, how and when he eventually arrived at the ideas which he communicated to Darwin.

Some of the islands to which Wallace travelled had never before been visited by an English collector, or lived upon alone (among the natives) by any European. His careful observations, not merely of the species as individuals, but as connected - or not, as the case might be - led him to make an observation which has stood the test of time and with which his name is still associated (pp. 358-359):

> In this archipelago there are two distinct faunas rigidly circumscribed ... The boundary line passes between islands closer together than others belonging to the same group. I believe the western part to be a separated portion of continental Asia, while the eastern part is a fragmentary prolongation

of a former west Pacific continent. In mammals and birds the distinction is marked by genera, families, and even orders confined to one region; in insects by a number of genera, and little groups of peculiar species, the families of insects having generally a very wide or universal distribution.

This separating boundary is known as 'The Wallace Line' to this day.

His brother-in-law, Thomas Sims, had written urging him to return home. In April, 1859, Wallace wrote, explaining why he could not do so - yet. Happiness came from following one's vocation. If he returned to England at that time, he would live a life of regret over lost opportunity. Some people saw their vocation as the acquisition of money and looked down upon others who had different aspirations. He was quite outspoken in response: "It strikes me that the power or capability of a man in getting rich is in an *inverse* proportion to his reflective powers and in *direct* proportion to his impudence" (p. 368). After he returned home in 1862, his attention turned more and more to the problem of wealth and its unequal distribution, and its effect upon humanity, as you will read when we study his writings.

If Wallace was happy, that was not because life was easy! He summarised his voyage from Waigiou back to Ternate as follows (pp. 370-371):

My first crew ran away in a body; two more men were lost on a desert island, and only recovered a month later after twice sending in search of them; we were ten times run aground on coral reefs; we lost four anchors; our sails were devoured by rats; our small boat was lost astern; we were thirty-eight days on a voyage which should not have taken twelve; we were many times short of food and water; we had no compass-lamp owing to there being not a drop of oil in Waigiou when we left; and, to crown it all, during our whole voyage from Goram to Ceram to Waigiou, and from Waigiou to Ternate ... we had *not one single day of fair wind* ... (Italics in original).

By January, 1861, Wallace was commencing preparations for his return home, "cleaning, arranging and preparing for packing for safe transmission to the other side of the world of about 16,000 specimens of insects, birds and shells" (p. 373). He made his way, leisurely, to Singapore, staying a month here, a month there, at various places along the way. Wallace wrote to his friend, George Silk, from Singapore on 20th January, 1862, saying that he might remain in Singapore another month, but from the account of his journey home, I conclude he must have left shortly after. He had purchased two birds of paradise, which he brought back with him to donate to the Zoological Gardens. They ate fruit and cockroaches - plenty of the latter of which he was usually able to catch aboard ship. He reached Suez some time in February, the weather being cold in Malta, and presumably even colder in England, he stayed an extra two weeks, fearing the cold would be detrimental to the welfare of the parrots, finally reaching London in the Spring of 1862 (p. 385) - I believe in April.

Chapter 2

Home Work

The second volume of Wallace's autobiography covered his life after returning to England, and page numbers given hereafter refer to Volume II.

On arriving home, Wallace moved in with his sister and brother-in-law, and his mother - although he does not mention her. Here Wallace sorted through the boxes of samples he had sent home at regular intervals, containing about three thousand bird skins of about a thousand species, twenty thousand species of beetle and seven thousand of butterflies. Wallace made frequent visits to the British Museum and regularly attended evening meetings of the Zoological, Entomological and Linnean societies. He wrote papers and books, and became an influential speaker. Some of the papers which he wrote were quite lengthy. He mentions two which filled about 200 pages of the society's *Transactions*. Initially, his topic was his travels, his findings, but, over time, he became increasingly interested in social issues.

Soon after returning to England, Charles Darwin invited Wallace to stay for a night at Down House and the two men struck up an unlikely friendship, which seemed to surprise them both. They should have been rivals, not friends, but friends they were. Distance precluded frequent meetings, except during Darwin's annual visit to London to stay with his older brother, Erasmus. At that time, they exchanged visits, sometimes alone, sometimes in the company of other naturalists. Both men were of a quiet, retiring nature, both enjoyed solitude and tended to avoid unnecessary company, if possible. They exchanged frequent letters, which have been preserved and are now available on-line, which correspondence continued until shortly before Darwin's death in 1882. Wallace was a pall-bearer at Darwin's funeral in Westminster Abbey.

Discussion between the two men was stimulated, not just by a common interest, but by areas of difference, which they debated. Both men advocated 'natural selection' as the means by which most physical change had become established, Wallace, if anything, holding to this position more firmly than Darwin! Not even in his first edition of *On the Origin of Species* (1859) had Darwin claimed natural selection as the *sole* means of change. Wallace argued more forcefully in this direction. Darwin always believed in the inheritance of acquired characteristics and, at first, Wallace had also accepted this - although many opponents did not. Later, Wallace abandoned the idea, chiefly in response to the work of Weismann and Mendel, by which time Darwin had died. Their main area of difference related to the mind. Wallace did not accept that mental attributes had been developed through natural selection. He did not see how abilities such as mathematics, art, music, philosophical thought, etc., could have been developed to the degree that they had through natural selection, since such attributes did not have any 'survival' significance. However, it was humanity's differing mental and philosophical attitudes towards each other which created, not only vast differences between societies, but divisions *within* societies, and it was these differences and divisions which increasingly came to consume Wallace's interest.

Another person whose acquaintance Wallace made soon after arriving home was Herbert Spencer, who wrote extensively on 'nature' and 'life' and whose work had included ideas very similar to that of Darwin and Wallace - some claim preceded them. Darwin and Wallace were both very aware that there was a big divide between 'origin of species' and 'origin of life'. Wallace, with his good friend Bates, called upon Spencer, hoping that he would be able to throw some light upon this mystery. Alas, they were to be disappointed. While Spencer believed 'life' to have been 'a development out of matter', that was as far as he was willing to speculate.

Of all the people Wallace met while living in London, the one with whom he formed the closest friendship was Darwin's good friend, Thomas Huxley, who lived in a house in Marlborough Place, with his young family. "I used often to go there on Sunday afternoons, or to spend the evening" (p. 34). It was to Huxley, Wallace believed, that he owed the medal awarded to him by the Royal Society and, perhaps, also his Darwin medal. Wallace was in awe of Huxley's knowledge and intellect, as he was of no other living human.

Another great friend was Professor St. George Mivart. Mivart had waited until Darwin published the 5th edition of *The Origin* before writing a scathing criticism, which was so well argued that it caused Darwin more problems than any other published comment. Wallace considered that Mivart's criticism of Darwin was sometimes 'unfair', but Mivart was 'excellent company, full of humour and anecdote' (pp. 43-44). He was a 'thoroughly liberal Catholic', a description I presume he earned because of his interest in psychical research and spiritualistic phenomena, subjects of great interest also to Wallace, who spent years researching them and on which subjects he wrote papers, as well as two books - the second an extension of the first.

Indeed, the first book Wallace wrote on matters totally unrelated to his travels and/or Natural Selection was *Miracles and Modern Spiritualism*, which he published in 1874. Wallace had become interested in mesmerism (hypnotism) as a young man, before starting out on his travels, but I have to wonder whether his interest in miracles and spiritualism had been, if not incited, then strengthened, by his contact with native people, most (if not all) of whom had strong beliefs in the supernatural. Spiritualism became an abiding interest and introduced Wallace to a completely separate group of friends – separate because he was unable to convert any of his 'scientific' friends to his beliefs, not for want of trying. One did turn up to one meeting, but never came again.

Wallace had occasionally met Professor, Sir Richard Owen, at Society meetings and had corresponded with him regarding the orang-utang specimens he had sent home while in the Archipelago, but later, through a mutual colleague, he and Sir Richard became friends.

Of great interest is Wallace's involvement in the publication of what is often considered to be England's greatest scientific journal, *Nature*. Quite who proposed the idea, Wallace does not say, although I know his good friend, Thomas Huxley, has been credited with being 'one of the founders' – if not the moving spirit. Be that as it may, Wallace records that he took part in the meetings in which was discussed the establishment of "a scientific weekly paper to serve as a record of progress for workers, to furnish reviews of scientific books by specialists dealing with them on their merits alone, to give reports of the meetings of societies and popular yet accurate accounts of all remarkable new facts or theories of general interest" (p. 54). For the next quarter of a century, almost every volume of Nature contained either reviews, letters or articles from his pen.

On first arriving back home, Wallace's circle of friends consisted, almost exclusively, of those whose interests were of Nature – flora, fauna, geology. However, his close friend,

George Silk, introduced him to a private chess club, where he met a Mr. L., to whose home he and George were often invited. I'm sure you have guessed what is coming. Wallace fell in love with one of Mr. L.'s daughters! Being somewhat older, Wallace was a bit unsure about whether or not he should try to court the young lady. He consulted his mother (this being the first time he even mentioned her) who encouraged him, and after two years the engagement was announced and a date set for the wedding. Unfortunately, the young lady changed her mind. Wallace was devastated.

In 1865, he took a small house in Regent's Park for himself and his mother, where he lived for five years. Wallace often went to Hurstpierpoint, in Sussex, to visit his friend, Mr. Mitten, who also had a daughter: "In the spring of the following year I was married to Mr. Mitten's eldest daughter, then about eighteen years old" (p. 412). For a girl as young as that to marry a man of 43, it must have been a true love match, recognized as such by her parents, who gave their consent, as was necessary for a young lady under twenty-one years of age. It would have been nice if he had told us her name but he continues to speak of "we" and "my wife" when he tells of their trip to Wales in the early autumn of that year. Armed with *Glaciers of Switzerland and North Wales* by Sir Andrew Ramsay, the pair explored the hills and valleys around Mount Snowdon, the Ice Age becoming a reality for Wallace in a way it never had been before. The former Ice Age (a new and controversial idea) became a life-long passion of Wallace's, one on which he became an acknowledged authority. The following year, he and his wife went - surprise, surprise, - to Switzerland, not his first visit to that country but one which he undertook with a new vision.

The (not-so-young) young couple, and their two children, William and Violet, relocated several times. In 1876, Wallace moved from London to Dorking, then to Croydon two years later, chiefly, wrote Wallace, because of the kindergarten and high school, although, since the family only stayed there until May, 1881, perhaps the choice of school was not as determining as Wallace had, at first, thought. The family moved to Godalming, where his children attended Charterhouse School.

In 1886, Wallace was invited to give a series of lectures in America, to which place he sailed, arriving in New York on 23rd October. He does not say how much he was paid, but he does tell us how much it cost him to stay at the hotel which was to be his 'home' for nearly three months - $3 a day! However, there was plenty of food. Dinner was at lunch time, lunch being at supper time. There was a smorgasbord of food: meat, poultry, game, dozens of vegetables as well as pastries, and Wallace could order as much as he wanted of as many items as he wished! While in New York, Wallace took the opportunity to visit as many museums, libraries and institutions as he could and also made the acquaintance of a number of eminent naturalists, including the botanist, Professor Asa Gray, close friend and associate of Sir Joseph Hooker and Charles Darwin. He also met and conversed in private with Oliver Wendell Holmes, who was much interested in Spiritualism.

In Boston, Wallace attended meetings of the National Academy of Science. Once Gray called upon him to speak. He was totally unprepared but spoke on the dispersion of seeds to oceanic islands by the wind - none of the islands having any flora which could be dispersed in any other way - and none that was unique, i.e., independently evolved. Prof. Gray made it up to him - inviting him to dinner so that he could meet most of the biological professors of Harvard University.

Wallace met with Professor Marsh, who lived near the Peabody Museum of Yale College, which enabled Wallace to visit "the largest collection of fossil skeletons, chiefly of mammals and reptiles of America, to be seen anywhere" (p. 112). The collection included "the huge bones of the atlantossaurus, a reptile nearly a hundred feet long and thirty feet high, supposed to be the largest land animal that has ever existed" (p. 112). There were horned dinosauria, flying pterodactyles, as well as ancient forms of horse, and much, much more. He visited a Lady's College, residential for about three hundred young ladies, who were awarded places, at the age of sixteen, after passing a stiff examination. The list of subjects studied was extensive. Besides lecturing at the Peabody Institute, Wallace also lectured at the John Hopkins University.

From Boston, Wallace travelled to Washington, where he met many more interesting people, and saw more interesting fossil remains, including those of 'early man', in the National Museum, which he described as being perhaps the most wonderful and interesting collection of such objects in the world. Wallace was even taken to a place where he could find old arrow-heads. Here he was received with great honour, more so than in either New York or Boston.

Many of the academics and scientists Wallace met were spiritualists. The practice and study of spiritualism was as great (if not greater) in America than it was in England.

Wallace also became quite knowledgeable about astronomy. This was hardly surprising. One can imagine him on those islands in the Archipelago, far away from the lamp lights of the city (no electricity in those days), staring in awe and wonder into the velvety blackness of the night, overwhelmed with the beauty of the stars of the southern sky. He also had the opportunity to study the stars at night when visiting the Naval Observatory in Washington, which had the finest telescope in the world, through which he was able to observe Saturn at magnifications of four and six hundred. He also observed Orion, although he deemed a fine cluster in Perseus as the most beautiful object he saw. The night was not considered a good night for viewing, otherwise even more powerful instruments would have been used.

Wallace lowered his sights but not his spirits when observing the Niagra Falls, staying four days on the Canadian side of the border. Although now Spring, it was still frosty and some of the spray was frozen; there were great ice mounds below and gigantic icicles near the margins. He explored falls on both sides of the border and especially mentions one on the American side: "the smallest twigs coated with glistening ice from the frozen spray, looked like groves of gigantic tree corals - the most magnificent and fairy-like scene I have ever beheld" (p. 127).

After his speaking engagements were complete in the north-east of America, Wallace travelled to the south-west - to California. This was a long journey, made the longer by constant stop-overs for the presenting of lectures. None of the people Wallace recalls having met on his journey were familiar to me so I have not selected any to mention here. Wallace clearly thoroughly enjoyed his journey. He took the opportunity during actual travelling time to admire the local scenery, especially the geology, in which he was becoming more and more interested. During his two or three day stays *en route,* he took the opportunity to explore the area, seeking out unusual plants and small creatures, mostly snails. Unfortunately, especially during the first part of his journey, it still being Spring, many flowers were not yet in bloom.

It is noticeable that, as he journeyed, his lectures came to be given more and more to educational establishments, rather than to naturalist Societies. Wallace was most impressed with the system of schools and colleges in the Western States. It was co-educational, at all ages and stages - even University. Furthermore, there were female teachers, even in schools with male students. One school had a female Principal! At the

Station Hotel in Kansas City, there were "female waiters instead of the usual white, brown, or black men waiters" (p. 147). In Sioux City, he stayed with a Mr. Talbot, who owned six thousand acres of land on which he was breeding (and studying) a great variety of animals, including solid-hoofed pigs, which were considered superior for fattening purposes. Mr. Talbot had also patented metallic tags for identifying cattle. On the train to Cheyenne, he observed a young lady chewing gum - not a pleasant experience for Wallace!

Wallace was most impressed by Salt Lake City. The Mormon Tabernacle seated six thousand people and had been so superbly designed that a speaker could be heard distinctly throughout the auditorium using but an ordinary, conversational tone. It was a 'Garden' city, each house being surrounded by anything from one half to one-and-a-half acres of land, full of flowers, as would be an English garden. The streets were about one hundred and thirty feet wide and lined with shady trees. In England, The Land Nationalisation Society had already been formed; Wallace was its President. It cannot be said that Wallace's views on housing had been inspired by Salt Lake City in the sense of having had their origins in that place but it almost certainly inspired him to continue to press for acceptance of his ideas, having seen them so successfully put into practice.

In San Francisco he met up with his brother, John, whom he had not seen since 1848, and whom he would never see again. They received many invitations to dine but the one which impressed Wallace the most was an invitation to breakfast with a wealthy merchant, Mr. Sutro, who lived in a beautiful cottage on a cliff overlooking the Pacific. Breakfast consisted of hot soup, fish, cutlets, game, etc., hot cakes of various kinds, with choice fruits, all 'washed down' with various delicate wines, as well as with tea and coffee. (In case you are wondering, it was the practice for servants to finish off what was left. They ate what the rich ate - only an hour or two later!)

Among the many millionaires to whom Wallace was introduced, and with whom he dined, was Senator Stanford, whose son had died at the age of sixteen. Through spiritualism, the grieving parents had had contact with their son and it was as spiritualists, not as naturalists, that the two men met. Stanford was preparing to build a large University in memory of his son. Preparatory work was in progress. Later Wallace saw pictures of the completed complex, which he described. It was intended for education from the lowest to the highest level, tuition to be free for residents of California.

Much as he admired Senator Stanford, Wallace was saddened that Stanford saw prosperity only through his own eyes, apparently being oblivious to the everyday struggle against poverty undertaken by his - and other - workers, from whose labour his own wealth had been accrued.

Having celebrated (!?) 4th July, Wallace bade farewell to his brother, sister-in-law, nephews, nieces, grand-nephew and grand-niece, made his way across the continent to Quebec, from whence he set sail for Liverpool. He 'dillied and dallied', not because he was 'lost and couldn't find his way home', but because he made numerous stops along the way, to explore, to collect, to admire - and, sometimes, to criticise. (He preferred the Swiss Alps to the Rocky Mountains.) He gave the last lecture of his tour in Michigan. He sailed from Quebec on Friday, 12th August, 1887, having been in America for more than ten months. At 6 a.m. on 17th August, the ship anchored off Portrush, Northern Ireland, to disembark some passengers and mail, reaching Liverpool late that night. By 5.30 p.m. the following day, he was home in Godalming.

Someone had commented that they had had trouble understanding Darwin's *The Origin,* finding Wallace's lecture far simpler. This inspired Wallace to write *Darwinism,* which consumed most of his time and effort for the following year. He continued writing, converting the lectures he had given in America into books and articles, as well as giving lectures in various parts of the country. In the Autumn of 1889, Oxford University bestowed upon him the honorary degree of Doctor of Civil Law (D.C.L.). Seven years previously, on 29th June, 1881, Dublin University had also conferred upon him the honorary Law degree of LL.D. It was following the conferral of these degrees that Wallace began to be addressed as 'Dr. Wallace'. For a lad who left school at the age of fourteen, he had not done badly!

When Wallace had return from the Archipelago, he had been unsuccessful in obtaining employment. He first applied for the position of Secretary to the Royal Geographical Society but was beaten for the position by his good friend, Henry Bates. That was in 1864. In 1869, he hoped for a directorship when the Government planned to establish a branch museum in Bethnal Green, which would combine art and natural history. Unfortunately, it was decided that the museum would be managed directly from South Kensington (London's premier museum). Wallace felt so fed up with London and its disappointments that in 1871 he purchased four acres of land at Grays, near Barking, building a house with beautiful views across North Kent, into which he moved at the end of 1872. Seven years later, in 1878, part of Epping Forest having been purchased by the Government, to be returned to the people, Wallace submitted proposals for the formation of what today would be recognized as a nature reserve, which he hoped to manage. The position was given to someone who proposed a large hotel, with a beer garden, swings and roundabouts.

Wallace had realized that the close study of all his samples was more than a life-time's work for one man and handed on some of his samples to students of other groups.

The breeding of some of the Malay butterflies had shown that some species had males of one colour and females of another - plural! There may be two or three females of completely different appearance which were the one species. Furthermore, the eggs from one female could produce offspring of all three or four varieties!

Birds and butterflies always held a special attraction for Wallace, who had seen so many beautifully coloured varieties during his travels. He became President of the Entomological Society and of the Biological Section of the British Association. He was asked to write the article on "Distribution - Zoology" for the *Encyclopædia Britannica*, for more than a hundred years *the* definitive authority on all matters. The information was carefully vetted before being published, something that does not necessarily take place with our modern 'on-line' system of sharing knowledge.

Wallace had been greatly struck by the distribution of birds in the Archipelago, particularly the difference between the eastern (Asian) portion and the western section, which he termed 'Australian'. Considered in comparison with the rest of the world, the Australian region was quite small, yet it contained nearly as many species of parrot as the rest of the world combined. The Australian region also contained three-quarters as many pigeons as the whole of the rest of the globe. These observations were not merely of interest, they helped scientists learn about the past geological history of the Earth, scientific information about which was not readily available in those times. Wallace deduced that the eastern islands of the Archipelago had once been associated with, if not joined to, Asia, the western islands similarly having been close to, or joined with, Australia. There was not then any concept of oceanic plates, which 'drifted', at times colliding, or separating. Wallace offered no 'explanation' for these changes, merely asserted that they had happened.

Wallace suggested the greater number of birds might be associated with lack of tree dwelling predators, such as monkeys, conspicuously absent from this region - another clue to the geological past. Every living entity, be it plant or animal, was dependent upon its food supply. For many animals, this was plants, and for many plants, this was climate. Wallace was fascinated with Earth's constantly changing climate, the concept of a past Ice Age still being fairly new and not yet universally accepted. Temperatures rose and fell, oceans warmed and cooled, their currents swept in new directions as the sea floor (and land) rose or fell; the wind affected temperature and temperature affected wind. The physics was constant, the result was constant change. Nor were temperature changes necessarily the same in the northern and southern hemispheres. It all depended on the Earth's position in relation to the Sun, on the position of the Sun (and our galaxy) in relation to other Suns and galaxies and also of the precession of the equinox. Wallace became very knowledgeable regarding astronomy - as you will see when we study his interesting writings on this fascinating subject.

In 1879, Wallace published a book, *Australia*, for "Stanford's Compendium of Geography and Travel", speculating as to the origin of the native peoples and claiming that they were "by no means so low in intellect as has been usually believed" (p. 101). The present book is not about Wallace's ideas on evolution, plant, animal or human, but about his other interests. If you want to know what Wallace thought about Australia and its people, you will have to read it for yourself!

Always one to look on the bright side, Wallace remarked that, had he obtained any of the permanent positions for which he applied, he would not have been able to travel to America, nor write his *Darwinism*, nor, possibly, any of his later books. Perhaps writing "and popular scientific work" was what he was best fitted to perform (p. 417)? By "popular scientific work" he may have also been referring, not only to his writing, but to the lectures he gave, which Wallace mentions frequently, 'in passing', rarely giving any details. In this, Wallace had a big advantage over Darwin: he did not stutter. Darwin was afflicted with what appears to have been quite a noticeable stammer. Stuttering was quite common in days gone by - even in my childhood. For some, it was a minor affliction, little more than a hesitation. For others, starting a sentence could take several seconds. The affliction disappeared when children, naturally left handed, were no longer forced to write with their right hand. In a time when many people prided themselves on their beautiful copperplate handwriting, Darwin was renowned for his atrocious handwriting, about which he constantly apologized. Almost certainly, Darwin would naturally have been left handed. Darwin, if you are listening 'up there', we understand and we forgive you!

When not reading, writing and lecturing, Wallace was gardening. He gardened for pure enjoyment. "I have never made any experiment with my plants, never attempted to study their minute structure or to write about them; the mere seeing them grow, noting the infinite diversities of their forms and habits, their likes and dislikes ... all this was to me a delight in itself ..." (p. 204). Alas, the soil at Godalming was not conducive to the growing of the plants he desired, so his family moved to Parkstone in June, 1889, where he lived until 1896.

In 1893, he prepared for Mr. Stanford a new edition of the Australian volume of his "compendium of Geography", Stanford University now being fully functional.

Another person with whom Wallace formed a friendship was John Stuart Mill, who, after reading the concluding pages of Wallace's *Malay Archipelago*, in which Wallace criticised our barbaric civilization, particularly in relation to the private ownership of land, invited Wallace to become a member of his proposed 'Land Tenure Reform Association', which, of course, he did. They saw eye to eye about most things, their major area of disagreement being 'God'. Mill declined to accept that a 'Good' God could, or would, have permitted evil, adopting an atheistic point of view. He rejected Wallace's suggestion that "evil may be essential to the ultimate development of the highest good" (p. 237), an argument which had been put forward by the Great Master, when he declared that it was necessary that evil come into this world but woe unto him by whom it came (Luke 17: 1), which hardly solved the problem! The Association died with the death of Mill in 1871.

One point Mill, and Spencer, did make which caused Wallace to stop to think, was that of the inevitable 'jobbery and favouritism' which would result if property were removed from the care of its present owners and placed in that of the human beings who would comprise the State agency, whose existence would become necessary if the present large land-owners were to be replaced. Government officials, who had no personal connection with the land or its people, could, and probably would, be just as uncaring of the welfare of the working man as some present owners.

Nevertheless, in 1880, Wallace, and a group of supporters, formed the *Land Nationalisation Society*, of which he was elected President. "Its lectures and its yellow vans have pervaded the country" (p. 240).

By 1899, the land surrounding his home at Parkstone was becoming built out, so it was time for the family to make another move. After some searching, a suitable place was found, almost by accident, a mere four miles away, where, in 1901, he purchased three acres, with a view over the moors and fields towards Poole, with a glimpse of the harbour. It took about a year for the new house to be built, but they were able to move in in time for Christmas, 1902.

Just before Wallace left America, he suffered his first asthma attack. These attacks continued after his return to England. They were cured in a rather unusual way. A Mr. Bruce-Joy called, he having been commissioned to model a medallion of Wallace, who happened to be suffering an attack at the time of his visit. Mr. Bruce-Joy assured him that he could be cured by changing his diet. Wallace explained to his reader that he was, *in principle* (his italics), a vegetarian but, being desperate, he agreed to try the recommended diet of complete abstention from starchy substances (carbohydrates) and watery vegetables, eating instead meat, with a fair proportion of fat, fruits and nuts, with a small proportion of eggs and milk. I am sure many readers will recognize this as the "High protein, moderate fat, low carbohydrate" diet popularized by Dr. Atkins in the second half of the 20th century. It worked. Wallace never had another attack. The diet was also recommended for rheumatic and other problems.

His travels and findings had taught him acute discrimination, necessary to determine the similarities and differences between varieties and species. He could not help but compare and contrast people as well. In some ways, all humans were alike; in other respects, no two were the same, nor were any two groups or societies of humans living together. Wallace had been particularly struck by what seemed to him to be two different types of people. On arriving at some islands of the Archipelago, the people ran down to the beach to greet him and his party. These people were excitable and voluble, quick moving, rarely standing (or sitting) still for long. They might amuse themselves by playing tricks on their fellows, possibly even taking something which did not belong to them, although always owning up when challenged. The second type would watch the arrival of his party from behind the bushes, emerging slowly, perhaps one at a time. They were every bit as friendly and welcoming; they merely took their time. They tended to walk, rather than run or jump, and their walk was slow and dignified. Like their movement, their speech tended to be considered and meaningful. Today, these two types would be labelled 'extrovert' and 'introvert' and they occur among all humans, at least to some degree. Neither was right or wrong; neither was inferior or superior, just different.

Differences such as these influenced societies, no two of which were exactly the same. There were some standards which seemed to be universal: one did not physically harm one's fellow citizen; one did not cheat or lie to one's fellow; one did not take another's mate. Other laws and traditions varied from people to people; what was acceptable to some was not acceptable to others. Were we all the same, how boring life might be! Differences of opinion stimulated thought and were essential to human happiness – and progress. Wallace believed passionately in freedom of thought, writing to Sir Charles Lyell in 1872, asking him to use his influence in this direction, saying (p. 431):

> ... it is a disgrace to civilization and a crime against posterity, that the great mass of the instructors of our youth should still be those who are fettered by creeds and dogmas which they are under a penalty to teach ... it is the very first duty of the Government of a free people to take away all such restraints from the national church ... It is the duty of the State to disqualify as teachers, in all schools and colleges under its control, those whose interests are in any way bound up with the promulgation of fixed creeds or dogmas of whatever nature.

Alas that was one battle Wallace did not win.

In 1890, Wallace declared himself a socialist, making his first declaration of his position in an article on *Human Selection*, published in the September edition of the

Fortnightly Review. Being such a gentle soul, Wallace insisted that socialism must be adopted voluntarily, its benefits being so obvious that, once established in a small way, it would rapidly spread. Compulsory socialism was a contradiction in terms.

My earlier work was concerned with theories of evolution, Darwin and Wallace being but two of the people whose life work and theories I considered. I only had the time – and need – to read the first volume of Wallace's *My Life*. The reading of Volume 2 came, in many ways, as quite an eye opener, none more so than when reading Chapter 39: *A Chapter on Money Matters*, in which Wallace discussed 'earnings and losses – speculations and law-suites', of which he had had plenty. I had made the choice to leave the reading of this volume, and the writing of this chapter, until last. I am so glad I did, because I read Wallace's books, and wrote my thoughts about them, in the same state of ignorance about Wallace's personal problems, experiences and changing pattern of thoughts as had his readers. I have not changed that which I wrote as the result of this greater understanding. You, if you have started this book at Chapter 1 and are working your way through, will be in a different position, bringing a far greater understanding to your reading of the ways in which Wallace's life experiences had shaped his thoughts than did I, or Wallace's original readers.

From the reading I had done, I had received the impression that Wallace returned from his eight year sojourn in the Archipelago in straitened circumstances, that Darwin had come to his aid by arranging for him to receive a State pension, for which Wallace was extremely grateful. Part of this is true, but it is far from the whole truth.

Wallace returned from the Archipelago a wealthy man!

Wallace started the chapter by reminding his reader of the shipwreck which caused the loss of all the samples he was bringing back with him, which he had hoped to sell for a tidy profit. He told how the £150 insurance money had enabled him to live in London for a year, buy a good outfit of clothes and still be left with sufficient funds for his Malayan journey. The Malay Archipelago being so little known, the insects and birds being of such exceptional beauty, and often size, the samples he brought (safely) back home fetched high prices. His agent invested the money in Indian railway stock, bringing him an income of about £300 a year – from the interest. Had he disposed of the remainder of his samples in a similar manner, that amount would have been £500 a year, a very large sum at that time. Alas, that was not to be!

Instead of leaving his finances in the hands of a competent professional, Wallace started to make his own investments. He had a friend who was making money buying and selling shares on the stock exchange. He sold some of his Indian stock and started to do the same. Alas, the times, they were a-changing, as you will learn when you read about the great trade depression of 1875-1885, which brought Wallace close to ruin. Before that, in 1866, he had brought shares in a slate quarry, at which a friend of his was employed as Secretary, which some four or five years later went broke. Another friend had shares in some lead mines in Shropshire and Montgomeryshire, in which Wallace invested a large portion of his capital. How was he to know that Spain would soon be mining lead, prolifically? Or that lead would be a 'by-product' of silver-mining in Nevada, sold at almost 'waste' prices?

By 1880, Wallace was, indeed, in a precarious financial situation and it was at that time, eighteen years after his return to England, that Darwin came to his rescue, arranging for him to receive that State pension of £200 per year, for life, for which Wallace was genuinely extremely grateful.

These were not Wallace's only problems. When building his house at Grays in 1871, he found that the builder had not paid the workmen for two weeks. Of course, he paid them, sacked the builder and oversaw the completion of the house himself. This necessitated paying, for a second time, for materials, the builder having kept the money given to him for that purpose. Five years after the house was finished, the builder sued him for breach of contract for having terminated his employment! Wallace won and was awarded costs – which he never received, so he had to pay them himself.

Worse was to come. In 1870, Mr. John Hampden put out a challenge to anyone believing that the Earth was round to prove their case by the taking of measurements over a large body of 'flat' water. He would put up £500; anyone accepting his challenge would put up a similar amount, to be held by an adjudicator until one or other proved their point. Of course, Wallace rose to the challenge. Wallace gave an account (with sketched illustrations) of how this was done (several pages). Of course, Wallace was proved right, there was a slight curvature. Mr. Hampden refused to accept the findings. If they were right, then the Bible was wrong! That was impossible! Hampden demanded his money back. Gambling debts between two people were not recoverable by law but, in this case, the money had been handed to a third party. This provided a 'loop-hole' which Hampden was able to utilise. He lost, but did not give up. Not only did he not pay, he embarked upon a campaign of vicious public vilification, which lasted more than fifteen years. Wallace sued for libel, compelling Hampden to print public apologies. Wallace was awarded damages, but Hampden had transferred his property to his son-in-law and declared himself bankrupt. Wallace not only did not receive any compensation, he had to pay costs. Hampden was sentenced to two months' imprisonment at Newgate, but that did not stop him, neither did a further one year's imprisonment in 1875. In 1876, he sued the adjudicator for return of his money – and won – so Wallace had to return the £500, and pay costs, of course. And so it went on, both publicly and privately, with Wallace and his wife receiving threatening and abusive letters. "And this man was educated at Oxford University!" exclaimed Wallace (p. 376).

There was another small matter which irked Wallace just as much. In 1865, the British Museum owed Wallace £5 for a skeleton they had purchased from him. They wrote asking him to send a receipt, after receiving which they would pay him. Wallace, being the trusting man that he was, complied. He duly received a postal order - for £4 19s. 6d. They had deducted 6d. being the amount charge by the Post Office for the issuing of the money order. (Bank cheques carried stamp duty. All financial transactions, other than cash, involved some cost to the *debtor*.) Wallace decided to keep the accompanying letters, with the intention of one day publicly shaming the Museum. That day had now come!

Wallace was forced to rely on his writing, and his State pension. Looking back, he believed that all the traumas and difficulties he had encountered had been for the best. Without them, he would never have written the books and published the articles that he had and for which many people had expressed their appreciation. He had been instrumental in bringing new thoughts and concepts to many people. He declared that he was constitutionally lazy. Once having commenced upon a project, he would persist doggedly to the end, but he never started a new one unless 'forced' to do so. Everything he had written had been in response to questions and requests from others. Had he never suffered financial hardship, he declared, he would simply have retired to the country and spent his life working in his garden, which was the occupation he most enjoyed.

Wallace clearly had no objections to being the recipient of interest on his investments when he was the beneficiary. His objection to some people receiving money, which they had lifted not one finger to earn, came later! There is nothing wrong with changing one's opinion in response to wisdom and insight gained from a life-time of experience. Better that than persisting with prejudice conceived in ignorance. Wallace became a changed person over his life-time, a better person, he believed.

Through adversity we grow - we just need to make sure that we turn those stumbling blocks into stepping stones! Wallace may have stumbled a few times, but he never fell. He persevered and rose to great heights, heights never truly acknowledge by himself, or history.

Note: In his autobiography, Wallace never mentioned the names of his wife or his children. That of his children, I told you earlier. What you do not yet know is the name of his wife.

Annie

Chapter 3

The Wonderful Century

In 1898, Wallace published an interesting book entitled *The Wonderful Century: Its Successes and Its Failures*. Despite being one of Wallace's later works, it seemed appropriate to consider it first, because I felt sure the content had been accumulating in Wallace's mind for decades. The book summarised and demonstrated the sense of awe and admiration Wallace came to feel for this Earth, this Universe, as he observed human beings increasingly discovering and utilising some of its secrets, secrets which had been held for millions, even billions, of years, until humans finally reached the stage of their evolution which enabled them to start to comprehend. Understanding did not always come easily. There were failures as well as successes, but a failure may not be a complete failure if something is learnt from the experience.

The book was divided into two parts, that devoted to 'Failures' being longer than that devoted to 'Successes'. This was not, Wallace hastened to explain in his *Introduction*, because there were more failures than successes, rather it was because people tended to be far more aware of the successes, which only needed to be *described*, whereas they were either unaware of, or chose to ignore/deny, failures, which needed to be *proved*.

There were six chapters of failures, fifteen of successes. Of the failures, four chapters were on subjects upon which Wallace wrote elsewhere, such as poverty and the use of natural resources, which are covered in other chapters of this book. The remaining two considered phrenology and mesmerism (hypnotism), upon which he wrote no other books, so they will be discussed here.

Wallace believed humans had, during the century then drawing towards its close, made more progress in understanding, and, in some cases, mastering, certain aspects of our Universe than they had in all the preceding millennia of human history combined. He was right - and still is! For the most part, the first half of the twentieth century saw but a development of the ideas of the nineteenth, electricity, radio waves, X-rays, photography, the telegraph and telephone, even cars and aeroplanes, these were all off-spring of nineteenth century discoveries and inventions. Mid twentieth century, the atom was split and the nuclear age was born - for better, for worse. A couple of decades later, came the silicon chip. It may be argued that the computer reaped a more profound change upon our social structure than any other single discovery (except possibly electricity?) but we still have only two completely new concepts for the twentieth century and none from the first two decades of the twenty-first.

But there is at least one more item to be added to that short list. Around the middle of the twentieth century, plastic made its appearance - once again, for better, for worse. This product has probably transformed our lives as much as bronze or iron did the lives of our ancestors. When physicists are using modern means for estimating the age of certain items, such as radio-carbon dating skeletal remains, ancient or modern, allowance has to be made for artificial radiation introduced post-1945, with the start of the atomic age. Increasingly, (archæology) text books are using 'B.P.' (Before

Present) to replace the traditional 'B.C.' (Before Christ). For convenience the year 1950 was selected as the line of demarcation. Whenever I see those two letters, 'B.P.', I think 'Before Plastic'. After all, if we can have a Stone Age, a Bronze Age and an Iron Age, why can we not have a 'Plastic Age'?

Wallace made no mention of cars or planes. Both of these innovations were under development in the last decade of the nineteenth century, although their transformation of society only took place in the twentieth. Each person must decide for themselves the century to which they wish these innovations to be attributed. I have seen it argued that even travel to the Moon was but an extension of nineteenth century innovation, 'flight' having been 'getting off the ground' in its final years.

Wallace commenced by outlining the major discoveries of humans past, the first being the use of fire, which was universal across the world and had been used by our most ancient forebears. Neanderthals had been discovered, but not any earlier humans, so this statement was true for the time at which Wallace wrote. Wallace did not mention the Eskimo, although their lack of use of fire was not through any lack of ability; rather it was caused by the lack of trees! Brummer (1993) told of how he spent two years living with some of the last Eskimo, who told him that he was welcome to join them, living their 'igloo' life, provided he was prepared to eat raw meat. Apparently, the word 'Eskimo' meant 'eater of raw meat' and these people looked down with disdain upon those who cooked their food, so they were perfectly well aware of the practice, but chose not to use it. There are no Eskimo left. All dwellers in the far northern latitudes now lead a Westernised existence and the term 'Inuit', which originally applied to Eskimo people from North Canada, now applies to all.

Without fire, there would have been no bronze nor iron age, and without these there would have been no improved tools or weapons – or even the rudiments of chemistry.

Wallace next wrote of the development of the railways. It seemed quite a jump from the use of fire by pre-historic man to the railways, but there was a certain logic, because the steam engine was driven by fire. Same tool - different use! The concept of the steam engine had been the product of the eighteenth century but it had been developed for industrial use only, powering machinery in factories. Its use for travel had taken place during the early part of the nineteenth century. Wallace started by recalling how, in his boyhood, there were only two short railways, that between Stockton and Darlington having opened in 1825 and that between Liverpool and Manchester in 1830. Before that, travel had been by foot or by horseback. "In previous ages the only modes of travelling or of conveying goods for long distances were by employing either men or animals as carriers" (p. 5). He made no mention of the wheel, although he did mention "the yellow post-chaise ... the hundreds of four-horse mail and stage coaches ... passing through every town or village" (p. 4). If he mentioned the taming of fire as an early achievement, surely he should have mentioned the invention of the wheel? The wheel had played a pivotal role in the advancement of Asian and European culture. It was unknown in the Southern Hemisphere - southern Africa, Australia and New Zealand - and, surprisingly, in both south and north America. The Native Americans of North America had quite a sophisticated culture, but they had domesticated no animals nor made use of any wheel. They quickly adopted the horse, soon outstripping Europeans in their bare-back riding skills, but still ignored the wheel.

Wallace would have been unaware of the great civilizations which had once existed in the southern part of the continent - that of the Maya and the Incas. The discovery, hidden in the jungle, of great buildings, temples and pyramids, decorated, not just with pictures, but also with hieroglyphics, led to the suggestion that these people must either have come from Egypt or had extensive contact with it. There is an obvious appeal to this idea, but, if it is true, then it makes all the more surprising that there is no evidence of any South American peoples ever having used the wheel! I find Wallace's not having mentioned the wheel as an early invention somewhat surprising, but he didn't.

What had impressed Wallace was the speed with which hundreds - *thousands* - of miles of railway track had been laid down, criss-crossing the country, allowing ordinary people to leave their towns/villages in the morning, enjoy a day out - possibly by the sea-side, seeing the sea for the very first time - and then returning back home that same day! Until then, travel had been time consuming and expensive. Travel of any distance necessitated over-night stays, which added to the cost. Travel could also be dangerous and was often undertaken in groups. Train travel was not only safe, it was punctual. Furthermore, not only had the tracks been laid, but it had been found that steam engines could pull incredible weights - hundreds of people, tons of goods. This mass movement was crucial to keeping costs down. Early carriages were pretty rough and ready. Many of the economy class had no roof. People sheltered from the weather as best they could, beneath blankets, packed in like cattle. But it was worth it!

Prior to the arrival of the railway had been that of the canals, which had greatly improved the transport of goods. They were only able to operate thanks to the ingenious system of lochs, but their comparatively slow speed, along with their small load capacity, put a stop to their further development - although some are still in use today.

By the end of the century, trains had become such an everyday part of life, not only in Britain (where they were invented) but across the world, that Wallace felt the younger generation may not be fully aware of quite how transformational their introduction had been.

Steam travel had also become a reality upon the seas. In 1838, the *Great Western* made the journey from Bristol to New York in fourteen days. Higher speeds were possible but were attained at the expense of greatly increased consumption of coal. Considerably higher speeds had been attained by torpedo-boats and torpedo-destroyers.

Finally, Wallace mentioned the wheel – in its role in the new method of locomotion: the bicycle – and the tricycle. It has often been commented upon that the bicycle made a surprisingly late appearance. Wallace explained this by the extraordinary delicacy needed in its construction, to enable it both to support the necessary weight and yet remain in perfect balance. In past times, the necessary combination of strength, accuracy and lightness would not have been attainable. Wallace predicted that, by the addition of a small motor to a bicycle, a speed of fifty miles an hour might soon be achieved.

In his next chapter, Wallace moved to labour-saving machinery, mentioning specifically the type-writer, the sewing machine and the combined-harvester. He devoted a paragraph to the complexities which had needed to be overcome to produce the type-writer, but the machine was so well-known that he did not need to allocate much space to it. Of the sewing machine, he had more to say, pointing out that its use was not restricted to the sewing of seams, but that it was able to button-hole, sew on buttons, was used for carpet-sewing, leather work and in the making, and repairing, of shoes. Machine-made boots and shoes were very cheap, although of an inferior quality to the old-fashioned hand-made variety. Nevertheless, their appearance had been greatly welcomed by the poorer classes, which (I believe) up until that time, had had to rely on hand-me-downs. I cannot believe that they would have been able to afford hand-made boots or shoes, at least, not since the advent of the Industrial Revolution. In times gone by, the Lord of the Manor may have paid the local shoe-maker to provide everybody on this estate with shoes? If that had been the case in the past, it most certainly was not the case in the nineteenth century.

Of the three machines mentioned in this chapter, Wallace placed the most importance on the harvesting-machine. The saving in time and energy compared with the old-fashioned method of hand-reaping, baling, the building of hay-stacks or the moving of hay for storage in barns, followed by dismantling for threshing, was immense. Perhaps the more important was the saving in time, not because it saved money but because it allowed the farmer to choose the day for harvesting. In the past, many a harvest had been adversely affect by rain. The weather may have been fine when harvesting commenced, but the whole process could take three or four weeks, depending upon how many fields there were to be cut. August was harvest month and the August weather was notoriously unreliable. To be able safely to cut and store the harvest in a few (fine) days was truly a blessing for mankind.

Having spoken of the public transport of the body, Wallace now turned his attention to the public transport of thought. Initially, communication between people at a distance had been by messenger, on foot (runner) or on horseback. The invention of writing had seen the verbal message give way to the written communication – the letter. In both cases, this exchange was mostly between Courts, or Courts and the Army and frequently consisted of one letter (or message) at a time. "Letters were carried on horseback until 1783, when mail coaches were first introduced; and these led to a great improvement in our main roads and the extension of the postal service to every town or village in the kingdom" (p. 18). Delivery still took time, a problem eased by the advent of the steam-ship and the railway. Cost, also, was a big factor but this was helped by the introduction of a fixed delivery charge, irrespective of distance. It was recognized that the principal cost lay not with the distance the letter needed to travel, but in the labour involved in its collection, sorting and delivery. Between 1840 and 1871, the cost of postage increased, not by distance, but by weight, "the half-ounce letter being a penny, while one of two ounces was four-pence" (p. 19).

The most profound change in communication had been brought about by the introduction of the electric telegraph, which enabled rapid (almost instantaneous) communication between people on opposite sides of the world! Even today, I marvel at this, be the communication by phone, face-book or via the television, which enables me to watch a tennis match being played at Wimbledon from the comfort of my own home in Australia. The first electric telegraph had been established in 1837, but only operated across land. It had not then been thought possible to lay cables across the Atlantic but the first submarine line had been laid between Dover and Calais only fourteen years later, in 1851. A cable laid between Ireland and Newfoundland in 1858 had had to be abandoned but another was laid in 1866 and, since then, a further fourteen lines had been laid across the Atlantic, "while all the other oceans have been electrically bridged so that messages can be sent to almost any part of the globe" (p. 21). In some cases, Wallace suggested, mischievously, an event could be reported before it had happened! If someone died in Calcutta at sunset, news of the death would be received in England at dawn of that same day.

Following the telegraph had come the telephone. This was not the actual transmission of the voice, but a reproduction of the pattern of vibration made by the voice at one end of the cable by a similar vibration at the other, which was so effective that the listener was able to distinguish between the voice of one person and another. Initially, the process was effective only over short distances but now could be used cross-Atlantic. There was even a news service. At certain fixed times, news was relayed to the homes or offices of subscribers, who could listen in, if they so desired.

These improvements in communication, which all took place during the nineteenth century, were truly astounding, although it must be said that the general use of the telephone in private homes took some time. When I was a child, one asked "Are you on the phone" in rather the same way that one now asks "Are you on the Internet?". By the 1960s, in England at least, I think that just about everybody who wanted a phone, had one, but that was about one hundred years after the technology had been introduced and it was by no means universal throughout the world.

Returning to the subject of fire at the beginning of Chapter IV, Wallace did mention that some tribes either did not know how to kindle fire, or chose not to, preferring to use fire sticks, which were kept permanently alight. If their fire stick did fail, these people would ask for a 're-light' from a neighbouring tribe, which was always given. The Tasmanians were one such people.

He speculated that the preservation of fire had originated either from its 'rescue' from some volcanic eruption, or even the procuring of it by the thrusting of sticks into volcanic lava flows, or by utilizing small branches from trees ignited by lightning. There were reports of trees spontaneously igniting by the constant rubbing together, by the wind, of dry twigs still on the tree. He did not give an origin for these reports, but the oil-rich Australian Eucalypt would be a likely candidate. Wallace suggested tribal people witnessing such an advent might then have copied the process, rubbing twigs together until fire was obtained. He then made the rather extraordinary statement that such a method only required materials that were available just about anywhere. This from a man who had lived for years in the tropics where it rained for months on end! Even when the rain stopped, it would take time for the land to dry out, as I am sure the aboriginal residents of Tasmania's forests found out.

Wallace made this return to the subject of fire because he was about to refer to the invention of the match. Flint and tinder had been in use for centuries. Wallace remembered it being used by the family cook each morning. It was a tedious process and sometimes people abandoned the attempt and turned to their next-door neighbour for a light. Around 1827, a Mr. John Walker had invented a match using wood splints dipped in chlorate of potash or sulphur, mixed with gum, which ignited when rubbed on sandpaper. About 1834, phosphorus started to be used, with other materials, and by 1840 had become so cheap as to be in general use.

Even though the act of striking was still necessary, Wallace considered this not to be an extension of an old practice, but a new departure, one which had brought great benefit to countless people around the world. (Unfortunately, it was later found that phosphorus was poisonous, causing cancer of the bone, known as 'phossy jaw', the phosphorus having been transferred from the fingers of those involved in their manufacture to their mouths. The 'safety match' was developed and is still in use today.)

For light, brush-wood torches had been used since time immemorial. Candles for indoor use were a comparatively recent invention but torches had still been used outside after dark "almost down to our times, an indication of which is seen in the iron torch-extinguishers at the doors of many of the older West End houses" (p. 27). Lamps, small clay dishes filled with animal fat and a wick, had been used for indoor lighting before the advent of candles, but their illumination was not very great. It was not until the end of the eighteenth century that the Argund burner had been introduced, a glass chimney with a regular supply of air, which allowed the candle to burn steadily and brightly. It was not until the 1830s that they had been sufficiently refined to become a common household item.

Then had come the introduction of the gas-light. The technology had been introduced at the end of the previous century but it was not until 1813 that it came into public use when Westminster Bridge was illuminated by it. So successful was this innovation that its use soon spread to every town in the kingdom, for the lighting of private houses as well as of streets. More recent was the introduction of the electric light which had "already attained a considerable extension for public and private illumination" (p. 29). More surprising was the medical use to which electric light was being put. "Small incandescent lamps are now used for examinations of the larynx and in dentistry, and a lamp has even been introduced into the stomach by which the condition of that organ can be examined" (p. 29). Other internal organs had been examined in the same way - I presume the bowel!

Wallace mentioned the illumination of submarines and the exploration of the interior of sunken vessels as other uses to which electric lighting had been put.

Until the nineteenth century, the means of lighting had changed little over time. In that century alone, three innovations had been made: the Argund burner, gas-lighting and various modes of electric lighting. Wallace did not explain what he meant by 'various methods' but battery lighting would seem to be the most appropriate means of lighting for exploring the interior of sunken vessels? The word 'battery' does not appear in his index.

Wallace's next chapter was devoted to photography. This was something completely new, not just a new method of solving an old problem.

That certain salts of silver were darkened by exposure to sunlight had been known to the alchemists of the sixteenth century, However, it was not until 1802 that Wedgewood described a method of copying paintings on glass by exposure to light but no way was found of making these copies permanent. In 1839 Daguerre perfected the method of making permanent portraits on silvered plates, but they were very costly and could not be reproduced.

In 1850, colloidal-film glass was perfected and negatives were taken in a *camera obscura*, by which I presume Wallace meant a box covered by a black velvet cloth, beneath which the photographer crouched. These were negatives. Soon after positives were printed from the negatives on suitably prepared paper. Photography had been born and soon grew and matured. "Moving crowds, then breaking waves, running horses, and other quickly moving objects were taken, while now a bullet fired from a rifle can be photographed in the air" (p. 33).

Photography was coming to the aid of science, enabling the meteorologist, the physicist, the biologist, to preserve accurate records of the most fleeting natural phenomena. They were able to study the motion of the wings of birds in flight; they were able to capture the (almost) instantaneous lightning flash. For Wallace, perhaps the most marvellous achievement was in the field of astronomy: "... by the aid of photography, stars are shown which no telescope that has been, or probably ever will be constructed, can render visible to the human eye. For by exposing the photographic plate ... for some hours, almost infinitely faint stars impress their image ..." (p. 34). Considering Wallace's passion for nature, the number of articles and books he had written about both flora and fauna, for him to find *anything* more fascinating than the movement of the wing of a bird in flight, let alone the path of a flash of lightning, was quite amazing. It bore witness to his growing interest in astronomy, which subject he also studied sufficiently to be able to write a book - *Man's Place in the Universe* - which was published in 1903. This will be discussed in Chapter 13.

It was now possible for photographs to be reproduced as illustrations in books and periodicals and progress was being made towards the development of colour photography. Problems at that time consisted of the colour photograph being more brilliant than in nature, expensive and difficult to reproduce. These problems were not easily solved. In my childhood, photographs were still black and white. I first remember colour photographs in my late teens (mid 1950s) but many people still preferred black and white, which gave a sharper picture.

The most incredible thing of all was the discovery of the Röntgen or X-Ray, by which it was possible to produce images of the interior of the body! These rays differed from standard light rays. They could not be refracted or reflected, but they could pass through solid objects in a way completely impossible for the standard ray of light. In fact, the image was not formed by refraction or reflexion; rather what was captured was the *shadow* formed as the rays passed through the object, that shadow being deeper for the solid parts of the body – the bone.

But Wallace was not done. There were yet more wonders of the nineteenth century to be brought before his readers' attention, spectrum analysis, for example. Spectrum analysis had given the scientist: "... a perfectly new engine of research, by which we are enabled to penetrate into the remotest depths of space, and learn something of the constitution and the motions of the constituent bodies of the stellar universe. Through its means we have acquired what are really the equivalents of new senses, which give us knowledge that before seemed absolutely and forever unattainable by man" (p. 42).

Humans had long been fascinated and entranced by the colours reflected by the dew drop, the crystal and, of course, the rainbow, but our appreciation of colour was limited to the wave lengths our eyes were designed to determine. In 1802, Dr. Wollaston had discovered that the solar-spectrum was crossed by very numerous black lines of various thickness, and at irregular distances from each other. Wallace then gave an explanation of the meaning and importance of this discovery, which I am not even going to attempt to summarize. The long and short of it was that scientists were now able to determine the composition of stellar bodies! "Thus hydrogen, sodium, iron, magnesium, copper, zinc, calcium, and many other elements have been proved to exist in the sun" (p. 44). Furthermore, a line unable to be correlated with any known substance on Earth was named helium, after the sun. Recently, the rare mineral had been identified on Earth.

The earlier suggestion that stars were really suns was now confirmed. Some of these sun/stars had spectrums similar to that of our Sun, being yellow in colour, and were therefore assumed to be composed of similar elements. Others, such as Sirius and Vega, were more white, seemed to be composed only of hydrogen and therefore supposed to be hotter than our Sun, in an earlier stage of development, while other 'red' stars were supposed to be cooling. Astronomers were grappling with the extreme remoteness of some star clusters.

It hardly seems possible that, in Wallace's youth, people were grappling with the concept of evolution having taken place upon the face of this Earth. Now they were accepting that the stars, the Heavens, were evolving!

[Note: My supervisor at University was an amateur astronomer. He argued that if Mercury, Mars, Venus, Jupiter and Saturn could have capital letters, then why not Sun, Earth and Moon - and, of course, the Heavens?]

Another great step forward which had been taken in the nineteenth century was an understanding of heat. It may seem strange to us now, but heat was quite a puzzle to early alchemists and physicists. It could be felt; it could be transferred; but what was it? Heat poured down upon the Earth from the Sun; it was clearly present beneath the surface of the Earth because it burst forth with volcanic eruptions and was also present in some hot springs. It was assumed to be some unknown form of matter, known as phlogiston or caloric. Caloric could be created by friction, but then dissipated. From where had it come, to where did it go? Substances heated did not change their weight but could change their form and even, just a little, their size. An understanding of the nature of matter, of atoms and molecules, had allowed an association to be drawn between matter, energy, movement and heat. Energy was required to create movement; movement produced heat. When energy was withdrawn, when stillness replaced movement, the temperature dropped to the ambient temperature – that of the environment. It came to be accepted that energy was neither created nor destroyed, merely changed from one form into another, and one of those other forms could be heat. Substances had three forms: solid, liquid, gas. Most needed a large energy transfer to mutate from one form to another. Water was the most malleable, being known in all three forms in a natural state.

Estimations were made of the increase/decrease in volume with the increase/decrease of heat. It was found that gases expanded or contracted 1/273rd of their volume for each degree of heat (Centigrade). From this it was estimated that -273°C was absolute zero because further contraction was impossible. Our Earth operated nearly at the bottom of the heat spectrum. "Heat, therefore, seems to be the source of all change in matter, and the essential condition of all life" (p. 58).

Around the middle of the century, scientists had experimented with beams of light in darkened rooms, reflected off angled mirrors and by dint of meticulous measurement had been able to estimate the speed of light. Not surprisingly, there was some discrepancy between the calculations made by different scientists, the estimated speed varying between 185,157 and 186,327 miles per second. A hundred years previously, few would have realized that light had a speed at all, let alone have conceived that human beings would be able to calculate it. What an incredible achievement. What an incredible speed!

Wallace mentioned the phonograph, or gramophone, as it became known, another invention of the genius, Edison. Like the telephone, it did not carry sound directly. It transferred the vibration made by sound to another medium, in this case the vibrations were registered permanently in a cylinder of very hard wax as an indented spiral line. This was accomplished by the aid of a fine steel point which cut a groove into the wax as the cylinder revolved at a perfectly uniform rate. The groove varied in depth, depending upon the vibration of the sound it was recording, which variation would reproduce, with amazing exactitude the original sound.

I grew up in the days of the old '78s', discs which revolved at 78 revolutions per minute. If the record became scratched, it was useless, so great care needed to be taken when handling. The steel needles could only be used once. Around the 1950s, a more slender, lighter-weight needle was introduced, identified by its yellow shaft, which could be used ten times! I remember the introduction of the '45s' and '33s', which, not only rotated more slowly, but, in the case of the 33's, were larger and could thus play for longer, making more practical the recording of orchestral music, rather than the single song. I had a basic understanding of how the thing worked – to about the same standard as Wallace's explanation – but what I did not understand then, and still do not understand today, is how that steel needle, vibrating in that groove, could reproduce several different sounds at the same time. The strings, the wind, the percussion instruments, possibly a vocalist, or even a choir, all could be distinctly heard. How was that accomplished?

It is perhaps difficult today to realize quite how great a bonus it was for people to be able to have a means of hearing beautiful music within their own homes, without the need to travel into town, to buy a ticket, for a professional concert. Large houses might have employed a small three or four piece *énsemble* to provide evening entertainment, but this option was not available to many. But, of course, the phonograph was not made only for pleasure. The technology was quickly adapted for use in the office "for rapid dictation of correspondence, which can be reproduced and copied by a clerk later on; to take down discussions verbatim ... and even the languages, songs, and folk-lore of dying-out tribes are being preserved on these wonderful cylinders" (p. 67).

Chapter 4

The Wonderful Century
(Cont'd)

In a book devoted to the wonders of the 19th century, who would have expected a chapter on the subject of *"The Importance of Dust"*? Its subtitle: *"A Source of Beauty and Essential to Life"* would surely have attracted attention!

Few people, Wallace surmised, would have thought that dust had any good use at all. Even setting aside its negative appearance within our homes, was not dust a source of disease? Did it not, in extreme cases in some countries, cause ophthalmia and even blindness? In the same way that a weed is merely a plant in the wrong place, so dust, Wallace assured us, was merely matter in the wrong place: "... whatever injurious or disagreeable effects it produces are largely due to our own dealings with nature" (p. 69).

Ever the optimist, Wallace declared that as soon as humans dispensed with horse-power and adopted purely mechanical means of conveyance, so soon would we almost wholly abolish disease-bearing dust from our streets. Wallace was, of course, referring to the manure which horses were constantly depositing upon the streets, which kept an army of street cleaners constantly employed. Wallace was aware that vehicles driven by an imperfect combustion of coal would result in another kind of dust, but that "... may be got rid of with equal facility so soon as we consider pure air, sunlight, and natural beauty to be more important to the population as a whole than are the prejudices or the vested interests of those who produce the smoke" (p. 70). This was pure political hyperbole – plenty of reassuring words, but no detail! Eliminating the impurities left behind by imperfect combustion is not easy – as many towns and cities have found to their cost.

Wallace was not to know that. Let us, therefore, imagine the clean, horse-free streets of his imagination. Where does dust come in?

Fortunately, we would never be able entirely to eliminate dust. 'Fortunately' because it had now been discovered that it was to dust that we owed much of the beauty we saw around us – "... perhaps even the very habitability of the earth we live upon" (p. 70). These were strong words.

It had now been discovered (realized) why the sky and the sea appeared to us to be blue. Air was not blue, water was not blue, although in the past it had indeed been thought that they were, only of such a pale shade that the colour was not visible to our human eye, except when the air/water was seen in great volume. Left unexplained were the glorious colours of the sunrise and sunset.

In 1868, Professor Tyndall had carried out some interesting experiments. Everybody was aware of the sight of dust floating in the air when caught in a beam of sunlight streaming through a window. Not everybody was aware that, if there was absolutely no dust whatsoever in the air, the path of the sunbeam would be totally black and invisible, while if only a very little dust was present, the air would be as blue as a summer sky (p. 71).

Tyndall's experiments had shown that, if a ray of electric light were passed through a long glass cylinder in the air of an ordinary room, no matter how clean and well-dusted, the cylinder would appear brilliantly illuminated. If the cylinder was filled with air which had repeatedly been filtered with extreme care so that it was as free of floating particles as it was possible for it to be, then the light would pass through the cylinder without illuminating the interior.

Had I been asked, I would probably have said space was dark because there was no atmosphere to refract the light. But what would I have meant by 'atmosphere'? 'Air'? Molecules? Atoms? According to my dictionary, I would have meant: "a spherical gaseous envelope" which, apparently, had a weight of 15 lb. per square inch. Obviously, atoms and molecules were involved, but if these atoms and molecules were perfectly 'clean', would they refract light or would the Earth be in darkness? That, it would seem, was not only a good question, in this context, it was the only question.

In the 'normal' atmosphere, the number of dust particles is so great that they reflect all wave lengths (both those that our eyes can see and those which they cannot, such as infra-red and ultra-violet, although Wallace was not aware of these). Where the air is thinner, and contains less dust particles, only the shorter wave-lengths are refracted, giving the air a bluish tinge, which, seen from our vantage point, being many miles thick, appears to our eye as the clear blue of the summer sky. At lower levels, some yellow-white light is also refracted, causing the blue to be less intense at sea level than at the top of mountains. The same principle applies to the sea. Rivers and streams appear clear - or muddy - but not blue. It needs the depth of the sea water, together with its impurities, to produce a blue colour, best seen in shallow waters, such as those around coral reefs, where there is little mud but sufficient particles.

It is to the impurities (dust) in the air that we owe the refraction of light by which we not only see the world, but see it in glorious colour. Following volcanic eruptions, or dust storms, when the air is thick with dust, the lower wavelengths are refracted, giving their typical red-glow. The sun appears red when rising and setting because we are looking at it through a more heavily polluted atmosphere, horizontally at ground level, rather than vertically, as at noon.

But wait - there's more!

"To the presence of dust in the higher atmosphere we owe the formation of mists, clouds, and gentle beneficial rains, instead of waterspouts and destructive torrents" (p. 77). Experiments with receptacles filled with ordinary and filtered air showed that, when steam was introduced, the former instantly filled with condensed vapour, while the contents of the latter remained quite transparent. Many experiments were carried out which confirmed that the mere cooling of air was not sufficient for the formation of mist/cloud, "unless particles *of solid matter* are present to form *nuclei* upon which condensation can begin ... If there were no dust in the air ... there would be no clouds in the sky" (p. 78 - italics in original).

Reading this reminded me of experiments carried out some years ago (1970s?) when it was hoped to be able to increase rainfall in drought stricken areas by 'seeding' clouds. There needed to be at least some small amount of cloud present for 'seeding' to commence. Nothing seemed to come of the idea. I think it was too uncertain; the small clouds came and went too quickly for them to be utilized. The whole process was too costly for its small, uncertain, result.

Without dust, water would return to the Earth, but as dense mists, not rain. This would not be sufficient to support the growth of trees. Water would swirl above the earth (soil - small 'e'), but would not be absorbed into it in any great amount. There would be no rivers, no lakes, no sea. Wallace wrote that, without solid matter in the upper atmosphere, all the moisture would be returned to the lower atmosphere in the form of dense mists, which in the forests would form torrents of rain (p. 79). I question this, because I doubt that there would have been enough moisture absorbed into the earth for trees to have evolved in the first place.

Not too long ago, I saw a documentary about rain-making in a mountainous area, I think somewhere on the west coast of South America. The tops of the mountains were constantly covered in mist, but no rain fell. The lower plains were scrubby desert. They had built mesh screens, upon which the water formed droplets, which ran down into gutters along the base of the frame, which was collected and piped down to irrigate the land below. This process was based upon the principles Wallace reported here.

Wallace (correctly) attributed to the increased pollution in the skies above Britain the increased amount of mists and fogs which were being noted, especially in the winter months, when, of course, more fires were burning. Such fogs came to be known as 'smogs'. We (in London) used to treat the whole thing as a bit of a joke until the Great Smog of 1952. Road vehicles were brought to a halt; even the trains had to proceed slowly. It was impossible to see one's hand in front of one's face – I remember, I was caught out in it. We walked in the gutter, using the kerb to guide us – and the cars which crawled along behind us. This event saw the introduction of the 'Clean Air Act' (1956) which heralded the demise of the well-known London fog.

That we owe the light of day to the fine particles present in our atmosphere, that without them our Earth would constantly be in total darkness, was certainly a novel thought. I now treat the coming of daylight with new respect and gaze upon the colours around me with an even deeper sense of awe.

Wallace concluded by saying that, while 'dust' was essential for life to exist on Earth, too much was detrimental. As always, we needed to keep a balance, to walk that elusive Middle Path.

The next chapter was a rejoicing that the scientists of the wonderful 19th century had managed to achieve something which had eluded their alchemist forebears – they had discovered how elements combined! True, they had not changed lead into gold – although, unbeknownst to Wallace, in the next (twentieth) century lead was to be associated with something far more valuable – uranium!

Atoms and molecules may not be visible to the human eye, not even with the help of powerful microscopes, but compelling logic testified to their existence. The notion of their (slightly) different composition being the contributing factor to their differing weight, gave rise to the concept of the Periodic Table. The elements were each given an abbreviation, one or two letters. Hydrogen was recognized as being the lightest gas and was given the number '1'. All other elements received their number according to their weight by comparison with hydrogen – nitrogen 14, oxygen 16, and so on. Solids, such as aluminium, iron, copper and silver, were heavier, as indicated by their numbers 27, 56, 63 and 107. Scientists had worked out, not only individual atomic weights, but also combinations. For example, pure alcohol was formed by $C2H2O$. As the Table was brought into being by the Russian chemist, Mendeleef, it formed an oblong, eight vertical columns with twelve horizontal lines. Mendeleef was able to predict that the blank spaces would eventually be filled by atoms at present unknown, and that was already starting to happen by the time Wallace was writing. Wallace specified the discovery of gallium, scandium and germanium.

From the elements of Earth to the elements of the Universe, Wallace moved on to astronomy. Uranus had been discovered in 1781, by Herschel. Ceres, a minor planet, was discovered in 1801 and by 1807 it had been joined by three other minor planets. There was a lull until a further two were observed in 1845 and 1847. Since then, no year had passed without the discovery of one, or more, minor planets until, by September 1896 (when Wallace was writing) their number had grown to 417. These small bodies formed a planetary ring between Mars and Jupiter. Astronomers had long suspected that there might be an unknown planet in that vicinity, because the distance between Mars and Jupiter was so much larger than that between the other planetary bodies of our solar system, which included Earth. At first, it was suggested that these bodies were the remains of a larger planet which had fragmented but now astronomers were leaning towards the notion that they were remnants of matter thrown off by the Sun, which had failed to aggregate into a larger planet.

Neptune was discovered by mathematics. In 1843, a Cambridge student, John Couch Adams, had observed that the movement of Uranus was not quite as it should be and had postulated that the perturbations were caused by the influence of another planet. The French astronomer, Leverrier, had reached a similar conclusion and published his work in 1845 and 1846. Discoveries continued to be made. Wallace was particularly fascinated by a system of symmetrical markings on Mars. Also found on Mars had been a system of 'canals' which appeared and disappeared and which were presumed to be associated in some way with water. Wallace wrote a book about Mars, which will be considered later. The rings of Saturn were discovered and were the subject of much theorising. The spectroscope had enabled scientists to ascertain that the inner edge of the ring was moving more rapidly than the outer, confirming that the rings were not solid, but gaseous or particulate.

The falling of stones from the sky had been reported from antiquity but happened so rarely that there was no means of undertaking any systematic observation, and many people were simply disbelieved. Finally, on 26th April, 1803, a brilliant fireball was seen hurtling through the sky over Aigle, in Normandy, which exploded, showering down stones, of which about three thousand were retrieved. It was now accepted that the Heavens were not empty, except for scattered stars, but full of matter, from the size of particles of dust to huge masses, several times the size of Earth.

Such happenings led towards a new concept of the possible origin of the Universe, one in which the solar and stellar systems had been formed by an aggregation of particles, molecules, atoms, which had come together under the influence of gravity, producing heat, incandescence and sometimes elemental vaporization, as opposed to having been formed by the cooling and contraction of a primitive cosmic vapour. It was now known that there was (pp. 104-105):

> ... a perfect gradation from the faintest and least condensed nebulæ to the most brilliant stars ... being different stages in the aggregation of meteoritic matter everywhere and always going on ... The nebulæ of various forms and intensity represent, therefore, the early stages in the development of stars, suns, and planetary systems out of diffused meteoritic matter; while stars themselves are of various temperatures, the heat increasing when the meteoritic matter is most rapidly aggregating, and afterward cooling till they become of so low a temperature as to cease to be luminous to our vision ... This conception of the meteoritic constitution of the whole stellar universe is one of the grandest achievements of the science of the nineteenth century.

Think back a hundred years, to the end of the second decade of the twentieth century. How much has our concept of the creation of the Universe changed since then? Very little. The much vaunted 'Big Bang' theory made no attempt to explain what went bang, or why. It merely made an attempt to insert one step further back, a step which 'explained' the presence of the particles which the nineteenth century astronomers had claimed had aggregated. Compare this with the change in thinking which had taken place in the century of which Wallace was writing! What a profound difference!

Wallace was aware of the shortcomings of the current theories. Whence the chemical forces? And more mysterious than all, whence the force of gravitation, infinite, unchangeable, and at the very root of cosmic development? (Gravity is all the more mysterious when considered in association with the concept of an ever-*expanding* Universe.)

It was theorised that matter had formed out of 'ether' - a primæval substance assumed, but never proven, to exist. It was the movement of the ether which caused the formation of atoms, molecules, particles. The concept of ether has now been abandoned but nothing has taken its place.

And when we had grappled with these inconceivabilities, Wallace warned, there still remained "the even greater inconceivability of how life, consciousness, affection, intellect, arose from this infinite clash of etheral vortex-rings!" (p. 109). All human intellectual effort had brought us "no nearer to the First Cause of this vast cosmos in which we live" (p. 109).

From the astronomical evolution of the Universe, Wallace turned to the geological evolution of the Earth. He acknowledged the foundation for modern geology had been lain in the latter part of the eighteenth century by workers such as Werner, Hutton and William Smith. I would like to add the names of Buffon and Erasmus Darwin, whose theories regarding the great antiquity of the Heavens and the Earth, as well as of their changing nature over time, provided the foundation upon which the others erected their theories.

They wrote in the second half of the eighteenth century. In the early part of the nineteenth century, of which Wallace was writing, Cuvier was the acknowledged expert. He had denied the evolution of species but had been forced to acknowledge, thanks to the finding of large numbers of fossils of creatures now extinct, that change had occurred over time. He came to believe that there had been a number of 'Ages', each separated by some form of catastrophe, after which God had created new creatures, which remained unchanged (apart from minor variation) until the end of that Age. Noah's Flood had been the last catastrophe. It wiped out most living things, plant as well as animal. God then 'replenished' the Earth. Cuvier's *Essay on the Theory of the Earth* was the dominant text until 1830, when the first volume of Lyell's *Principles of Geology* was published. Lyell's theory became known as 'Uniformitarianism' since it argued that the laws governing the Universe were the same now as they had ever been. Any changes which had occurred, had occurred in conformity with these universal and unchanging laws.

The great advancement of the 19th century was the acknowledgement that there had been at some time in the past a Great Ice Age. Perhaps it is not so surprising that it was a Swiss engineer named Venetz who first made the deduction! He noted that where modern glaciers had retreated, the rocks they had previously covered were either rounded, smooth and polished or grooved and striated in the direction of the glacier's movement. There were many such rocks, far away from any modern-day glacier. There must have been glaciers in the past where none exist today.

People had long been puzzled by large rocks, perched in the middle of some stream or meadow, bearing no relationship to the landscape around them. How had they come to be where they now were? Put there by giants, who used to roam the land was the usual answer. Carried into position by ice, which then melted and left them stranded, was a far more satisfactory explanation. Fossil evidence proved that this Great Ice Age had occurred during the period of human existence - which was now acknowledged to be but a short time compared with the existence of the planet.

There was evidence of an Ice Age in New Zealand, Tasmania and the southern-most part of the Andes, although it was not known whether these two Ice Ages, that of the northern and that of the southern hemispheres, had occurred concurrently. The northern Ice Age had been estimated to have occurred between 20,000-100,000 years ago, probably including one or more milder inter-glacial periods. This was a good estimation. The temperature did, indeed, undergo several quite noticeable fluctuations over that period of time.

We now know that there have been several Great Ice Ages, interspersed with minor Ice Ages, and even Mini or Little Ice Ages. The time between these events are known as interstadials. The last Great Ice Age was from 30,000 B.C.-10,000 B.C. The last Little Ice Age was from approximately 1350 A.D.-1750 A.D. We are still coming out of it, temperatures not yet having reached the level of Norman times. (Rising temperatures melted the ice cap; even King Canute could not turn back the rising tide. It was not only Holland and Denmark which built protective sea walls. They were built along the east coast of England as well, where some may still be seen to this day.)

The final part of this chapter was devoted to a discussion on the antiquity of Man. Initially, evidence had been by the finding of well-worked flint tools, which were acknowledged to have been quite ancient. Then had come the discovery of human remains in the Neander Valley and the recognition that there had once existed a form of human with a cranium shape distinctly different from that of modern humans. The Neanderthals were assumed to be ancestral to modern humans. The suggestion that the human line had been subject to speciation was to be made in the 20th century. When, where and how frequently is still a matter of debate.

In Chapter 13, Wallace approached a subject very dear to his heart – evolution by natural selection. He acknowledged the early work of Buffon, Erasmus Darwin and of the poet, Goethe, who had: "put forth various hints and suggestions pointing to evolution in the organic world" (p. 135). He mentioned Lamarck's *Philosophie Zoologique* (published 1809) which contained an elaborate exposition of progressive development but which theory had gained few converts because it was too far ahead of its time. The next great work, that of Robert Chambers, *Vestiges of the Natural History of Creation*, published anonymously in 1844, reviewed the coming into being of the solar systems, the geological history of the Earth and the progressive development of plants and animals. It was a comprehensive volume, but no attempt had been made to explain *how* or *why* this progressive development had occurred. Wallace recalled how his interest had been excited by Chambers' book, which was highly successful. In 1852, Herbert Spencer had published his well-known essay on *Creation and Development*. However, it was not until 1858 that any theory had been put forward suggesting *how* changes had occurred in species.

In 1855, while in Sarawak, Wallace had written what became known as his 'Law' paper in which he claimed: "Every species has come into existence coincident both in Space and Time with a Pre-existing closely allied Species" (p. 139). In other words, species had evolved. Had new species been separately created by God, would not at least some of them have been found in places far removed from already existing similar species? In his paper, Wallace referred only to change in the wild. At that time, Wallace wrote, he had no conception of *how* or *why* new forms had come into existence.

Wallace gave an account of how light on the subject had suddenly come to him in February, 1858, during a severe attack of intermittent fever. He had been led to think of Malthus' Essay, on the checks on population exerted by war, disease and famine. It occurred to him that these checks must also occur on animals in nature and thus the concept of *the survival of the fittest* suddenly flashed upon him (p. 140):

> ... the whole method of specific modification became clear to me, and in the two hours of my fit I had thought out the main points of the theory. That same evening I sketched out the draft of a paper; in the two succeeding evenings I wrote it out, and sent it by the next post to Mr. Darwin.

It has been suggested that later in life Wallace began to suspect what we now know, that Darwin had not been as far ahead of him as he, Wallace, had thought, that he had come to this realization when Darwin's letters started to be published by his son, Sir Francis, after his father's death. One cannot help but feel that this chapter is a quiet claim on his own behalf for acknowledgement of a greater share of the credit for the discovery of the principle of Natural Selection.

Wallace referred again to Chamber's great work, *Vestiges*, to his own earlier 'Law' paper. He mentioned the term *'survival of the fittest'*, so associated with the name and work of Herbert Spencer. Then came his recollection of his surprise that his idea was not new to Darwin because Darwin had told him that his book was only to be about differences between species and varieties. He seemed to be implying that Darwin had 'misled', if not deliberately 'deceived' him. He subtly reminded his reader that Darwin had committed his thoughts to paper as early as 1844, not in a published paper, but in an informal essay which he had shown to Lyell and Hooker. Wallace concluded (p. 142):

> Probably so complete a change of educated opinion, on a question of such vast difficulty and

complexity, was never before effected in so short a time. It not only places the name of Darwin on a level with that of Newton, but his work will always be considered as one of the greatest, if not the very greatest, of the scientific achievements of the nineteenth century, rich as that century has been in great discoveries in every part of physical science.

Was Wallace hoping that his reader would silently place his name alongside that of Darwin as being on a level with Newton? Or was he hoping his reader would *replace* Darwin's name with his?

Wallace now turned his attention to physiology, which was almost wholly a product of the nineteenth century. Past physicians had been extremely interested in the anatomy of the body, but had very little knowledge of its physiology. Even when Harvey established the circulation of the blood, very little was known about the *function* of blood. Wallace having made a positive comment about Lamarck's work, from which it appeared he had read the book, I was very disappointed when Wallace dated the establishment of the cell theory, as far as plants were concerned, to 1838. Lamarck (1809) had definitely stated, and believed he was the first person so to do, that the cell was the basic unit of all living things, both plant and animal. The cell consisted of a solid outer shell which encased a mucilaginous (plant) or gelatinous (animal) material.

From the basic understanding that all living things developed from single cells had come the theory of recapitulation. It had been recognized that there was a strong similarity between the fœtus of vertebrates in the early stages of their development, even though they may grow up to be vastly different from each other. Embryos were believed to recapitulate the forms of their earlier ancestors during their development and this was seen as a method of learning more about our past.

Another, extremely important, understanding had been that related to white blood cells, whose function had previously been unknown. Also unknown had been the function of the spleen. The crucial role they played in the destruction of harmful bacteria and germs was now recognized. This pleased Wallace's love of all things natural: live a natural, healthy life, eat healthy foods, breathe fresh air, and one's body would have sufficient resources of its own to overcome most problems, without the 'aid' of the doctor's medicines, which were acknowledged often to be quite injurious.

Wallace acknowledged the beneficial role of bacteria, how they were responsible for the decomposition of dead material, both plant and animal, rendering it suitable to be returned to nature, ready for another cycle of nutrition. In their correct place, bacteria were essential to life, but they could kill, if introduced into the wrong environment. Bacteria could cause wounds to fester and, if not treated, the infection could become so serious as to cause death. He listed the introduction of antiseptics in 1865 as one of the century's wonders. He also listed the discovery of anæsthetics, whose beneficial use was so obvious that it required little coverage. "More lives are probably now saved by surgery than by any other branch of medicine" (p. 149).

Wallace gave a surprisingly short mention of cold in preserving meat and of the canning of food, preservation being accomplished by subjection to heat to boiling point to destroy bacteria and germs before the application of an air-tight fastening. Considering the vast number of tins of food which now adorn our supermarket shelves, more space might have been expected to be devoted to this development, which, not only made available food out of season, but allowed it to be transported around the globe without expensive refrigeration. The household refrigerator had not yet come into existence. Did Wallace not fully appreciate the potential of these two factors in bringing food to the people, or was he simply just more interested in bringing people to the food – by encouraging them to return to the country, to grow their own?

This brought to an end Wallace's catalogue of the achievements of the nineteenth century. Most were technological – even the discoveries within the field of physiology were a form of technology. Only one had profound philosophical implications and that one was Wallace's own – the theory of how life had evolved on this planet.

Over the years, Wallace's theory came to differ from that of Darwin. Wallace became more and more spiritual with age and perceived evolution as having occurred under the guidance of the First Cause. Darwin became more and more agnostic, allowing the theory of Natural Selection to be used to support a humanistic approach to life, both that of the individual and that of society. Wallace believed that the 19th century had seen a more profound change in belief in a comparatively short space of time than had ever occurred before in human history.

Chapter 5

The Wonderful Century
(Cont'd)

The second half of Wallace's book was devoted to what he perceived to be failures. Most were topics on which he had written elsewhere, which will be covered later, only two chapters covering topics which need to be considered here. Chapter XVI was about phrenology, and was quite lengthy (thirty-four pages). Chapter XVII combined consideration of hypnosis with psychic research.

It was not the topics which were the failures; it was society's disregard of them which was the problem.

Phrenology is the science of reading the character and capabilities of a person by the shape of their skull. Initially, the estimates were based on little more than the size of the cranium, the shape of the forehead and, possibly, the jaw. As the science progressed, not only were other features of the face, such as lips, nose, eyes and eyebrows, also included in the assessment, but the shape of the cranium - not merely the overall shape but individual 'bumps'. It was now realized that the brain was not merely one overall mass of cells, but that various parts performed different tasks. Brocca's area was known to control speech, the visual cortex at the base of the skull controlled sight. These discoveries had originally been made following trauma, but doctors were now actively seeking ways of increasing this knowledge, including by the use of animals. Phrenology offered a non-violent alternative.

Size was important. The bigger the head, the bigger the brain. Females, on average, had smaller brains than males, which 'explained' why they were inferior. Large foreheads were a quickly recognizable indication of brain size and, therefore, capability. Low foreheads were not only a sign of small intellectual capacity, but could also be an indication of low morals. Criminals were depicted as having small foreheads, low brows. The terms 'high brow' and 'low brow' are still in use today. These ideas had to be abandoned when it became clear to Westerners quite how intelligent were the Japanese, and other Asians, even though their cranial size was considerably less. An alternative became popular: comparative ratio between body mass and cranial capacity. This formula had the advantage of allowing the denial of genius status to a largely built man, merely because of his cranial capacity.

The front of the brain was the seat of perception and reflection, the top, higher sentiments, the back and sides, the seat of animal instincts. This must have been a relief when Neanderthal skulls started to be discovered. Their cranial capacity was greater than ours, but the larger size was mostly attained by the protrusion at the rear, for which the Neanderthal skull is so well known. More animal instincts. What else could be expected of primitive Man?

Some people had 'domed' shaped skulls; others had skulls which were quite flat on the top - even if they did not live in a culture which routinely used the head for the carrying of objects. Some had heads which were quite flat at the back; others had crania which were quite rounded, even 'protruding' at the back. Skilled examiners claimed to be able to feel extremely slight differences in the shape of the bone, which might appear quite even to a cursory visual examination.

A Dr. François Joseph Gall discovered (or rediscovered) this science in the latter part of the eighteenth century, but its use as a tool to assist in the understanding of the character and capabilities of individual people had been perfected in the nineteenth. A full reading was expensive. Wallace had had two quick readings as a young man in his early twenties, carried out by two different lecturers, who had visited his town. He quoted from the readings, summarising them as having said that he would pay great attention to facts, would seek reason for the facts, searching for causes, be firm when believing he was right, yet lack self-confidence; want self-confidence, learn easily, remember well, some vanity but more ambition, love of music but lack of ability, fond of argument but not easily convinced. One reader suggested he could excel in mathematics, the other, more correctly, disagreed. This was but a shortened summary of their findings, which, looking back on his life, Wallace thought had been remarkably good.

One of the reasons this chapter was so long was that Wallace also cited the readings of other people, who confirmed the accuracy of their readings. And that, surely, was the problem. Of what use were years of study if the only benefit was to confirm that which people already knew about themselves? Captain Fitzroy, seeking a person with some knowledge of the newly emerging science of geology to accompany him on his next voyage south of the equator, nearly rejected the young Cambridge graduate, Charles Darwin, despite his having attended lectures and field trips with John Henslow, because the shape of his nose indicated that he might not be tough enough to withstand the rigours of the voyage. Darwin proved him wrong, but his health was poor the remainder of his life, mostly digestive problems. Had

Fitzroy adhered to his understanding of phrenology, such as it was, how much would that have changed the world?

If Darwin had never embraced the notion of natural selection, if the concept had been Wallace's and Wallace's alone, would that have made any difference? Yes, it would! The phrenologists were right. Wallace had a good head for facts and reason, but lacked self-confidence. Despite the enormous amount of reading and study he undertook in the second half of his life, despite the large number of articles and books which he wrote, despite his celebrity, it must be said that Wallace's efforts produced little in the way of reward. Indeed, the very fact that I have considered it necessary to write this book at all, is testimony to the fact that Wallace's work is all but forgotten. Compare that with Darwin's! Had Wallace's spiritual approach to evolution become dominant instead of Darwin's agnostic/atheistic one, how much of a difference would that have made to 'politically correct' attitudes towards religion and 'God' during the twentieth century – and forward into the twenty-first?

Wallace was confident that phrenology would become generally accepted in the coming century. He believed rejection of phrenology was due, in part, to its promotion by itinerant lecturers, who did not necessarily know a great deal about the subject, and to its incorrect association with mesmerism, or hypnotism, which was also opposed and which was the subject of his next chapter.

The Austrian, Franz Anton Mesmer, had discovered the phenomenon of 'Animal Magnetism', now usually referred to as Mesmerism or Hypnotism, although something similar had been known in times past. Mesmer induced a state of trance by the passing of his hands, several inches above the body, in a downward direction, from head to foot, a number of times. This seemed to have an effect on the body's energy flow such that it induced a relaxed, trance-like state, or even sleep.

Mesmer found that people in this state became 'detached' from their bodies inasmuch as they seemed to have very little awareness of it, to feel very little in the way of pain. Mesmer, and his followers, utilized this phenomenon in a way that enabled people to undergo dentistry, including the extraction of teeth, with very little, or no, pain. The practice was soon extended to the surgical field, with patients, under Mesmeric trance, undergoing operations, some quite serious, such as amputation, without feeling any pain. Repeated mesmeric sessions sped up the induction of the trance state. Some disbelievers in painless surgery claimed that the patient had been 'trained' not to feel pain (p. 207). Quite so!

The discovery of chloroform made mesmerism unnecessary before surgical procedures, but it is still used today for childbirth, where it enjoys a high rate of success. It is universally agreed that the less medical analgæsics administered during labour, the better for the baby. For a while 'Stage Hypnotism' was popular, but fell out of favour when it became apparent that some participants re-enacted the ridiculous behaviour that had happily performed on stage after they returned home, if some sound they heard resembled the 'prompt' used by the hypnotist. These re-enactments faded after a time, but were an embarrassment.

Initially, while all hypnotists were men, their clients were usually female. These 'hysterical females' were generally considered to be exhibiting, under hypnosis, the type of behaviour which a man could expect from a female of lesser intelligence. It came to be realized that not all people were equally susceptible to the hypnotic trance. One group of people never could be hypnotised – those of low intelligence, the mentally defective, as they were then called. When it was acknowledged that a degree of intelligence was essential for hypnotisability, men suddenly became very interested, especially the medical profession.

Apart from pain relief, the mesmeric induced trance was most frequently employed for entertainment, or used in much the same way as a clairvoyant trance, another subject in which Wallace was extremely interested. He wrote two books on this subject, which will be considered in Chapter 17, so they will not be considered any further here.

Chapter 6

Studies Scientific and Social

When Wallace published, in 1900, under the title *Studies Scientific and Social*, 'reprints' of various papers he had previously written, he advised his reader that he had made revisions, in some cases almost to the extent of making them new papers. Unfortunately, he did not make clear to his readers where these alterations occurred. All we know is that these two volumes contained the opinions and ideas which he held in 1900. Volume 1 was devoted to nature - not just evolution, not just animals, but the Earth (geology) as well. Simple geology, botany, zoology and anthropology, interesting though they may be, do not come within the scope of this book, which is looking at Wallace's 'other' work; Volume 1 will not be covered here.

Volume 2 contained papers on social issues (humanity). The paper on morals submitted to the Agnostic Annual, 1895, was a reproduction of Spiritualist teaching on ethics, taken from his book on Spiritualism, which will be discussed in Chapter 17. His papers on political reform, land nationalisation and trade are covered in Chapters 7, 8 and 9. This volume also included several other miscellaneous topics, which are the subject of this chapter.

Origin of Language

While most philologists (language experts) involved themselves with establishing the existence of, and trying to trace the root of, words and expression common between neighbouring groups of languages, Wallace felt there was an even more fundamental commonality between *all* languages, wherever, and whenever, they evolved.

When we communicate in person, whether by speech or by body language, our first message falls into one of two basic categories: 'welcome' or 'go away', or so claimed Wallace, although he tacitly acknowledged a third response: 'I'm not quite sure abut this'. Speech was formed by the movement of the mouth and of the breath, and there were certain movements which were universal, for example, the gasp. This most universal of all sounds is not, strictly speaking a 'word' but everyone, even a very young child, understands its meaning: surprise. That surprise may be one of pleasure or horror, but, whichever it is, it is immediately apparent that the articulator of this sound has been taken unawares by something. I checked in my Oxford Pocket Dictionary and found: *Catch breath with open mouth as in exhaustion or surprise.* The second part of the definition referred to 'last gasp'. Perhaps that is why they placed 'exhaustion' before 'surprise'. What I found interesting was that the dictionary did not so much *explain* the word as describe it.

Wallace believed that many words (p. 115):

> ... are so constructed as to proclaim their meaning more or less distinctly, sometimes by means of imitative sounds, but also, in a large number of cases, by the shape or the movements of the various parts of the mouth used in pronouncing them, and by peculiarities of breathing or in vocalisation, which may express a meaning quite independent of mere sound-imitation.

It was during his long sojourn among the native peoples of South America and the Malay Archipelago, as he struggled to understand what was being said, that Wallace came to understand the importance of body language, facial expression and verbal expression, many of which, he came to believe, were universal across the human race. The finger in front of the mouth, while expressing the sound "shhh..." is easily understood. This sound is 'open', can be extended for as long as the speaker wishes, or has breath enough, and invites co-operation. 'Shush' is less open, more commanding, and impels immediate silence. Both sounds are understood by all people.

Some sounds, both vowel and consonant, are 'open', such as *a*, *o*, and derivatives such as *ah*. They can be 'extended' and are made with the lips apart. Other sounds, such as *e* or *u* are made with the lips much closer together. Capital 'I' is sounded with the lips wide apart; small 'i' with the lips more closed. These may be associated with 'terminal consonants', such as *d, m, n, p, t.* The word *up* necessitates an upward movement of the jaw, whereas *down* is quite the opposite. Unassisted, we cannot rise very far and the very word *up*, being so short, seems to express this, whereas, alas, we can fall a long way and the 'open' word *down* can be extended to express this concept, if so desired (as can the word 'fall'). A couple of extra letters are needed to convert *up* into *jump*. The *u* sound has the similar meaning but the terminal *mp* clearly indicates how most of us can expect to finish – with a bump or a thump – with at least some of the breath knocked out of us! If you were imagining a gymnast jumping to grasp a bar over head, you would have used slightly different breath control which would have lightened the sound. That word *grasp.* No doubt, you have already mentally analysed it. The initial *gr* implies effort, as with grip and grab, but the final *sp* carries with it almost a feeling of relief, compared with grip and grab. The *ip* in *grip* is slightly shorter than the *ab* in *grab*, the quickness of the movement being implied in the speed with which the word itself is articulated, *grab* bringing to mind that desperate moment as the hand flays out to find the support that *grip* implies already exists.

Breath is important also, as in the word *heaving*, which is best expressed with a distinct inward pull of the breath through a slightly closed throat. Wallace offered *high* and *low* as further examples of 'breath/throat' words. It is difficult to say either word in reverse: *high* in a deep tone and *low* in a high voice. The same is true of the word *deep*. It is easy enough, if one wishes, to drop the voice, but hard to lift it when pronouncing *deep*.

When occurring at, or near, the end of words, the letters *b, d, g, k, p,* and *t,* all contribute to an abruptness and were referred to as 'non-continuous' letter sounds. Wallace listed *step, hop, jump, leap, halt, stop, drop, bump, wink, strike, hit, knock, pat, slap, stamp* and *kick*. Other letters, with or without a following vowel, were 'continuous': *f, l, m, n, ny, r, v, s, z*. As examples, Wallace offered *roar, snore, hiss, sing, hum, scream, wail, purr* and *buzz*. The word 'yawn' necessitated the opening of the mouth in a manner resembling the commencement of a yawn, and *moan, groan, wail, yell, sigh* and *sob* also imitated the cries they portrayed, as *bubble* imitated the sound of boiling water. Other combinations of letters were deliberately obscuring: *bumble, fumble, jumble, mumble, rumble, tumble*. (If you did several of these things at one time, you might very well feel *humble*.).

Wallace gave many other examples, but basically he was arguing that our language today, whatever it is, binds us far more closely to all humanity, past and present, than we may realize. We use similar sounds to express the same emotions whoever we are, wherever we are.

The Sabbath (October 1894)

In Victorian times, the Sabbath was strictly observed. While the Seventh Day Adventists observed the Jewish Sabbath (Saturday), most Christian denominations observed the Christian Sabbath, which, since the earliest times of Christianity, had fallen on Sunday, officially the first day of the week, the day upon which Jesus had risen from the dead. Wallace fully supported the concept of a day of rest, but took issue with its form of observance.

Wallace drew attention to the fact that the Fourth Commandment was the longest. It was the only Commandment to which was attached a detailed explanation of its requirements. The Commandments, Wallace claimed, were either Divinely ordained or they were not. If Divinely ordained, they should be obeyed. If not, they could be ignored. What could not be done was pick and choose – obey some bits and ignore others.

The fourth commandment said: "Six days shalt thou labour and do all thy work" – and so should all your family, servants and livestock (cattle). On the seventh day, one was to rest – and so should all one's family, servants and livestock. Wallace pointed out that it was only 'work' which was forbidden on the seventh day/Sabbath. There was no prohibition against relaxing, enjoyable activity. Everything depended upon the interpretation of the word 'work'.

When his gardener worked in his (Wallace's) garden, that was his 'work'. However, when Wallace worked in his garden, that was his relaxation. Not only did this activity refresh and rejuvenate Wallace, it also helped his gardener. What was wrong with doing that on the Sabbath?

Wallace pointed out that many of the people who claimed that they strictly observed the Sabbath, not only arrived at Church in a carriage drawn by horses (livestock), who were definitely not enjoying a Sabbath rest as ordained, but in a carriage driven by a coachman, who also was working on the Sabbath. How 'Christian' was it to save one's own soul by forcing another to sin?

'A change is as good as a rest' – or so it is said – and that was what Wallace proposed. Why should people not sing, and whistle, take walks and picnics, on their day of rest? How had 'rest' come to mean sitting quietly reading a book? Surely, the original intent of the commandment was to ensure that everybody (including livestock) had one day a week on which they were not required to perform their usual duties, their 'work', whatever that may be.

Wallace's solution? Everybody swapped roles!

The servants/employees should all have the day off to enjoy themselves with family and friends in whatever way they chose. While businesses could close, it was obvious that there were some things which needed to be done around the house, and that was where the employers/householders would step in. They would make their own beds, cook their own meals, drive their own coaches to Church. Wallace was of the opinion that, once engaged in this way, the employers would actually quite enjoy the experience. Not only would it provide them with first-hand knowledge of household tasks, but, done in the right spirit, would be quite fun. Knowing that, by their effort, they were enabling another human being to enjoy themselves, would be its own reward. Wallace was obviously a firm believer in the dictum that 'Charity begins at home'! If one family did not have any sons capable of driving a coach to Church, another family probably had more than one. Everybody would pitch in and share the tasks. Others might enjoy cooking and be happy to prepare meals for more than one family – meals which could be taken as a picnic, perhaps, weather permitting. Wallace did not address the issue of the horse still working on the Sabbath. Presumably he envisaged the horse being given another day off?

The Sabbath should be a day of rest from one's usual occupation; it should be a day of fun.

War (1899)

Wallace included his paper on *The Causes of War* in his section on Ethics, not that on politics. War, said Wallace, was caused by greed. Defending one's country did not cause war. That was the result of another person's/country's aggression, usually fuelled by animosity or greed. What was so shocking was that this animosity or greed was so frequently personal – a dispute between two rulers could plunge a country – or, rather, *two* countries, into war, causing untold misery to both their populations, even though the people being called upon the do the fighting, to pay the price, had no quarrel whatsoever with the people they were fighting (killing) and only wanted to be left in peace to till the soil and tend their flocks.

Sometimes the greed was a greed for power. The ruler wanted more territory. More territory increased his (self) image, making him a great ruler, not because of the wisdom of his rule, but because of its extent. Clearly this form of greed was driven by pride, but it was associated with another, very basic, form of greed – the desire for profit. More land meant more wealth – and it was not only the ruler who so thought. His advisers, the superior classes, as Wallace called them, thought so to. Indeed, so entwined were the thoughts of war and money that these rulers, these superior classes, would not only devote much time and money to the manufacture of superior weapons, they would then *sell* these weapons to other countries, with apparent disregard as to the future use to which these weapons might be put. Where, Wallace wondered, was the logic in that?

Surely, if one country developed a superior weapon for its own defence, it should keep that weapon for itself? The possession of it would be the best defence the country could have. Selling the weapons to people who might at some time in the future use those self-same weapons against you, made no sense at all, particularly in the case of the British who, at the time Wallace was writing, had colonies/territories across the globe. Wallace believed that all modern wars were (p. 390):

> ... caused by the ambition, the interests, the jealousies, and the insatiable greed of power of their rulers, or of the wealthy mercantile and financial classes which have the greatest influence over their rulers ... nothing is more inconsistent, more foolish, and more wicked than the universal practice of civilized and Christian nationals in selling all the most improved weapons and instruments of destruction to semi-civilized, barbarous, or savage rulers.

This practice, continued Wallace, made it even more difficult for advanced nations to disarm. The only reason for indulging in this behaviour which Wallace could suggest was money. What made everything even worse was that the nation selling the arms was counting on the purchasing country *using* these weapons, creating untold death and destruction. Then they would 'need' to buy more - a lucrative arms trade (p. 391):

> ... the supply of modern instruments of war to barbarous rulers should be absolutely forbidden ... The only rational mode of procedure would be to forbid altogether the private manufacture or sale of war material.

Quite what criteria could, or should, be used to distinguish between 'barbarous' and 'civilized' nations was not entirely clear. Surely *any* nation initiating, or encouraging, war anywhere in the world, with an eye to financial gain, was 'barbarous'?

Wallace also spoke out against the use of fire-arms for crowd control. Crowd control may sometimes be necessary, but would it not be better to call the fire-brigade, to use a jet of high-powered water to disperse them? He did not believe any group of protesters, however passionate they were about their cause, could withstand the jet of one, or several, fire-engines.

Wallace drew attention to the fact that it was the 'common people' who bore most of the burden of war. They provided most of the soldiers; they bore the greatest emotional burden when their sons went to war. Not only did they not know in what condition they would be when they returned (if they returned) but their families had to make do without their contribution of labour, whatever that may have been. In addition, it was the worker who bore the financial burden. Some manufacturers benefited directly; others may contribute by means of taxes, but those taxes were paid on money gained from sales of goods to - you know whom - the workers. Any wealth the superior classes may possess came originally from work done on the land and in the factories.

Did no good come from war? There was one benefit, but Wallace thought that benefit could be gained in another way. Young men in the forces learnt discipline, organization, cleanliness, obedience and, perhaps most importantly of all, *esprit de corps*. These skills were not only utilized in times of war; they were called upon in times of national disaster, when the army was drafted in to assist other emergency services. Wallace suggested that young men should still be trained to serve their country, but their training should be as emergency relief workers in times of fire, flood, storm and tempest, not forgetting earthquake and volcano. (Remember, the British Army served overseas more than it did at home.) Then, and now, our Defence Forces train first for war, then utilize their skills to help in times of other emergency. Wallace wanted the situation to be reversed. Training should be directed towards Disaster Relief. If necessary, these healthy, well-organized and disciplined young men could quickly learn to supplement their training by using it in the defence of their country. Wallace did not specifically mention this, but the implication is clear. I doubt the thought that another country might even contemplate invading Britain ever crossed his mind but he would have been well aware of the action of British forces in places such as India when there was a rebellion.

If the Forces were recognized by the natives of the colonies as being there primarily for their assistance, not for their destruction, their whole attitude towards the colonizing presence might be changed.

(When National Service was abolished in England, there were suggestions that it be retained as a civil force for just the reasons which Wallace suggested more than a century ago. These were not listened to. They should have been.)

Much as Wallace might deplore the greed which led to war, he was not naïve enough to disregard it. He cited "guard the country against attack by foreign enemies" as the first duty of any ruler/government (p. 150). This article had been published in 1873 and Wallace expressed the popular opinion that "No cost is too great, no preparations are too tedious, in order to deter an enemy from venturing to attack us" (p. 151). His following comments regarding this being seen as sufficient justification for thousands of young men being kept in a state of unproductive activity, or idleness, and of expensive, unused equipment being discarded and replaced by even more expensive (and, hopefully, never to be used) equipment, clearly foreshadowed opinions expressed later, more forcefully (see Chapter 9). Much as he might deplore the amount of money which was then being spent by many countries on their armed forces, he never suggested radical disarmament.

Justice

The second, and only other, duty of the Government was the administration of its laws, justice, which could be seen as protecting its citizens from attack by internal enemies. Far more people were attacked, even killed, by their countrymen than were attacked by foreign invaders. Yet, by comparison with the emphasis on updating the armed forces, the attention paid to updating the system of justice paled into insignificance. "Here everything is antiquated, cumbrous, and inefficient ... the mode of procedure, handed down from the dark ages, is often circuitous and ineffective ..." (p. 151). The aggressor might receive punishment, but the victim received no compensation. On the contrary, the victim often incurred great expense when seeking justice – if 'justice' this could be called. "The fixed money fine, the same for the beggar and the millionaire, though almost universally admitted to be unjust, is not yet abolished" (pp. 151-152). Only the very wealthy, Wallace asserted, could afford to pay to obtain justice. This injustice continues to this day. I fail to understand why fines are not fixed at a certain percentage of income. In this day of computers, this information is readily available.

Britain's laws were so complex that the layman could not understand them. The legal profession relied upon this confusion for their business. If the law was crystal clear, there would be no lengthy arguments in Court – and solicitors were paid by the hour.

Trusts

The first step in reducing the work-load of the Courts would be taken by addressing the issue of Trusts. Anybody could place their assets (money/property) in Trust, imposing whatever conditions they chose, which, for reasons which Wallace failed to understand, were treated as 'sacred', even though conditions might have changed. No one, Wallace asserted, had the right to control their wealth from the grave, to dictate how their property should be handled, not only by their children, and possibly grandchildren, but by others who may follow hundreds of years later. The Law should be involved only in ensuring the absolute, unconditional, transfer of the deceased's wealth to specified individuals or institutions. Leaving money in Trust was an exercise of power. 'Even from the grave, I can, and will, tell you what to do.' This was immoral and the Courts should have nothing to do with it.

Wallace made another point - one with which I have been in one hundred percent agreement for many years. If you want to give money away, do it during your life-time, when the money belongs to you and is yours to give. Why are those who leave money to charity in their Will held in such high regard? The money is of no use to them once they are dead. What they are, in fact, doing is giving away somebody else's money.

Wallace also saw no reason for Court intervention in the case of Bankruptcy. Bankruptcy stemmed from the practice of trading on credit. If people and businesses paid for their purchases at the time of purchase, they would never incur debts which they could not pay. The decision as to whether to demand payment at the time of delivery, or whether to allow the person or business to trade on credit, rested solely with the vendor. If the decision made turned out to be an unwise one, that was the responsibility of the vendor, not the State. Those who chose to engage in speculative trading, chose to risk their own capital. There was no reason whatsoever for the time and other resources of the Court to be expended upon such personal matters. At times, it seemed to Wallace, the Law seemed to favour the defaulter, particularly since the passing of the Limited Liability Act during the 1860s. Knowing that they would never be asked to repay more than they had originally put into the business when registering it as a 'Limited Liability' Company encouraged owners to order goods/services for which they had, at that time, no means of paying, in the hope that they would accrue sufficient funds at some time in the future. This encouraged overspending and over-borrowing by means of interest-bearing loans, incurring greater debt in the attempt to settle lesser debt.

Human Progress

Human progress was not a uniform process. Material progress was something completely separate from metal and moral progress. Material progress was cumulative. Once something new had been invented, all benefited. Wallace cited printing and the steam engine as examples. The European world had received much from the enterprise of its forebears but that did not mean that any particular European person alive in Wallace's time, (or now), would not be able to come up with that idea *de nouveau*, had it not already been thought of by someone else. The same was true of mathematics. Today's mathematicians may have built upon the mathematics of Newton, but that did not mean to say that they were greater mathematicians than Newton, or ancient Greeks, such as Euclid or Archimedes, nor did it mean that they could not have come up with the same mathematical theories, had they not been preceded. The pyramids of Egypt bore witness to great mathematical accuracy. Since Wallace's time, the pyramids have been explored in great detail and they continue to astound. To this day, they have not been replicated and quite how these mammoth structures were built in the middle of desert land has still not been definitively determined. (Not *all* knowledge is cumulative. Some does seem to be lost.) The ancient Indian scriptures, as well as Greek literature, bore witness to the intellectual capabilities of these cultures. Wallace quoted Sir Frances Galton as having estimated that their 'average ability' (whatever that was) was very nearly two grades higher than that of Europeans of his day, although quite what constituted 'two grades' was not explained. I assume the reference was to school grades? However, Galton had claimed that the Greeks of yesteryear were as much higher than present day Europeans as Europeans were above Africans.

While material progress was being made, there was some evidence that humanity's intellectual level had dropped.

According to the dictates of natural selection, the superior (in any way) should out-compete and, eventually, replace the inferior. Why had this (apparently) not happened? Wallace cited celibacy, not only of the clergy, but also of monks and nuns, of which there had been many in past times. The policy of the Church was contributing to the diminished reproduction of the very characteristics which it claimed to value most highly. Wallace also believed that being born to wealth had a detrimental effect on the young, who did not need to strive for success, or even for necessities, as did the less intellectual classes. (Evolution worked in both directions. That which was not used tended to fade.) Elsewhere, Wallace had mentioned the loss of humanity's fittest in useless wars. He made no mention of war here, presumably because there was no specific correlation between fitness of body and superiority of intellect. Our intellectual faculties may not be as great as those of ancient times, but Wallace did believe there had been gains in other areas. He believed the people of his time were more kind and considerate, not only towards their fellow humans, but also towards animals. The terrible tortures and persecutions of earlier times were no more. He believed humans had become more gentle in their nature.

Wallace found the early intellectual abilities of our forebears somewhat of a mystery. Under the laws of natural selection, which operated in association with the environment, Wallace could not identify any cause which had forced the development of these faculties. In his present society, he knew that 'education' would be claimed as the causative factor if intellectual faculties were seen to be increasing, but there was no general education in past times. (Indeed, someone must have the knowledge to pass it on. From where did that knowledge come in the first place?) Wallace was still of the opinion that some of the improvement effected by education would be passed on to the next generation, although this was increasingly being questioned by people, such as Professor Weismann, who claimed that all inheritance came from the germ cells alone, none from somatic (body) cells, as had been claimed by Darwin in his theory of *pangenesis*. If Weismann was right, it would be difficult to maintain the position that external circumstances had any influence on evolution.

If intellectual and/or artistic abilities were passed on by inheritance, then it would be expected that these characteristics would run in families, but this was not the case. On the contrary, nearly all great discoveries, all artistic genius, manifested in persons born into families with no such abilities at all. Wallace then listed a number of inventors/engineers who had been born into farming families, with little or no education and no engineering abilities. He then mentioned other, well known, people, including Faraday, Sir Christopher Wren, Herschel, Rembrandt and Shelley, all of whom came from 'working' families, the 'highest' being the son of a clergyman. Furthermore, none of those mentioned sired offspring who followed in their footsteps or gave any indication of having inherited their father's abilities. The main area of disagreement between Wallace and Darwin had been Wallace's insistence that natural selection operated on the physical body alone, that our moral and mental evolution was due to some other (higher) cause.

There was an up-side to all of this. If good/uplifting mental/moral characteristics were not inherited, then neither were the bad! "Throughout all trade and commerce lying and deceit abound to such an extent that it has come to be considered essential to success. No dealer ever tells the exact truth about the goods he advertises ..." (p. 505). These things had become so common that they had ceased to shock. Indeed, so rife were they that subsequent generations of parliamentarians passed legislation designed to promote honesty in business, for which I am sure we are all very grateful.

There was one other reform that could, and should, be hastened – the education of women! Educated women would insist on better behaviour by men. Already there were many women refusing to marry because they could not find a man who measured up to their standard. In times gone by, women were more or less forced to marry. Now they were becoming more independent, they were exercising more choice. The lower grade of man would find himself without a wife and over successive generations, the general standard would improve.

General education has been compulsory for well over a century. Women have more independence and influence than at any other time in Western history. Have our standards of morals and ethics improved? I leave that for you to judge.

Individualism

"Now that we have entered the last year of this our Nineteenth Century, in many respects the most eventful century for good and evil the world has witnessed, most thinking men are looking forward with anxious hope as to what of real good the Twentieth Century may have in store for humanity" (p. 510). It was thus that Wallace opened the penultimate chapter of his work. He went on to say that he was convinced that the society of the future would embrace some form of socialism, which would embrace the concept of *"the organization of labour for the good of all"* (p. 512. Italics in original). Britain's extremely efficient postal service had been enabled to achieve its high level of organization because it operated under one authority. Numerous manufacturers producing competing products was wasteful. Money was wasted in advertising; there were competing stores, where one per district was all that was required to demonstrate the product. All unnecessary and useless occupations should be abolished, which included nine-tenths of all lawyers, and all financiers and stock-gamblers. When the resultant labour needs were shared among the population, each person should not need to work more than three or four hours a day; the rest of the time could, and should, be spent in rest and recreation - *enjoying* life.

Wallace was hopeful that such a system would eventuate - but probably not in the coming century, although he did anticipate that there would be some steps in that direction. He stressed that he only believe in *voluntary* organization for the common good (p. 513). As a preliminary step, he proposed a period of competition under strictly equal conditions. This way the best would emerge, which could then be generally adopted. In sport, every care was taken to ensure that conditions of competition were the same for all. The same care should be taken in business, and this included access to wealth. When the wealthy had the means to buy their way into business, a chance denied to an equally able, but poorer, person, then the best may not succeed. Equality of opportunity was essential. Wallace had first used this phrase in an address to the Land Nationalization Society in 1892. It had since been adopted by many others.

Equal opportunity required that all should have the best education they were capable of receiving, which did not necessarily mean that all should have the *same* education (Wallace's italics). Different people may need, want, to learn different things. Education needed to be adaptive. It needed to be able to ascertain the faculties best suited to each individual for the good of society and the future happiness of the individual. Furthermore, each should receive an 'endowment' to assist them through the transition period between education and profitable employment and to furnish them with whatever was necessary for their chosen occupation.

Wallace's next suggestion was somewhat more controversial. Wallace claimed that since Society had made such a substantial contribution to the individual's education and training, Society was entitled to claim any surplus wealth which the individual accumulated during his lifetime. Wealth should not be passed on to the next generation. Wallace did not specify quite what qualified as 'surplus wealth' but elsewhere he did acknowledge that it was human nature to want to pass on something to the next generation, knowledge and wisdom as well as material possessions. I assume he would have allowed a degree of inheritance, since he believed that only when they felt they were achieving *both* of these aims, did men work to their very best ability.

Wallace was particularly opposed to the passing on to the next generation of stocks and shares, allowing future generations to enjoy an income for which they had contributed nothing. Wealth produced by society should be shared by society, current society, not future society.

Wallace applauded the fact that governments were finally acknowledging the need for some level of 'reasonable subsistence wage' (p. 482). He also did not believe that any work should be permitted which would be permanently injurious to the worker's health (p. 488). However, his third suggestion was more controversial – he felt it necessary also to fix a maximum income (p. 448). This is something with which I wholeheartedly agree! Of course, Wallace was referring to inherited wealth, by which people, such as Darwin, were able to live in comfort, supported by their staff, without ever needing to work – in paid employment – for a single day of their lives. In times gone by, such luxury had been the province of the aristocratic class. Not any more. Industrialisation had seen many 'middle class' people acquire wealth beyond that of the aristocrat. One would like to think that Charles Darwin's grandfather, Erasmus, made his money from the books which he wrote, not from the charging of high fees to his patients. His other grandfather, Benjamin Wedgwood, became rich from the proceeds of his highly successful 'Wedgwood Pottery' business. Charles was not the only grandchild. He received but a share of their fortunes, but that share was enough to support him in luxury all his life. Wallace worked hard to support himself by the writing of books but, without any office/business experience, was unable to obtain regular paid employment. A willing worker struggling while another person lived in comfort, without lifting a finger - no wonder Wallace felt the system was unjust!

I, too, object to what I perceive to be 'unearned' income. I do not believe that ANYONE *earns* more than $1,000,000 a year. They may receive it but I do not believe they *earn* it. For a 40 hour week, $1,000,000 per year works out at $480 per hour, or $19,230 per week. Yet many people do receive that amount - or more, much more. Nor is it only CEOs, bankers, etc. who command high salaries. Many people in the sports and entertainment industries do as well. Whether a person contributes more to society playing football than by cleaning, I leave you to judge!

The complaint today is the same as it was in Wallace's time – the rich are getting richer and the poor are getting poorer. I am going to stick my neck out and follow in Wallace's footsteps by making a suggestion. I do not think the highest paid employee of any company (and Directors/CEOs are employees) should be paid more than 10X the salary of the lowest paid employee. If Directors cannot manage on less than, say, $5,000 a week, why should they expect any of their employees to manage on less $500? If the company does well, then the pay of *all* the employees should increase. The amount could still be 10X more for the top earners than the bottom, which I think is more than generous!

Wallace finished by submitting that the principle of Equality of Opportunity for all should be the principle for all future legislation. This was the supreme Justice.

Not charity but Justice

Wallace's last chapter was a final appeal to his readers. He reminded them that, in the past, eternal salvation and a place in Heaven was believed to be earned by belief and by observance. There were certain beliefs which formed Church dogma and only people expressing a belief in those dogmas would enter Heaven. So profoundly was this held to be true that any amount of punishment or torture was considered justified if it resulted in the recalcitrant person expressing acceptance of the dogma. (Others before me have pointed out that 'dogma' spelt backwards gives 'am god' - which was what the proponents of the dogma seemed to believe they were!). As an expression of the acceptance of these dogmas, adherents were required to perform certain observances: baptism, attendance at Church, no eating of meat on Fridays, and so forth.

Things were now changing, largely, Wallace claimed, because of Spiritualist beliefs which were gradually permeating society. It was what one *did* which was important, how one lived one's life. Every human being had some degree of control over their actions, but not complete control, since one's actions were influenced by one's condition and situation in society. A person born to poverty, condemned to a life of grinding labour, with no cheering hope of a happy and peaceful old age, could not be expected to develop a happy, cheerful, generous nature. Society was allowing millions of infants to die prematurely, a slaughter far worse than that of Herod, which was a disgrace. Many people gave to charity; many people devoted their lives to charity, but the problem persisted because their actions were directed at the result, not the cause. In a truly just society, these causes would cease to exist.

There must be equality of opportunity. There must be no inequality of inheritance. Being born to an easy life deprived the soul of the opportunity to develop moral character. Wallace made no mention of Buddha, who was born to wealth and prestige, but who renounced his position, showing that character can overcome even this obstacle! One cannot but wonder how much of the Buddha's teaching Wallace absorbed during his time in the Malay, whether he was aware of it or not. Wallace referred to the parable of Lazarus in the bosom of Abraham, but not to the saying that it was easier for a camel to pass through the eye of a needle than for a rich man to enter the Kingdom of Heaven. There is a path through the hills outside Jerusalem which narrows at one point as it passes between two rock faces. It is known as the Eye of the Needle. A camel can pass between it, but not if it is burdened with goods - which the camels of the traders usually were. Once again, it was the wealth which was the problem. Also, surprisingly, Wallace did not cite one of Jesus' best known sayings: *The love of money is the root of all evil.*

Every soul which incarnated upon this Earth had done so for the purpose of developing all of its moral faculties and powers. It was our duty to ensure that every single child born was provided with the maximum opportunity for the development of these powers, not just for its happiness while on this plane of existence, but because this development was crucial for the soul's future existence in the after life. That every soul born should have, not just an *equal* opportunity, but the *greatest* opportunity to develop its full potential was, said Wallace, "the hope nearest to my heart" (p. 527).

Chapter 7

The Lower House of Lords

When, in 1905, Wallace published his autobiography, *My Life*, he seemed quite proud of his ancestry. He claimed descent from the great Scottish hero, Sir William Wallace. He believed his father's middle name, Vere, had been obtained from a connection with the Dukes of St. Albans, 'Vere' being their family name. His mother was descended from the French family, the Greenells, who had fled to England in 1572 to escape the St. Batholomew massacre.

That was then. This was now. Then, the aristocracy earned their fame (and fortune). Now, Wallace, who described himself as an extreme radical, seemed to have come to the conclusion that the aristocracy were 'good for nothing', certainly not deserving of automatic representation at Westminster, not even in the Upper House, the House of Lords.

Wallace's campaign for 'universal suffrage' did not seem to include the vote for women, although I am sure he would have supported the idea had someone else suggested it. Keen as he was that working people should not only be allowed to vote, but should also be eligible to stand for election, he seemed to be remarkably unaffected by the knowledge that the aristocrats had been disenfranchised for centuries! Way back when – when the British Isles was a collection of small kingdoms and kings summoned whom they would to advise them, first the Witan, then the parliament gradually evolved, along with the size of the individual kingdoms until Britain eventually came under one Crown and one Parliament. The country became divided into a number of areas, which came to be known as 'constituencies', which were responsible for choosing who would represent them.

These historical details are necessary to bring into focus quite how separate the Lower House of Parliament, the Commons, had became from the Upper House, the House of Lords. It was not only the Sovereign who was forbidden entry to their chamber, but also his aristocratic advisers, who could not vote and who could never become members of the House of Commons. Gradually, a two-tiered system evolved. The aristocrats throughout the land formed an automatic body of persons upon whom the sovereign could rely for advice. Most (if not all) had some form of blood relationship with the sovereign, even if it was becoming remote. They were his extended family. He trusted them. Then there were the representatives of the people. By the time of Charles I, this Lower House had become quite independent of the Crown, and could even be quite antagonistic towards it. Charles I was quite aware of the machinations of Oliver Cromwell and his fellow Parliamentarians, but bursting in upon one of their sittings was seen as outrageous. The Sovereign was not allowed to enter the Parliament of the people – and still is not to this day, except by their special invitation once a year at the Opening of Parliament. Charles I's action probably cost him his head. He was not deposed and exiled; he was deposed and beheaded. And it was from the House of Commons that all legislation emanated! Quite extraordinary!

So, what good was the House of Lords? What did they do? Why did it not only remain in existence, but was copied, inasmuch as both America and Australia enshrined an Upper House, which they called the Senate after the Greeks, into their respective Constitutions? For the answer to this question, we must consider the development of the Commons.

For centuries, there was no such thing as Party Politics. The Members of Parliament represented their constituents, that was all. Things changed when international trade entered the equation. 'World Trade' became a reality, a fact of life affecting everyday citizens, especially the workers, as Britain's interests spread across the globe. Britain was not only trading with Europe and with her own colonies, she was trading with her former colony, America, with the colonies of her European friends and with anybody else she could, including, of course, India and China. Many of these countries were producing items at a lower price than were home manufacturers of the same product. Tariffs (import duties) were imposed to bring parity. Some opposed this idea – most traders and business men who were the importers of the products or who owned the ships which brought them! They were known as 'Free Traders' and became the Liberal (Whig) Party in Parliament. Others were 'Protectionists', later forming the Conservative (Tory) Party. Parliament became divided into two sides, much as it is today. The Sovereign, in this case Queen Victoria, no longer chose whom she would as her Prime Minister. She became obliged to 'offer' this position to the leader of the Party which held the majority of seats in Parliament.

The Party with the majority of seats held the power. Increasingly it became expected that members would support the official position of their Party, whether they were privately in agreement or not. Although an 'Opposition' member could introduce a Bill into Parliament, increasingly legislation was proposed by the majority Party. 'Her Majesty's Loyal Opposition' had an important role to play. It was their duty to 'oppose' all legislation, whether they agreed with it or not. It was their duty to find every fault, every flaw which they could, thus ensuring that every Act which was passed was as perfect as it could be. The Governing Party considered the points raised by the Opposition and presented their Amended legislation for a Second Reading.

While the system generally worked well, there was one obvious problem. The Government had a majority and could push through any legislation it wanted, Opposition or no Opposition. However, the process was not complete. The Bill now went before the House of Lords for review. Here there were no Party politics. Members held their seat by right of inheritance - and they could not lose it! They were answerable to no one. Members considered proposed legislation impartially, making their individual judgement. After careful consideration, the Lords might pass the Bill, or send it back to the Lower House for further amendment. By the time the legislation had finally been passed by both Houses and presented to the Crown for signature into Law, it was supposed that it would be as good, as free from the potential of unwanted side-effects, as humanly possible.

Wallace appreciated the value of the Upper House. He did not want to abolish it. He wanted to reform it. He objected to the fact that it was composed of two different types of Lords: the one hereditary, the other Episcopal. In the first instance, Wallace did not see being born to wealth and status as being character building; rather, he perceived such a circumstance as being character destroying. Whatever great thing their ancestors may have undertaken or accomplished to be awarded their title, offspring of many generations later had nothing in particular to recommend them for the automatic assumption of such an important position. In the second case, Bishops served first the Church, second the nation. They could never be completely unbiased in their opinion. Although the Sovereign was the Head of the Church of

England, the two Institutions, Church and State, should be kept separate.

Wallace wanted to abolish both the hereditary right to legislate and the right of the Church, through its Bishops, to be involved in the legislative process. While there might be a chance of achieving the latter, Wallace recognized that to achieve the former would be virtually impossible. If you can't beat them, join them. Wallace proposed the introduction of life peerages.

Wallace estimated that, counting the three Ridings of Yorkshire as separate entities, the number of counties in Britain numbered around one hundred. He proposed that two Lords should be elected to represent each county. He was prepared to allow the hereditary Lords to stand for election. The Life Peers, who would gradually increase in number following their first introduction, would have been created from among persons of exceptional achievement in the fields of science, art, literature or philanthropy – industrialists and businessmen were not mentioned. Wallace made no suggestion as to the length of time which should exist between elections – that was a matter for later consideration – but he did specify that there should be no campaigning. A person, whose achievements had warranted the bestowal of a life peerage, should be well enough known for his nomination alone to be sufficient. Nor did Wallace think that the general public should be put to the trouble and expense of a general election. Election would take place by the vote of the members of the several Town and County Councils, together with District and Parish Councils.

Wallace was also aware of the danger of 'stacking' – of the Party in power recommending its supporters for peerages. This was interesting, since it showed that even Queen Victoria had limited control over upon whom she conferred a peerage. Clearly, even then, it was the Prime

Minister and his cabinet who were the chief decision makers. Wallace proposed to limit the number of peerages granted each year and, if possible, to keep even the number representing each side of politics. Wallace was not entirely clear upon this point. If, as he seemed to want, each of these Life Peers was chosen because of his contribution to society, was there any reason to suppose that any one would have a particular affiliation with any Party? Perhaps Wallace was anticipating peerages being granted to retiring politicians from the Lower House?

Britain has now introduced Life Peerages. However, the entitlement to a Seat in the House of Lords also lasts for life. The House of Lords remains an unelected House – and that is its strength! Wallace completely ignored the fact that no one in the Lords needed to worry about loosing his seat at the next election. They thought for themselves, spoke their own minds and were answerable to no one – not even the Sovereign! Unfortunately, the Senate in both America and Australia is elected, making them vulnerable to the vicissitudes of Party Politics, along with the pressures of lobbying, and the possibility of bribery and corruption.

Having dealt with the Lords Temporal, Wallace turned his attention to the Lords Ecclesiastical. He republished an article he had written in 1873 outlining a proposal for the disestablishment of the English Church. He did not refer to it as the 'Church of England' or the 'Anglican Church' because he did not consider it to be such. Henry VIII may have envisioned one Church for the whole of England, with the Sovereign, not a priest (the Pope), at its head, but things had not turned out that way. Not only were many English people still loyal to Rome, but many now belonged to other post-Reformation Churches.

There were countless village Churches which were centuries old; many had been built in pre-Reformation times.

Wallace did not mention St. Paul's Cathedral or Westminster Abbey, but these were places of worship built by the State (i.e. with public money) for the people, at least, for all the Christian people of England. Wallace considered it an injustice that many sincere Christians were denied the right to worship in these places, both great and small, because of doctrinal differences, which were relatively small compared with their more significant points of agreement.

The English Church should be disestablished but continue to exist under the same conditions as those which governed other denominations. Current Church property, which would revert to ownership by the State, should be available for use by *all* Christians, regardless of their denomination. The buildings, from parish churches to cathedrals, should be returned to the use for which they had originally been established – "the moral and social advancement of the whole community" (p. 236). I question this. I believe that the churches and cathedrals had been built as places for the worship of God. Moral advancement would follow worship, not precede it. I doubt that 'social advancement' was a consideration.

Wallace suggested that administration of each 'parish' should be under the control of a man, for whom he suggested the title 'Rector', which, he claimed, did not imply a religious teacher. (My, somewhat ancient, dictionary, gives *rectitude* as moral uprightness, *recto* as right-hand page of an open book and *rector* as Parson of Parish or head of an educational or religious establishment.) This person should be (pp. 240-241):

> ... chosen, primarily, for moral, intellectual, and social qualities of a much higher character than are now expected ... His moral character should be unexceptionable. He should be specially trained in the laws of health and their practical application, and in the principles of the most advanced political and social economy. His religion should be quite

free from sectarian prejudices, and his private opinions on religious matters would be no subject of enquiry. He should, however, be of a religious frame of mind ... He must have a fair knowledge of physiology, and of simple medicine and surgery, of the rudiments of law and legal procedure, of the principles of scientific agriculture, and of the natural history sciences, as well as whatever is considered essential to the education of a cultivated man.

Be it remembered that the social worker did not exist in those days - although I do feel that the social worker of today would have fallen somewhat short of Wallace's exacting standards!

Wallace placed one important restriction upon this Rector's activities (p. 241): *... he would never conduct religious services of any kind* (italics in original). The Rector was to service *all* his parishioners; this he could not do, to maximum effect, if the parishioner knew that the Rector held religious views not compatible with his own. Although banned from preaching on religious matters, there was no reason why the Rector should not lecture in the Church on moral, social, sanitary, historical, philosophical, or any other suitable topics. His knowledge of the law and position as an *ex-officio* magistrate would enable him to settle most petty disputes; he would also be an *ex-officio* member of the School Board and of the governing body of any other public educational institution in the district. If asked, he would visit the sick and, most importantly, he would maintain friendly relations with other ministers and help them to keep friendly relationships with each other. His position would be one of 'weight and dignity', well respected, which would encourage some of the best of the young people to make this position their calling. Of course, there would be higher officers, fulfilling the managerial role of current bishops, and over the whole a Supreme Board or a Minister of Public Instruction.

The Rector would be responsible for fair allocation of Service time for such recognized religious denominations as wished to avail themselves of the Church premises and facilities. Apart from that, his duties, although numerous, would not be laborious and would leave him a considerable amount of time for leisure (p. 251).

Wallace had done his homework. He had ascertained, not only how many parishes there were in England, but their size and the number of their parishioners. There were small parishes, there were large parishes; there were heavily populated parishes, there were scantily populated parishes; but there was no consistency. Wallace estimated that, if parish boundaries were to be redrawn in a more practical manner, there number could be halved. He suggested this be done over a period of time. When the incumbent of a small parish retired (one way or another), that small parish should be combined with another, either a larger, nearby, parish, or another small one, if there were three or four small adjacent parishes which could eventually combine into one. This would happen gradually, over thirty years or so. No present incumbent would be affected in any way. With the number of parishes halved, the stipend could be doubled. As the size of the current parishes varied, as did the number of parishioners, so also did the stipend but Wallace had determined that an average amount was £275 per annum. This, he believed, could be raised to £600.

Because the changes would take place over a generation, and only after the incumbent priest had retired, there should be little disruption and plenty of time to educate and train the next generation of Rectors.

That Wallace thought the Rector's duties would not be laborious, and would leave him with plenty of free time, must, I feel, be taken alongside his suggestions for Land Reform (see next chapter). With thousands of families relocated in the country, with sufficient land upon which to produce most of their own food, with clean air, fresh water, good sanitation and security of tenure, the welfare of these people would be vastly improved and poverty all but abolished. With health and wealth assured, could happiness be far behind?

Wallace had surprisingly little to say about representation in the Lower House. He thought it ridiculous that a young person, hardly out of school or finished with their education, should be permitted to vote, let alone stand for Parliament. He proposed that thirty should be the minimum voting age and forty the minimum age for taking a Seat in Parliament, in the revamped House of Lords, at least. But who were these young people who might vote, and even stand for Parliament, as soon as they reached the age of majority, which was twenty-one?

Over the centuries, almost by default, it was the land owners who represented their people in Parliament. They voted among themselves to select their representative. Gradually, as industrialisation took hold, more people became property owners but the vast majority of the population either rented their homes or were provided with them, free of charge, as part of their payment for labour, either on the land or in the factory. At the turn of the nineteenth century, less then 3% of the population were entitled to vote. The French Revolution had had a profound effect upon the whole of Europe and the English, who had experienced revolution before, in Cromwellian times, were only too aware of dissatisfaction with the current system.

In 1819, a demonstration at St. Peter's Field, near Manchester, had resulted in the death of eleven people. This incident became known as 'The Peterloo Massacre' and it was the catalyst for reform, although it was to be a further thirteen years before the first Reform Act was passed in Parliament.

The Great Reform Act of 1832 gave the vote to men who owned property with an annual value of £10 or more. This still excluded six out of seven men. The 'annual value' (I presume rateable value?) was later reduced to £6 for country properties. Only the person who directly paid the rates was entitled to vote, other adult males occupying the same property were still excluded. This would have greatly reduced the number who qualified in the early days after its enactment, especially among the upper classes. The Manor traditionally housed a number of relatives, some of whom, with their families, had use of one wing. These younger brothers, uncles, cousins, whatever, would not have qualified to vote. However, industrialisation, and the rise of the middle class, meant that more and more people were purchasing a property, albeit much smaller than previously. Nevertheless, there was a growing movement pushing for universal suffrage. There were demonstrations, and unrest, in many parts of Britain on both sides of the border. These culminated in May, 1867, with the demonstration in Hyde Park, London, which had been banned by the Government. Troops and police were on hand to dispel the protesters, but the crowds were so huge that they did not dare to act. The Home Secretary, Spencer Walpole, resigned, and the planned Act was amended to increase the number of persons entitled to vote. After 1867, approximately two out of every five men had the right to vote.

The Reform Act of 1867 had been intended to address the gross inequality which existed between boroughs when it came to representation. Representation was grossly unequal. The right to send a representative to Parliament had been passed down through the ages. It had not adjusted to post-Industrial Britain. For example, newly emerged industrial centres, such as Birmingham, Leeds and Manchester, had no representative, while the old borough of Dunwich, Suffolk, which, in 1831 had a population of 32, was still sending two representatives. While the major provisions of the Act were still concerned with the (re)creation of boroughs to ensure fairer representation in relation to population, the demonstrations forced the Government to amend its proposed Act to increase voting eligibility. All those directly responsible for the payment of rates received the vote. There were extra votes for professionals, graduates and those with £50 savings. This last provision may have been intended to address the problem of male residents of country houses, mentioned above, who were very well educated and every bit as deserving of the right to vote as some of the new home owners.

A third Reform Act, passed in 1884 gave the vote to all male house owners, which increased the franchise by some six million - a huge number. Nevertheless, some were still excluded: men not house owners, and women.

It should be pointed out that, on occasions, females did inherit property. If there were no sons, a daughter would inherit. However, on marriage her husband took control of the property. Women were not allowed to manage money. They were not considered competent to do so. Any money they inherited was also 'managed' by the husband, who gave his wife an allowance to spend on clothing and other personal items. The person 'directly paying the rates' would have been the husband. He claimed the vote, even if the property did belong to his wife. That there is no mention in Wallace's writing of 'votes for women' does surprise me, since he supported their equal education and looked to them, by their wise marriage choices, to improve males. Would their wisdom not also have improved Parliament?

Chapter 8

Land Nationalisation:
Its necessity and Its Aims

(First published in 1892, 4th edition 1906)

The problem, Wallace wrote, was that the rich were getting richer and the poor were sinking into pauperism. This had happened in every society which had abandoned its traditional lifestyle of hunting and gathering. Among such people, everything was shared. Every member of the tribe/community, male, female or child, had an equal right to walk the tribal/communal land, eat its produce and sleep peacefully at night under whatever shelter was deemed desirable or necessary. Everybody helped everybody else. There was always a leader, whose decision was final. This leader always acted as fairly as he could (and it always was a 'he') and his authority was never questioned. The native peoples may have had fewer material possessions than the Europeans, but in many ways, it seemed to Wallace, their life was more idyllic.

What had gone wrong?

It was in 1853, soon after he had returned from his travels in the Amazon, that Wallace had read Herbert Spencer's book, *Social Statics*, which first alerted him to what he came to perceive as the social injustice of privately owned land (Wallace 1900, vol.2: 333). The following year, he set out on his travels once again, this time to the Malay Archipelago. He does not say how often the thoughts and ideas of Herbert Spencer imposed themselves upon his mind during his travels, but, somewhere, a deep passion was forming in his heart and mind, which compelled him, upon his return to his home country, to devote much of the remainder of his life to the cause of social change. He addressed a number of different issues, but that of the ownership of land was forefront. He cited Spencer's claim that it was a crime to deprive others of their right to the use of the land, that land upon which they had been born. Chapter XVI was entitled "How to Nationalise the Land" and this Wallace was determined should happen. He joined with others to form the Land Nationalisation Society in 1881.

Since the British system of land tenure had evolved from that imposed at the time of the Norman Conquest, that was the time with which Wallace chose to commence his analysis. He assumed his readers would have a working knowledge of English history in pre-Norman times, but that may not be the case today. Here is a quick synopsis.

The Ancient Britons may not have had the material wealth of the Ancient Greeks, of the Babylonians, or the Egyptians, but they were conversant with the use of metals; not only iron and bronze but also of copper, tin and gold, which were mined in Cornwall and exported, via the Straits of Gibraltar, to those other places, which had such a need for these items. There was no centralized government, although the Druid priests exerted great influence and similar religious beliefs were a unifying factor. We know little about any system of governance, although I do remember being shown, many moons ago, a set of 'laws' of some ancient ruler of part of England. I cannot remember his name, or the exact location over which he ruled, but I do remember two regulations which had been set down.

The first related to the hand-shake. Any agreement made between two people, and sealed with a hand-shake, was legally binding. I do not know whether any later rulers, kings or Parliaments, re-enacted – or retracted – this law, but it is still powerful today. It may not be possible to enforce such an agreement in a Court of Law, but no one would want to be caught on camera, making an undertaking, sealed with a hand-shake, upon which they later rénéged. All politicians recognize the power of the hand-shake, both at the beginning of a meeting and, *more importantly*, at the end, after each leader has recited the 'understandings' at which they have mutually arrived.

(Incidentally, in ancient Briton, marriage was also sealed with a handshake – known as 'hand-fasting'. Marriage was for nine years, after which time it could be renewed, if desired.)

The other decree which I remember from this ancient document was the one which allocated to each man five acres of land. Pretty good, eh? Well, no. Not according to Wallace.

The earliest reference to the allocation of land given by Wallace was that made by Elizabeth I, whose statute required that a mere four acres of land be attached to each new cottage. Wallace made the very good point that it was not the quantity of land which was important, but its quality. If the land was fertile, vegetables could be grown, along with some fruit trees, chickens kept, a few sheep and possibly a cow or two, then an area of three or four acres might be sufficient for a man and his family. If the land was less fertile, included rivers, ponds, marsh land, woodland, hills, and so on, then even ten acres might not be enough. In addition to their personal acreage, these people were automatically entitled to collect mushrooms, chestnuts, acorns, nuts and berries, and anything else edible, from common land, as well as fish from the river. They could collect birds' eggs, shoot pigeons, kills hedgehogs, badgers, and so forth.

The same was true, I should imagine, in other European countries, before, during and after Roman occupation.

The Roman Empire was different from any which had come before it. The Roman Empire did not pillage and plunder its conquered territories. It annexed them. It did not try to impose direct rule over the conquered countries which constituted its Empire. So long as the defeated country acknowledged its vassal status and paid due tribute, Rome was content to allow the country to continue very much as it had before, with its own rules - and rulers! The Romans built (or *had* built) long, straight roads connecting towns, for the convenience of their soldiers, but in what the country people were doing amidst the winding country lanes, they had very little interest.

The greatest gift the Romans gave the British was an increased knowledge of the world beyond the Channel. Of course, they knew there was a world beyond. They traded with it, but traders came and went. The Romans came and stayed and Briton was, for the first time, *part* of a larger community and a common way of life. Legend has it that Joseph of Arimathæa traded with Britain and that, on at least one occasion, he brought the Carpenter's Son with him, even that after the 'Resurrection' the family returned to Glastonbury, England then being outside the Roman Empire and, therefore, safe. Whether or not some early form of Christianity became established in England, there can be no doubt that becoming part of the Roman Empire opened Britain up to Christianity, and the influence of Rome, this time through the Papacy. The Church, including its Monasteries, was a massive land-owner. Henry VIII not only reclaimed his country's religion, he reclaimed its land. Church land became *de facto* Crown land, although it retained its individuality –

until the time of Cromwell. Then the Monasteries received a second blow.

Wallace makes no mention of Church land in his book – or not, at least, in relation to Nationalisation. His chapter on reforming the House of Lords made clear that he considered Churches, and Church land, as already belonging to the people. Here he is concerned only with private ownership. Nevertheless, I feel it is prudent to bear some of this in mind, because the idea that the land belonged, not necessarily to those who lived upon it, who worked it, but to some greater entity, possibly never seen, possibly domiciled far, far away, even overseas, had seeped into the British consciousness over, not hundreds, but *thousands* of years – well, nearly two thousand at least!

After the Romans left, the Vikings took the opportunity to undertake a bit of pillaging and plundering. The temperature had dropped, growing crops in northern regions had became increasingly difficult. Having stolen the annual harvest, the Vikings headed home for another year. They were not interested in the land itself, only its produce. After a few centuries, the temperatures rose again so they stayed home and grew their own crops. The Brits made use of those Roman roads; communication improved; trade improved and a gradual coalescence took place between neighbours which resulted in fewer kings and larger kingdoms, until England became united under Alfred, the Great, who ruled from 871-899 A.D. Although he only inherited the Kingdom of Wessex, such was his influence that he became *de facto* ruler of most of the land, a land which had enjoyed peace for hundreds of years. So contented were its people, there was very little crime. It was said that a woman and child could walk the length and breadth of the kingdom without fear. So peaceful and so prosperous was England under Alfred, that the rulers of Wales asked to come under Alfred's protection, although Wales, of course, remained a separate country. For the next century-and-a-half, there were a number of kings, most notable of whom was probably Canute, who, by dint of marriage, ended up being king of England as well as of Denmark! This diversion did not last long and the Crown reverted to good Anglo stock. So 'good' were the English kings that one of them eventually became a Saint – Edward, the Confessor, who reigned from 1044-1066 A.D.

Edward failed his country in one important matter. He left no heir! His two brothers had predeceased him, but he was survived by a sister-in-law, who was now married to Harold, son of the Earl of Wessex (and thus a descendant of Alfred the Great). The Witan decided to make Harold King, but there were those who were not happy with this somewhat sideways inheritance via the female line. They wanted a direct male heir – and one was available: William, Duke of Normandy. There was a problem. He was illegitimate, not that that worried him. In Normandy, he overcame any opposition, quite brutally at times, and was just the man the English thought they wanted. A faction of English Lords invited him over and he duly arrived, with a small army.

Harold met him at Hastings, also with a small army, that being all that he could muster. Harold lost the battle, lost his life, and William was duly crowned King – and that was when everything changed!

William knew little about the country over which he now ruled, a deficit he set about rectifying with all speed. He set his minions to work, travelling the length and breadth of the land, recording *everything*, particularly land and its ownership, much to the delight of later historians, who still consult the Domesday Book to this day. He knew he could not govern alone; he needed help and he knew exactly where to find it! He sent for his friends in France and made them Dukes, responsible on his behalf for large areas of land. They were required to swear fealty to him, to promise to raise an army in his service if required, and, in exchange, they each received what was, in fact, a little kingdom of their own. For England, it was psychological devastation. No doubt, some of the Lords who had welcomed him were also rewarded but, in other parts of the land, those who would not submit to the surrender of their land, disappeared from the pages of history.

It was at this time that the system of serfdom was introduced. The peasants were left in peace to farm their land as they had in times of yore, but now they were bound to it. They could not leave and move elsewhere. Neither, of course, could the Dukes! Too bad if the Duke of York thought the climate might be better in Cornwall! York was what he had been given, and in York he stayed! Some have claimed that the serfs were little better than slaves. Not so, said Wallace – along, of course, with many others. The peasant could not be evicted. He was as entitled to live upon the land he had inherited as was the King, or the Duke – or the Earl, or the Baron, or any other titled person, who received smaller parcels of land upon the making of a similar loyalty pledge to their immediate superior. *All* were required to make some form of payment for the land they were granted, be it cash or produce, but this was reasonable. The small-holders were left pretty much on their own to decide the use to which their plot would be put and England prospered, for about a hundred years.

It was this, which Wallace clearly saw as an almost idyllic situation, that he wanted to try to recreate, at least in country areas and in a manner suitable for his time, with the land reforms for which he fought, as an ardent member of the Land Reform Society.

That Normandy blood! That fighting spirit! It resurfaced in William's great-great-grandson, Richard I, or Richard the Lionheart, as he was also known. He ruled from 1189-1199 A.D., and spent about a year of his reign in his own country, not long, but long enough to plan his next Crusade! On one such occasion, Richard was captured by the Germans, (or whatever it was that the people from that area called themselves at that time), who held him hostage for a couple of years (1192–1194 A.D.) and it was his poor, younger brother, later King John, who had the unenviable task of travelling the country, to raise the ransom money.

That was not the worst of it. He might be a mighty lion, but Richard did not set out to reclaim the Holy Land from the Infidel all on his ownsome. He took with him, not hundreds, but *thousands*, of England's finest young men – men who should have been at home, ploughing the fields. Many never returned. Those that did had been away, not for months, but for *years*. It is difficult to imagine the psychological impact this must have had on the population. However deep their faith that God would bless their Christian endeavour, how could the people not be torn apart by an event such as this, which had never, ever, occurred before in the history of their country? Traditionally, battles were fought on a single day. It took a few days to marshal the troops, to march them to the chosen battleground, but the battle itself was quickly over. Now loved ones were gone for an extended period of time, with no means of communication and no guarantee of return. For the first time, there were hints of a labour shortage. For the first time, at least since the Conquest, a man choosing to leave his home for whatever reason might have a reasonable expectation that he would be made welcome somewhere else, no questions asked. Cracks in the system had begun to appear.

Nevertheless, the system held good for a while yet. The climate changed. The temperature dropped - again. Europe was heading for an Ice Age. No one knew about climate change back then; no one knew that Ice Ages had even existed. Gradually the Shetland Islands, the Hebrides, became uninhabitable. Temperatures fell over Scotland and many people resettled in the north of Ireland. The cold spread down through England, the boundary of the Ice Age officially being the River Thames. Climate change happens gradually, but, for convenience, this 'Little Ice Age' is deemed to have lasted from approximately 1350-1750 A.D. Farming practices had to change. Some land in the north or in mountainous areas, simply had to be abandoned. The cracks deepened, but it was not only the geographical climate which was changing. The Age of Exploration had begun and the Industrial Revolution was not far behind.

Despite their traumas, the Crusades had gripped the English imagination as had nothing before them. They may have *heard* about Rome from the Romans, but they had *seen* the Middle East with their own eyes during the Crusades. Some had lived there for several years. During their sojourn, they heard about other lands to the Far East and to the South, beyond Egypt. People from Cornwall and Devon had been used to trading with people from Spain and Africa, Spain having been occupied by the Muslims for several centuries. They had seen black people, although probably not as many in recent times after the Muslims withdrew. For others, however, the Crusades probably afforded their first introduction to people of distinctly different races and colours. The Vikings had discovered Greenland and had reported further land beyond but no one (that we know of) had sailed west in search of land. However, Aztec pyramids raise the question of contact between the Middle East and America at some time in the past. Certainly, there were people who believed there was land to the west. And so it was, that as England, and Europe, sank into a deep freeze, intrepid sailors set off to explore the world to discover new horizons, most of which were a lot warmer! Trade was transformed. Silk was introduced but did not replace traditional clothing. On the contrary, there was a huge world-wide demand for wool (remember, it was cold in Europe!), and more and more land was given over to sheep and cattle rather than to the growing of crops, made increasingly difficult by the continually deteriorating weather. The first cotton mill was established at Derwent in England and the Industrial Revolution had begun.

Industry needed workers and there was only one place from where workers could be obtained: the land. The tradition of the landowner/employer (factory owner) providing free housing persisted, but there were no four acres surrounding each cottage. Rather, houses were built in rows, terraces, with but a small back yard. Little or no thought was given to sanitation. Farmers knew exactly what to do with 'waste'. Factory workers did not. Wages which sounded astronomical to the farm worker, and which enticed many to leave the land for the towns, turned out to be totally inadequate when needed for buying both food *and* clothing. For the first time, poverty became a problem in Britain. The industrialists were doing very nicely, thank you. The workers were sinking into poverty, even debt, something never before experienced. People who could not work, because of sickness or age, lost the right to their house and, again for the first time in the history of the country, people became homeless.

There was some good news. The Ice Age was over. No longer were market stalls erected on the ice of the River Thames each winter; no longer was there even skating on the ice of the River Thames each winter! As the ice melted, it became apparent that the 'cracks' which had appeared in the social structure had now become 'crevasses' and many people were falling down, becoming lost in their cold darkness. The Land no longer belonged to everybody, administered by the Crown and its representatives; it belonged to the Crown and its representatives, who held legal title, vouched for by documentation, which land could be sold, in whole or in part, as they wished. Leases could be terminated; tenants could be evicted – and frequently were when land changed hands. The situation was becoming worse and worse.

Having drawn attention to the benefits of serfdom, Wallace made little reference to the intervening years, apart from his brief mention of Elizabeth I's four acres. His book concentrated on the happenings of the past fifty years, the events he recalled having happened in his own lifetime. He devoted a chapter to Landlordism in Ireland, to land 'clearing' and evictions, which was followed by a chapter on Landlordism in Scotland and one on Landlordism in England. He then discussed 'Occupying Ownership' as distinct from 'Landlordism', finishing with the vision which he, and his fellow campaigners, had of a better and fairer land.

Irish Landlordism

There will be few people who are not familiar, at least in some small degree, with the difficulties faced by the Irish peasant people during the nineteenth century, particularly during the years of the potato famine, when three million people are believed to have died from starvation or associated disease. Wallace noted that Ireland had some of the largest estates and the largest number of absentee landlords. How had this situation come about?

Undoubtedly, some landlords of genuine Irish stock had chosen to purchase properties in England for political reasons. London and its environs was the place to meet other landowners, to discuss finance and trade, keep up with what was going on in the world, a world dominated by England. To these must be added landowners not of original Irish descent. Before Georgian times, it was expected practice for the Sovereign to reward loyal service by the awarding of a title and some land. (It is no coincidence that the term 'title' related both to the person and the property they owned.) Those who fell out of favour might be allowed to leave Court but keep their land and title. Others forfeited both, which made land available to be awarded to another loyal subject. After the Union of Scotland and England, when James VI of Scotland inherited the throne of England and became James I of England, stability became more evident. There was little justification for forfeiture and so the Stuarts gave away the only land not already allocated – that in Ireland. Some of these landlords are believed never to have visited their land, or if they did, their visit was but perfunctory. Land was often leased out, sometimes 'in perpetuity' or for a very long time, at a very low rent (p. 31).

Land was let, sub-let; there were middle-men and agents, extravagant rack-rents and "... the most merciless appropriation by the landlords of the improvements and actual property of the tenants. Nowhere else in our country do we find the land so generally treated as mere rent-producing property" (p. 31).

Here Wallace referred to what he saw as one of the major problems, if not *the* major problem, with the system of land ownership as it then operated throughout the United Kingdom. It is doubtful if anybody would complain if the house, built by a tenant who had been granted a 99-year lease on a vacant piece of land, were to revert to the landlord's descendants after the ninety-nine years was up. However, the system did not seem quite so fair if the lease were for only ten years, or five, or two. Why would any tenant make any improvement upon a leased piece of land, or to a leased property, at his own expense, if that improvement was to devolve to the owner after a short period of time, with no reparation to the tenant? The most any tenant would do would be maintain the property in the state in which it was at the commencement of the tenancy. But there was worse! Under the law as it stood, if a tenant improved the property in any way such that its value was increased, the tenant could be charged increased rent! It was hardly surprising that tenants, who could be evicted if they refused to pay the increased rent, did nothing even to keep the properties in reasonable repair, let alone make any improvement.

Rents were collected by agents. Agents preferred to collect large rents from a small number of tenants rather than small rents from a large number of tenants. Such agents, Wallace believed, encouraged owners to dispossess small tenants in favour of larger ones. Such larger tenants may, or may not, employ labour but they were unlikely to offer much by way of a residence. Such houses as there were, were often not much more than planks of wood nailed together. Not only had millions died in the two years of the potato famine (1847-1848), as a result of the famine, many tenants fell behind in their rent and were subject to eviction "... in the four years 1849-1852 there were 221,845 evictions" (pp. 39-40). Each eviction probably involved a family. In place of the tenants, the land was given over to cattle and sheep, which were deemed more profitable.

Evictions themselves were bad enough, but they were made worse by the callousness of those carrying out the evictions, who were not the landowners, but their agents. Wallace makes the point that many of the landowners had no idea what was going on, being dependent upon reports from those self-same agents, who, of course, made everything sound orderly and desirable. "The houses, which had been built by their own labour ... were pulled down; and when the houseless families, having nowhere to go, lighted fires in the ditches to cook some food, the fires were extinguished in order to drive them off the land" (p. 40). Many occupants were forced out of their houses at night during the winter. Where did these people go?

To America mostly. This was the other side of the coin. Not only was it more profitable for landowners to run cattle or sheep, but there was a desperate need for people in the

New World. When, "In Fourteen Hundred and Ninety-two, Columbus sailed the ocean blue", he did not arrive in America. He arrived at the Caribbean Islands, although he always insisted that he had reached the coast of the mythical western continent. However, other Spanish sailors did make it to America; having sailed in a south-westerly direction they reached South America, which was populated - populated by a people well familiar with gold! The Spanish claimed South America, which took most of their time and energy, so the northern part of the American continent was left for the English. The French were later to show an interest too, particularly in Canada, but Napoleon's attention had been directed towards Russia and the Middle East, so the French mostly missed out. The early settlement of this vast new land was slow, but steady. The land was populated by people with a completely different life-style from that of the Europeans, but they were well-clothed and well-housed in their unique wigwams, and their footwear - the moccasin - was an instant hit! There was a steady trickle of migrants, mostly with religious aspirations, sufficient, after a couple of hundred years, for the new arrivals to have reached the far coast. Then gold was found and there was a gold rush. Not surprisingly, some of the people who joined this rush were the dispossessed of Ireland.

Australia was another story. It was perceived as being an empty, desolate land. It was sparsely populated by naked people, but was 'uninhabited', there being no fixed dwellings, no habitations. There was no farming, no industry, nothing to trade. Nobody wanted to go there. The British Government had no alternative but to 'draft' labour, which they did, via the prison system. The Government made the mistake of contracting out the first shipment of convicts, the contractor increasing his profits by cramming as many people on board as he could. The suffering of these poor men, the death toll, was horrendous and the mistake was not repeated. Those sentenced to penal labour in the colonies were carefully chosen; they had mostly been convicted of non-violent crimes, were deemed to be healthy men who would do good work. With sentences of around two-seven years, a small number of recalcitrants landed up in Port Arthur Prison, Tasmania, but the majority worked on building: houses, roads, infrastructure for the Harbour, the docks, ship repair, there was plenty to do. Others worked on farms. They probably considered themselves the lucky ones. This must have been much better than rotting in a cold, damp gaol 'back home'. And after they had completed their (comparatively) short sentence, they were offered the choice: continue working and save enough from their wages to pay for their journey home or *accept* a parcel of free land, stay and work it. Many chose to stay. The parcels of land being offered far exceeded in size those allocated in the Mother Country, be that England, Scotland or Ireland. People started to migrate to Australia, voluntarily, and some of these people were Irish.

Nevertheless, the number leaving voluntarily (mostly single men) was nowhere near enough to relieve the pressure at home. "For a time,", wrote Wallace (p. 41), "all was thought to be going well." Then the potato famine hit (1847-1849). About three million people are estimated to have died. There may have been no radio or television in those days, but there were newspapers and reports were certainly received on the mainland, but nobody seemed to know what to do. It is easy to condemn with the benefit of hindsight but it must be remembered that in those days organized help centred around 'Parish Relief' - the Poor Laws. Each parish was responsible for its own poor, but that was all. Today, all over the world, there are Government and private bodies with vast reserves of emergency food, shelter and medical supplies, ready to be rushed to the aid of people in need - although, let's be honest, millions are still starving. At that time, there was no organized response at the ready. This was not the first time

126

that the potato crop had failed, but a famine of this magnitude had never occurred before. The population of Ireland dropped from eight to five million, although it is not clear how much of this drop was due to death and how much to migration.

Where did the money for 'Poor Relief' come from. What today is the Local Council was then the Parish Council. It was the responsibility of each Council to raise the money used in Poor Relief and this they did by taxing the landowners a certain amount for every dwelling on their land. Red flag? A landowner, whose income had been drastically reduced as a result of the failure of his crops, was being asked to pay *extra* according to the number of peasants for whom he had provided (free) housing on his land. Getting rid of the tenants and putting the land over to more profitable and less troublesome sheep must have seemed like a very good idea. And that is what happened.

Wallace had built his ideas, in part, upon those of John Stuart Mill, of whom he was a great admirer. Mill had written that commercial rents could be left to market forces, but not those of the peasants. They were tied to their piece of land and, if the rent was fixed solely at the discretion of the landlord, were subject to extortion. Mill argued that, if an equitable rent could not be agreed, then it should be fixed by an authority. Today, at least in Australia, we do have a Rent Tribunal, so some of the problems identified by Wallace and his fellow campaigners have been addressed, if only in a small degree.

(Rents in Australia are undoubtedly high, but not at 'starvation' levels. I could not help but smile when I read Wallace's horror that a man, whose wages were about 9s. or 10s. a week, was expected to pay 1s. 6d. a week in rent! That was about 1/6th of his wage. Wallace wondered how a man could be expected to provide for his family when such a large proportion of his wages was needed to pay the rent. Today, some rents are closer to double that, half of unemployment benefits if not of the minimum wage!)

Mill suggested (p. 43) "that whoever reclaims waste land becomes the owner of it, at a fixed quit-rent equal to a moderate interest on its mere value as waste". This was the first time I had ever heard of a 'quit-rent', but not the last! It featured frequently in Wallace's on-going arguments. Quite why anybody should pay 'quit' rent when taking up a lease, was beyond me, but the puzzle was solved thanks to Wikipedia.

Its origins dated back to Norman times. According to the Conquerer, the land belonged to *him* – or, at least, to the Crown. Not only did those to whom he allocated land (the Dukes) owe him loyalty, they also owed him service, be that raising an army, supplying an army, feeding an army, or anything else he might require of them. As the Dukes sub-divided their land among Earls, Barons, whoever, not only was an undertaking of loyalty required, so was service. The requirement was proportional to the land acquired, i.e. that imposed by the Crown upon the largest estate owners was split between lesser owners in proportion to the amount of land for which they were now responsible. At some point in time, it became the practice for a sum of money to paid to the immediate 'higher' authority in lieu of service. This was known as *Quietus Redditus*, and seems to have been the price one paid for being left in peace and quiet! It not only bought freedom from service, it re-inforced rights to the use of the land. For example, if the owner/tenant, the payer of the quit-rent, as it came to be known, wanted to put a piece of land to agricultural use, he could refuse others the right to hunt over that particular area. Whereas the *selling* of land was accompanied by a proportionate re-allocation of quit-rent, with the *leasing* of land, it was up to the landlord to decide the 'share' of quit-rent to be paid by the tenant, and, it would seem, some landowners were quite creative with their mathematics! Quit-rents gave rights to the *use* of land, not to its ownership.

As land was claimed for the Crown around the world, so did quit-rents spread across the Empire. Collecting rents may have been a simple task in Britain and Ireland, but was well-nigh impossible in Australia, where land packages were sometimes vast. In the first half of the nineteenth century, New South Wales extended north to Cape York. The State of Queensland became a separate entity in 1859. It will readily be recognized how impossible it must have been for a Government agent to travel thousands of miles to collect a few dollars in quit rent - especially those properties which were owned and for which no other form of rent was payable. Most of the outback properties, many comprising thousands of acres, fell into this category. In 1831, quit-rent was all but abolished in New South Wales. What is particularly interesting is that it was retained in a nominal form, 'a peppercorn or one penny'. It had to be retained in some way, however nominal, because it was an acknowledgement of the ultimate ownership of the land by the Crown and of service/duty owed to the Crown.

Quit-rent may have been abandoned in New South Wales, but it was still very real in Britain in the 1880s, when Wallace was campaigning for his version of Land Rights.

Landlordism in Scotland

If you thought Ireland was bad, just wait until you hear about Scotland!

Scotland was different from Ireland in some ways, similar in others. Firstly, Scotland was not as densely populated. Recovering from centuries of Ice Age conditions, land was becoming available for farming which had been laid waste. Not having been farmed for hundreds of years, it was not very fertile and was more suitable for sheep and cattle than it was for crops. For the first time in history, Scottish Lairds were not thinking so much about how they could keep all their tenants gainfully employed as how they could maximise the use of their land with the minimum of labour. Secondly, the Scottish were less likely to blame the English for their problems or to look to them for answers.

It had been the Scottish King, James VI, who had inherited the English throne. He wasted no time in relocating his Court from Icy Scotland to the melting point in London. James wanted his two kingdoms to become one, but this was staunchly resisted by the English. It took three years for James to come up with a compromise which the English were prepared to accept: united under one Crown, the two countries wold retain their separate identities. They would retain their own flag and their own Patron Saint (George for England and Andrew for Scotland). As far as possible, Scotland would retain its own laws. Those passed in Westminster, in the interest of all the King's subjects and signed into Law by him, would over-ride any pre-existing laws, be they English or Scottish, but local administrators would still be able to pass laws, in either country, applicable to their people only. There was to be a new flag, flown when it was deemed appropriate to emphasize the unity under the Crown. Uniquely, I believe, in the history of the world, this flag was not a new design, created especially for this momentous event. It was a union of the two flags, the white background behind the red cross of St. George cleverly melding with the white cross of St. Andrew on its blue background. Later, Ireland's flag, the red diagonal cross of St. Patrick on its white background was to complete this most special of flags. The Principality of Wales, which had mastered the art of flying under the radar long before radar was invented, kept well clear of all this.

Wallace emphasized that all that was done was done within the law. Initially, as in Ireland, evictions happened with at least some semblance of mutual consent. Peasants were offered alternative land – close to the sea, with access to fishing, beaches to scavenge for shell fish and kelp, cliffs from which to collect eggs, and, of course, the land itself. Sounded idyllic, and it was, in summer! People had been allowed to move their belongings, including the wood from which their houses had been made, but when the winter storms blew, these provided little shelter from the bitter cold. Boats overturned; people were washed off the rocks. Many men drowned, leaving destitute families. Resistance to moving grew. It must not be thought, stressed Wallace, that the failure successfully to become established on their newly allotted land was due in any way to the mental or physical shortcomings of the peasants. They were well bred and deemed to be the most intelligent of peasants anywhere in the world. But times were changing. The age-old practice of land passing down through the generations, not only among the Clan Chiefs but among the peasants also, began to fail with the advent of Industrialism. Suddenly, some people had more money than others; some people bought more land from others; estates became larger, owned by fewer people.

The uniting of the two kingdoms meant that Scotland followed England from serfdom to peasantry, from Chieftan to Lord, from being protector of the land and its people to being the owner, with the right of disposal. "... almost all the evils so prevalent in Ireland exist as fully and to as disastrous an extent in Scotland at the present day" (p. 73). As his first example, Wallace cited the Sutherland estates (p. 56).

> "One of the most celebrated of these wholesale clearances was made on the great estate of the lords of Sutherland, then in the possession of an English nobleman, the Marquis of Stafford, who had acquired it by marriage. The estate consisted of more than 700,000 acres, or the larger half of the entire country and was inhabited by a population of 15,000 herdsmen and small farmers ...".

From this information, one can make certain deductions. Firstly, the new owner had no emotional attachment to the land he had acquired. He did not personally know any of its inhabitants. Secondly, the land was sparsely populated. Even allowing that the figure of 15,000 referred only to the men who were the legal tenants, and allowing that each had a family of around six people, that would still not bring the population of the estate – which was 'nearly half the entire country' – to more than 100,000. One can perhaps understand the logic of using this land for pasture, relocating the people. The problem was the place of relocation. It is highly unlikely that the new owner was personally familiar with the chosen land, which would almost certainly have been selected by his agent/manager. What is of particular interest is the early date. The clearances took place between 1812 and 1820 and apparently passed unnoticed by the English. Why on earth would the English be interested in what a Scottish Lord was doing on his own property?

The English may not have noticed, but perhaps the Irish did. There had always been a closer relationship between the Irish and the Scottish than between the Irish and the English, those in the northern parts of Ireland sharing, not only surnames, but whisky, bagpipes, religion and many other things as well.

Evictions became more violent. Houses were torn down, having been deemed unfit for habitation, which they probably were. When the peasants tried to rebuild, the timber was burnt. Sometimes peasants were given time to collect belongings; at other times their meagre belongings were burnt, along with their homes. The peasants were offered new homes in a new land – Canada!

Canada was in desperate need of people. The founding of colonies in the New World (America) had taken place during the European Ice Age – which, of course, affected America as well. It had also taken place during a period of unprecedented religious persecution. Henry VIII's take over of the Church in England had been reasonably peaceful, but when his daughter, Mary, a Catholic, came to the throne, there ensued bitter persecution of heretics. People were burned at the stake, something which had never, ever, happened before in any of the Islands. Protestantism spread from Europe and was embraced particularly warmly in Scotland. There was never any need to force people to emigrate to America; many went willingly and white people spread slowly, but surely, from coast to coast. The situation was different in the north, in what is today Canada. Most of the land was frozen over – as much of it still is today. There was some settlement, both by the English and the French, who fought for the land. The English won – sort of. There has always been a strong French influence in Canada. The Brits needed more people in Canada – and who better to settle this land than the Scots, who were used to such a climate and would know how best to utilize the land? So many Scots migrated to Canada that part of it became known as 'New Scotland' – Nova Scotia!

There were boats at the Scottish ports ready to take these displaced people to their new life, with a promise, of course, of land, a promise I am sure was kept, because it *needed* to be kept, although Wallace did reproduce one letter written by a party of new disembarkees, who had not been met by the expected welcoming committee. The letter had been written immediately and sent back to Scotland by the Captain of the boat upon which they had arrived.. Frightening as this experience would have been, I am sure they would have been greeted the next day. Every single one of the people who embarked on these ships did so 'voluntarily' – i.e. no overt force was used, no one was arrested, no one was shackled. They were told that this was what had been arranged and, being law abiding people, they did as they were told. If the agent told the Lord that all had gone smoothly, that everybody had embarked peaceably, he would have spoken nothing but the truth and the Lord would no doubt have been well satisfied. Wallace did not state directly by whom the evacuations were funded but there is an implication that it was the Lords who were financing the whole procedure, which would make sense. No doubt they thought they were being generous, that their generosity was welcomed and appreciated - a case of the 'right hand' not having a clue what the 'left hand' was doing!

Person by person, acre by acre, the clearings in Scotland far exceeded those in Ireland. The brutality of the evictions was far greater: the burning of the houses and the people's belongings often taking place in winter and at night, in weather far worse than anything experienced in more southerly Ireland. And, by the way, there was a potato famine in Scotland as well, at the same time as that in Ireland. Wallace gave no figures, either for population or casualties. The fiercely independent Scots kept their problems to themselves. Nevertheless, it is clear that any problems Ireland faced due to positions of Law were suffered also in Scotland; any problems faced in Ireland due to geographical/climatic conditions, was suffered in Scotland also, but to a greater degree.

English Landlordism

There must have been a reason why Wallace gave this chapter a slightly different form of title from that used for the two previous chapters. Was Landlordism in England different from that in Scotland and Ireland? Legally, no. In practice, yes, for better, for worse.

Wallace's opening comments were very positive. "In England pure Landlordism is seen at its best" (p. 97). Landlordism had evolved over some eight hundred years. Large, ancestral estates still existed but they were buffered by countless smaller estates, owned, not necessarily by aristocrats, but by the country squire – a younger son of a younger son, etc. These people "usually lived among their tenants, have been accustomed to treat them liberally, and have had sympathy with their pursuits and a desire for their prosperity" (p. 97). He went on to say that the tenant farmers themselves were usually men of some education and of some capital. Their families had probably lived on the same tenanted property for several generations and the 'prosperity' of which Wallace had just spoken was evident.

The problem in England was the reverse of that in Ireland and Scotland. The tenants were not being forced from their land; they were deserting it!

The world over, there has always been a problem with younger sons. Several healthy boys were welcome as teenagers to help work the land, but what to do when they became old enough to marry and needed a home of their own? Robert Malthus (1766-1834) travelled widely across Europe and Asia, as far as China. In his book, *An Essay on the Principles of Population* (1798), he gave interesting accounts of the methods he had seen employed in various countries, during his travels. Scandinavia, for example, required ten years' military service of their men, the longest time of any nation. Men were around thirty years of age before they became available for marriage. But there was another hurdle they had to overcome. They could not marry until they were a 'householder' – i.e. they owned a house. And they could not become a householder until someone died! No new houses were being built. This novel arrangement kept the population low and individual wealth high! China was a complete contrast. On his death, the father's plot of land was divided equally among all his sons with the result that each son now had but a tiny parcel. Despite being the most peaceable, most hard-working people Malthus had encountered on his travels, the Chinese peasants lived in the greatest poverty.

England was somewhere in between.

The rule of *primogenitor* had applied since Norman times. The large estates passed down to the eldest son or closest male heir. That heir was responsible for the well-being of close family members – siblings, aunts and uncles, cousins. Some had 'rooms', or even a wing, within the main house. Others had separate homes. All received some form of allowance. As family relationships became more distant, so the families were expected to become more self-supporting. The minor aristocracy and their descendants joined the military, the Church, became doctors, lawyers, teachers. In other words, they formed the 'professional classes. The non-landed class had no land to leave. The passing of property to the next generation was largely at the discretion of the landowner, but personal property was more likely to be shared. With the increase of wealth among the newly created 'middle class' following the Industrial Revolution, there came far greater opportunities for choice as to the distribution of wealth, the industrialist being free to leave his money (and his land) where he willed. Increasingly, money was being left to daughters, especially in America. The wealthy heiress, many of whom married 'up', became a notable phenomenon, particularly in America. Land ownership was changing in England; whether for the better or worse remained to be seen.

One thing about which there was no doubt was the attraction of the towns for many of the young men – and girls, who followed them. Initially, the new homes provided by the factory owners, the comradeship of the work place, were well received. Lack of outdoor space and poor hygiene have already been mentioned, as has the vacating of one's house on leaving one's job. The loss of the home if unable to work because of sickness or old age soon became a major problem. The working environment, which could well involve the handling of toxic substances, such as phosphorous, impacted people's health and even youngish people were becoming ill in a way never before seen. Not only were more and more factories belching more and more smoke from their chimneys, more and more steam engines were doing the same as they criss-crossed the country upon their shiny new rails. So bad was the pollution that, famously, the wings of the brown Manchester Moth turned black to match the sooty blackness of the bark of the trunk of the trees upon which it slept! After the Clean Air Act, passed in 1956, Britain's air cleaned sufficiently for the moth's wings to regain their former colour.

With no sick pay, no retirement pay, and certainly no holiday pay, poverty, homelessness, destitution and despair were the unexpected harvest of seeds sown, and allowed to grow and prosper, without proper care and attention. In an attempt to redress increasingly evident wrongs, a New Domesday Book was assembled (p. 107). It was shown that 525 members of the peerage owned 1,593 estates, covering around 15,000,000 acres, or approximately one-third of the land of the United Kingdom. Many 'private gentlemen' also possessed several estates in more than one county. Most of these estates, both those owned by the peers and those owned by private gentlemen, must have been managed by agents. That feeling of 'oneness' which had existed in Norman times between the Duke, his minions and his serfs, and between all of them and the land, was gone. The agents probably had no more feeling towards the peasants upon the land than they did towards the cattle.

It might be wise to point out that most of the 'peers' (aristocrats) who owned those 15,000,000 acres were not Members of Parliament. The Laws of the Land were the responsibility of the House of Commons – the House of the Common People. No peer of the realm was eligible to sit in the Lower House. If the Lords of the Realm were receiving some unfair advantage as far as land ownership was concerned, then its was up to the House of Commons to remedy the situation.

At the time Wallace was writing, England's fate was in the hands of the Members of the Lower House. And who were these Members? One thing we know, they were not women. They were not the top of the Upper Class, who were also banned. They were not the lower class, the peasants, the workers in the factories. To qualify to vote, one must needs be a property owner. In times passed, this had meant 'land owner', but the rise of industrialization, and the move to the towns and the cities, had meant that some men owned houses with very little land. Some of the 'landless' properties were quite grand – particularly the terraced houses in London and Bath. So, the Members of Parliament were lesser aristocrats, landed gentry, and the newly rich merchant and industrialist. How many of those were likely to pass legislation designed to retard the acquisition of wealth? The merchants and bankers were helping to create a new 'class' in Britain – the Middle Class – neither aristocrat nor worker. They were competing with the aristocrats for ownership of land and this competition was driving up prices. A Mr. George was quoted as saying: "... as the value of land increases, so does the contrast between wealth and want." Where money leads the way, can selfishness be far behind?

In England the situation was the exact opposite of that in Ireland and Scotland. Far from trying to drive people from the land, the problem was to attract people back to it. In Scotland the problem of 'absentee landlordism' related mostly to landlords who lived on a small part of their vast estates and knew little of the rest, rarely, if ever, visiting it, leaving nearly all decisions in the hands of one or more 'agents'. In Ireland, absentee landlords may not live on their land at all; they may not even live in the same country. However, in both countries, large landowners were actively seeking to *reduce* the number of tenants on their land. In England, absentee landlords mostly lived in one of the big cities – London being a popular choice, but it could have been Manchester, or one of the other industrial centres, as more and more merchants/industrialists owned land. Manufacturers needed labour and did their best to *entice* workers to leave the land to work in their factories. No one was *forced* to leave the country for the towns. They were doing so in increasing numbers of their own volition. Now the landowners were facing a lack of labour on their land! Scotland and Ireland might have been able to get away with giving over their land to cattle and sheep, which provided meat, leather and wool, but if England did so too, how was everybody to be fed? Already Wallace was reporting food shortages in the country: milk, butter, eggs, poultry, (nearly) all of which, Wallace claimed, if produced were sent away to the cities. but we know that many people in the cities were suffering from hunger, so the unthinkable was already starting to manifest. England was not producing enough food to feed its people!

This system would appear to be a forerunner of the mass production/marketing of today, under which large conglomerates enter into contracts with producers, often with the assistance of government sponsored marketing boards, which results in the growers/country dwellers having very little say in distribution. Wallace's vision was one of hundreds, thousands of small holdings: a man, his family, his house and his land, those precious few acres upon which he would grow sufficient food to feed his family. Any extra eggs, milk, or even vegetables, could be sold to pay for any items he could not produce himself; Wallace mentioned tea and coffee. He did not want Englishmen to be forced to labour in factories; he did not want them surrendering their produce to their landlord. He wanted as many English families as possible to be self-supporting.

Because Wallace worked with others on Land Reform, it is difficult to tell if any of the solutions offered in his book *originated* with him, or whether he was but promoting the ideas of others. However, it is not difficult to tell to which ideas and beliefs he was firmly committed: "... we maintain that land ought to be owned only for personal occupation" (p. 108). If the rich could only live in one place, would they choose the city or the country? Wallace said that his opponents argued for the first option; he argued for the second. He believed that the Englishman's love of the country ran true and deep. If a man could only have one *permanent* residence, most would choose the country. They would stay in Inns or hotels when they needed to visit a town or city. Of course, they would not be able to rent a property for their visit because Wallace's plan made no provision for the ownership of a second domestic property which could be rented out on short-term let. He still allowed for large estates, but envisioned these being manned by farm workers, who would increasingly become the owners of their house and small acreage, attracted back to the country by the very prospect of being able to purchase their own abode.

The advantage to the landowner would be freedom from his responsibilities towards his workers. He would no longer be required to provide them with free housing. He would no longer be required to contribute towards the Parish Poor Relief Fund.

Where was this newly available land to be found? There was only one place: the large estates – the *very large* estates.

Wallace did not suggest wholesale seizure of land. He proposed that land should gradually be made available, initially on the outskirts of the nominated estates. The new holdings would be out of sight of the main house and, bearing in mind the enormous acreage of some of these properties, would scarcely be noticed. Far from detracting from the value of the estate, Wallace believed that people, knowing that the land was *theirs*, would take great pride in it. He believed the cottages built would be of a standard superior to that currently provided by the landlord. The land around the cottage would be carefully husbanded. The garden would be tended with beautiful flowers; there would be a vegetable garden, a herb garden, fruit trees, an area for the chickens, for the sheep and the cow or two. These beautiful country cottages, if they did anything, would enhance the value of the adjacent estate, not detract from it. Wallace further suggested that not more than 10% of the land should be surrendered during the life-time of the owner and his heirs, born during his life-time, a time span which Wallace suggested would be approximately 50-70 years.

And how were these workers to pay for their land? It is here that Wallace (and his colleagues?) came up with a unique suggestion.

Wallace pointed out that there were two parts to the value of any property – the property itself, the building or other use to which the land had been put, and the location. Any property dealer will tell you it is all about location, location, location! The location may be fixed, but the *locality* can change. What if a new railway became established nearby? That would greatly increase the value of the property to the advantage of the owner, yet he had done nothing to deserve it. He had not contributed a penny piece to the cost of the building the railway. At the time Wallace wrote, a new factory estate nearby might also increase the value of property, since it would offer the possibility of work, and if the property on offer was a worker's dwelling, it could be in great demand.

Wallace spoke mostly of unwarranted/undeserved increases in property value, but, of course, the reverse was also true. Rezoning, such that industrial buildings could be erected adjacent to some person's back fence, or even the building of a multi-story apartment block, whose residents could look down upon what previously had been a private back garden, could decrease the value of a property, sometimes to the extent of making it all but unsaleable. This, said Wallace, was unjust.

The two-tiered nature of the value of property had long been recognized in English Law. It was the basis of quit-rent. The original quit-rent of Norman times had been determined by the owner of the land and this practice had continued down until the 19th century. Then, all land had belonged to the Crown - and it still did, in theory, something which Wallace never acknowledged. Early in his book, he made two passing references to the 'Crown', but thereafter he referred only to the State. Those acres of land which were gradually to be surrendered by the landowners to the State, were to be purchased from the landowner by the State, by repayment of the quit-rent. Since the quit-rent was paid annually, how many years' worth of quit-rent would the State need to pay to recompense the landowner for his loss? That was 'to be determined', but it would be quite a few. However, the State would now be receiving quit-rent, not from the former landowner but from the new 'private' owner, so the State could just forward the money on. The precise details were unclear. The original quit-rent of Norman times was paid up the chain of 'owners' to the Duke, nobody truly 'owning' the land. Now people were perceived as owning land and quit-rent applied to tenants. If I have read Wallace correctly, he was envisioning the new owner of the few acres paying a 'one off' quit-rent at the time of purchase, although he would be able to spread the payment over several yeas, as if it were a mortgage. Unlike the traditional landowner, the State's receipt of quit-rent would be short-term.

Who, or what, was the State? Wallace never defined this entity. The Law only applies to people. A business has an owner; a company has (at least three) directors. A car has an owner, whose ownership must be registered before the car is allowed to be taken on the road. Domestic animals have owners, who are legally responsible for them and liable for any damage they may cause.

So, who was the 'State'? If a group of people, such as 'every living Englishman', were they all equally responsible? That would be unworkable. In business, shareholders are somewhat protected. Their shares might loose value if the Company made some mistake or broke the Law, but the individual shareholders would not be prosecuted. The Directors might be. They might be fined or even gaoled if their Company was found to be in violation of the law. So, who would be responsible for the 'State'. There is only one group of people I can think of and that is the Members of Parliament with seats in the House at Westminster. And who were those people who held those seats, in whom Wallace wished to place such trust? Some, no doubt, were people like Wallace, genuinely determined to make a difference, a difference which would benefit 'the people'. Others would be those who saw a seat at Westminster as enhancing their position of prestige and power. Wallace never carried his thinking this far. He left his theory with the State purchasing the 'reclaimed' land from the landowner, for onward sale to the tenant farmer, who would pay the State the quit-rent, that amount which had, for centuries, determined the right to the use of the land, which amount would be refunded to the tenant on sale of the property.

Members of Parliament enjoy 'Parliamentary privilege' when speaking in the House. They cannot be sued for any defamatory comments they may make, be those comments true or untrue. What redress would an owner have if he considered that the law, or the administration of the law, was unfair to him? People do 'take on' Government departments, so maybe such action would have been possible, but it probably would have been expensive. Wallace's trust in the State to act as a benevolent parent was quite touching.

Wallace never specified what proportion of the over-all price was to be quit-rent, paid to the State, and what proportion was to be paid to the previous owner, if buildings, or other improvements, were involved. He tacitly recognized that the sum might be significant by suggesting that the tenant-now-to-be-owner should be allowed to pay the amount off in instalments, as with a mortgage, if necessary over a period of years. Since the change of ownership would be taking place quite gradually, presumably the quit-rent received by the State from one buyer would be used to pay out the quit-rent owed to another seller. Apart from administration, the cost to the community would not be large. The reduction in the size of the estate of any one person during their life-time would be no more than 10% and knowing that the ownership of the remaining 90% would be secure for the remainder of his life-time would help soften any blow felt by the landowner at being forced to relinquish any at all.

There remained the question of where the buyers would obtain their funds. This would be by traditional borrowing, both the quit-rent and property price being paid off at the same time. Wallace recognized that this could be a potential problem since, in effect, two mortgages were being paid off simultaneously. However, Wallace assumed that the State would do everything it could to facilitate the purchase, being very generous in its repayment demands, even allowing a year or two's 'grace'. Once in the property, the new owners would not be paying rent. What had been rent, gone for ever, would now become a payment towards permanent ownership – an idea to which many people of today will relate. Pride of ownership would ensure that the property was not only maintained, but almost certainly improved. It must be remembered that Wallace was not speaking of town or city dwellings. He was referring to country acreage – smallholdings. At the end of his book, he did make reference to ways in which his ideas could be adjusted to make them suitable for application to town/city situations, but he was looking a century ahead and his suggestions were very general.

Although fuzzy in some of its detail, the broad outline of Wallace's ideas are clear and so have some appeal. Wallace concentrated on undeserved profit resulting from locality improvement, but, of course, the reverse would be true. A property could loose value as the result of re-zoning, or some such. If a property lost 25% of its value because the local council had chosen the empty land behind the back fence as the place for its new rubbish tip, the owner may still be able to find a buyer at the reduced price. Under Wallace's system, he would be entitled to the full value of his house. The reduced price would occur because of the reduced quit-rent. By how much would the *national* body, the State, be prepared to lower its income, the quit-rent, due to a decision taken by a *local* body, the Parish or Local Council? Wallace assumed that the State would always act in an impartial way, safe-guarding the interests of citizens.

Wallace summarized his views on pp. 192-193. These included:

> Arrangements to be made by which every British subject may secure a portion of land for personal occupation at its fair agricultural value.

> A person must own land only so long as he occupies it personally; that is, he must be a perpetual holder of the land, not its absolute *owner*.

> The State must in no way deal with individual landowners, except through the medium of special Courts.

> The State should be the actual owner of the land, in order that it may be untrammelled in making from time to time such general rules and regulations for its tenure as may be found needful for the public good.

> The State alone, as universal landowner, will be able to provide means by which every man, from the labourer upwards, may procure suitable land for his personal occupation.

Every human being has to live somewhere upon the face of this Earth. Some may choose to emigrate; that would be their own concern. Those who chose to live their lives in the country of their birth had an inherent right to share in its ownership. A few should not be allowed to own huge swathes of land, parcelling it out in bits and pieces to others at their whim and pleasure. "Every Englishman should be allowed, *once in his life*, to select a plot of land for his personal occupation ... not less than one acre or more than five acres (pp. 216-217).

In 1900, Wallace published his two volume work, *Studies Scientific and Social*, which has already been considered and in which he devoted much space to Land Nationalisation, most of which was repetition of previous writing.

There was only one chapter (XXIII) which contained new thought, and that related to the past rather than to the future. *The Social Quagmire and the Way Out of It* had appeared as an article in the Boston *Arena* in March and April 1893. It related to problems in America which country, you will remember, he had visited. He commenced by telling how much English readers in the early years of the century had enjoyed reading works of fiction portraying rural life, in the days before trains and telegraphs, when "all beyond the Mississippi was 'the far west' and California and Texas were foreign countries". The life portrayed was almost idyllic, plenty of home-grown food and plenty of home-grown friendliness. He suggested that newly arriving migrants, from Europe as well as from Britain, tended to attribute this happiness, this freedom, to lack of authoritarian rule by Church and State. Since the arrival of the Pilgrim Fathers, and the establishment of the Plymouth Brethren, there had been freedom of religion such that it had allowed the establishment of many new religions – Baptists, Mormons, Seventh Day Adventists, Jehovah's Witness, Quakers among the best known. All were variants of Christianity. All were free to interpret the Gospels according to their own understanding and worship God according to their own conscience. The 'Church' was no longer a threat. There was no Inquisition. The Church was no longer seen as the wealthy autocracy, they but the poor, ignorant people.

But there was more. Not so long before (1776), the American Colonies had declared themselves a Republic! There was no King to tell them what to do. They elected their own President, who was one of them. Wallace postulated that many of the immigrants attributed their poor condition of life in the home country which they had just left to these two authorities, and many still did, a century later. The truth of the matter was that unemployment, homelessness, poverty, pauperism and crime were not only as prevalent in America then as they were in Europe, *they were worse!* The rich in America were even richer and the poor were were becoming even poorer – or, rather, the percentage of poor was becoming greater. He estimated that there were over a thousand millionaires and that 250,000 people, out of 6,000,000, owned three-quarters of the wealth of the country. It was not the method of maintaining law and order which was the problem; it was the law itself. It was *society* which need to change, not its method of rule. Common-born people could be just as selfish, just as greedy, as the aristocratic – and aristocratic people could be just as kind and caring as the poor.

Unfortunately, throughout his writings, Wallace tended to portray the poor as selfless and hardworking, attributing the increasing crime rate to their poverty. He rarely mentioned anything good done by an aristocrat, the exception being Lord Carrington (1900: vol.2, p. 419) who had eight hundred tenants on small plots of land around the town of High Wycombe, whose produce (type unstated) was around forty pounds per acre compared with seven pounds an acre for other, larger, ploughed acreage.

If poverty was the *cause* of crime, then all poor people would be criminals. Clearly they were not. On the contrary, many extremely poor people led exemplary lives, never stealing. A white collar criminal could steal more in one day, with the stroke of a pen, than an unemployed person might steal in a life-time of petty crime. The social conditions under which these two individuals were raised might *direct* their criminal tendency. It would not create it. Some people were greedy, some were not. Their social situation allowed different avenues for the expression of their personality; it did not create the personality. This was the lesson learnt by the French as well as the Americans. Becoming a Republic was not the simple solution to all life's problems. The problem was human nature.

There were enough hints in Wallace's writings to show that he was aware of this, but they were only hints. His sanctification of the working people was palpable. He died in 1913, four years before the Russian Revolution. Had he lived to hear of those events, I am sure he would have been thrilled. Not only the land, but *everything* belonged to the people. Alas, the farm people became every bit as oppressed. They were not only told what to do, what to cultivate, but even where to live, being moved to another place if their labour was deemed to be more needed there. They were allowed to keep enough of their crops to feed themselves, if but meagrely, the rest being appropriated by the State to feed the people in the towns and cities. Same old, same old! They were never out of work. If the salt mines of Siberia were in need of labour, that was where they might be sent - although criminals were the first choice. In fairness, I must say that I have seen short interviews on television documentaries with older people living in Russia who look back to the days of Communism with longing. The shelves may have been nearly bare, but they all got *something*, they were all treated equally. Now the shops were full of beautiful items, of clothing, of accessories, such as they never dreamed of. They looked at them with longing, but they could not afford to buy them. They now felt 'devalued' in a way that they had not before.

Wallace, were he alive today, would no doubt be pleased with the fact of the minimum wage, even if not the amount. He would also be pleased with Work Place Health and Safety, at least the concept if not always its application. Apart from that, I think he would be appalled, especially by 'Investment Portfolios' which see a small number of people acquiring more and more properties, purchased, not with their own money, but with the money received from their tenants, who must struggle to save the deposit for a place of their own out of what is left after rent (used to pay another person's mortgage), and all other living expenses, have been paid. Remember, Wallace advocated that each person should only be allowed to own one property, the one in which he (and his family) lived.

Plenty to think about!

Chapter 9

Depressed Trade

In Chapter 12 of *Studies Scientific and Social*, Wallace wrote an extremely interesting article outlining what he believed to be the causes of the downturn in trade which Britain was then experiencing. The downturn had become noticeable to all over the previous two or three years, but Wallace believed the problem had started to emerge much earlier, quite suddenly at the end of the year 1874. Wallace had done his homework. The term 'depression' was synonymous with 'bad trade' and 'bad trade' simply meant 'deficiency of purchasers' (p. 191). Why was there a deficiency of purchasers? Not because people did not want to buy. It was because people no longer had the money to spend. Why had people become deficient in spending money?

The country *as a whole* might be richer, but people *on the whole* were poorer. Obviously, the population had increased. *National* increase in wealth did not equate to *per capita* increase, nor was there any equality *per capita*. Some were becoming exceedingly wealthy while others were becoming exceedingly poor. This had been true for some time, so was not, of itself, the reason for the downturn in trade. Wallace had studied trade figures, imports and exports, from 1864 to 1883. Always imports exceeded exports. In 1863 imports had valued £222 million, exports £160 million.

With minor variations, this gap had remained fairly stable until about 1870. For the next four years, exports had risen sharply, reducing the trade gap from £62 million to £31 million. 1871-1872 had seen a sharp rise in exports; the (positive) trade gap fell to £41 million. 1873 was almost steady, nothing more than a small downward fluctuation, but between 1874 and 1879 there had been a sharp decline in exports and a sharp rise in imports. Wallace showed on his graph that exports had fallen to £191.5 million, but did not specifically state the value of imports. From the graph, the amount would appear to have been around £310 million, perhaps a little less, giving a trade gap of approximately £190 million. Exports had improved in comparison with imports, but the gap in 1883 had still been £120 million. Why?

Wallace identified four causes and I will deal with them in reverse order because the fourth one was our old friend: rural depopulation. From his study of the 1871 and 1881 census, Wallace had learned that the overall population of England and Wales had increased by 15%, but that over about half the area of England and Wales, population had actually fallen. Most of the arguments he then set out for the repopulation of the rural areas were much the same as those covered in the previous chapter of this book and need not be repeated here, but he did made one or two interesting points, which do bear repeating.

There had been an enormous increase in the import of certain foods. "Mr. Giffen and other statisticians" (p. 212) had cited this increase as evidence of increased prosperity. Wallace saw it as evidence that the country was not producing enough food to feed itself and people were being forced to spend money buying food, which previously had been obtained 'free' from their own back yards, thus having less money to spend on other things, which, Wallace argued, was a contributing factor to the depression. Wallace compared 1870 (the year of the lowest trade gap) with 1883, the last year for which he had figures (p. 212):

> In 1870 we imported less than a million – 860,000 – cwts. [hundredweight] of bacon and pork, whereas in 1883 it had risen to 5,000,000 cwts. Of potatoes there were imported 127,000 cwts. in 1870, and 4,000,000 cwts. in 1883; of eggs in 1870, 430,000,000, and in 1883, 800,000,000.

I found the numbers relating to eggs particularly staggering. I could not believe that England did not have enough chickens to produce sufficient eggs for its own requirements. I could only suppose that in times gone by, eggs had been considered too fragile to move *en masse*, leaving town dwellers without eggs. Clearly, England's overseas competitors had addressed this problem. Wallace had pointed out that only about one third of those migrating from the country to the city were farm workers; the rest were village traders, who had relied on the farm workers for their trade. Without the farm workers, their businesses were no longer viable. They followed the farm workers to the towns and cities.

In support of his argument in favour of encouraging the return of people to the land, Wallace cited the estate of Lord Carrington, mentioned in the last chapter. Lord Carrington had allocated about eight hundred allotments of land to labourers. These allotments, on average, returned a yield of about £33 an acre *more* than had been the yield under normal farming, i.e. the farmer labouring on the Lord's land for payment. £33 was a lot of money in those days and an acre is not really that large a piece of land. Remember, this was £33 *more*, not £33 all up. If each man had several acres, just think of the purchasing power which would be released! Reducing food imports would bring down the trade deficit. No more depression!

Thirty years later, the catch-cry of the Marxist movement was: "From each according to his ability; to each according to his need." Unfortunately, when the workers were working for the State, 'abilities' suddenly declined while 'needs' rose. People wanted what they could get - for the minimum output of their labour. Human beings labour for themselves, their families, their tribe. Few labour for those they do not know - not unless they can be persuaded to relate to them in some way. Believing in evolution, as he so firmly did, Wallace was only too aware of the emotions and feelings which human beings still shared with their animal forebears. If a pride of lions gives any thought to the other pride on the opposite side of the valley, it is not as to how they might help them but how they might kill them! It was thus throughout nature. Our greatest rivals are other members of our own species. All creatures look after themselves, some look after their family, even less look after their friends, but *none* look after their rivals. Charity organizations are well aware of this human characteristic which is why they give a name to the girl sleeping in the street, trying to keep warm, and promise to send you a cuddly replica of the animal you are 'adopting'. If the recipient cannot be personalized, donations will be small.

The next cause of the depression in trade mentioned by Wallace (going backwards, it was actually the third he mentioned) was the increase in the number of millionaires. Wallace had checked probate duty paid - a matter of public information - for the ten years before 1874, when the depression started, with the ten years after. He pointed out that probate was only paid on personal property, not property held by the family estate, so his figures underestimated many people's wealth during their life times. In the first of the decades, he was considering [1864-1874] 162 persons had died with a personal wealth of more than a quarter of a million. In the second [1874-1884] that number had risen to 208, an increase of 29%. He reiterated his claim that if a few people had more, then most people had less. There was only a certain amount of money to go around.

Wallace had also consulted the two census carried out in 1871 and 1881 in reference to manufacturing. Persons engaged in cotton manufacturing had decreased by 20%, those in the linen and wool trade by 15%, metal workers had remained the same and drapers had diminished by 7%. These were all manufacturers of 'every day' items, such as might be purchased by 'the masses'. When it came to manufacturers of items likely to be purchased by the wealthy, milliners had increased 4%, carpet makers 9%, florists and gardeners 10%, musicians and musical instrument makers 23%. "The rich have grown richer and have been able to indulge in greater luxuries, while the poor have grown poorer and have been obliged to do with less of the bare necessaries of life" (p. 204).

There was another area, connected with the wealthy, which had also grown. Persons registered as bankers or bankers' clerks had increased by 21%. Insurance agents or brokers had increased by 300%, by which Wallace could only assume that: "there are an immense number of people who live in the city by speculation who find it convenient to call themselves insurance agents or brokers" (p. 205). He believed that the mania for speculation had been increasing and its effects were becoming more injurious. He attributed this to the passing "more than twenty years ago" of the Limited Liability Act, an Act which had received wide-spread support, even from persons usually supportive of the working classes, such as John Stuart Mill. This Act stipulated that, when a business/ company was established and registered as 'Limited Liability', should that company close down for any reason, financial failure being the most likely, the persons who established the business could not be asked to pay out in settlement more than they had put in. All such registered businesses were required to added the term "Limited"/"Ltd." after their name, so that any person or company trading with them would be aware of this limited liability.

The hope of the Act had been to increase trade. It had. It had encouraged many people, who really did not have the business acumen to succeed, to start out in businesses, many of which were more or less doomed to failure from the outset. Two years previously, a Parliamentary Report had been published summarizing the results of the Act, but he could find no one who seemed to be aware of it, not even an accountant in the City who specialized in the winding up of companies. The report covered twenty-one years. In the first seven, 4,782 companies had been formed; in the second seven, the number had risen to 6,000 and in the third, the number was 8,643. Some 20,000 companies had been formed, 8,000 were still in existence, 12,000 had been wound up, not a great success rate. The average paid-up capital of these 8,000 companies was £55,000. Those which had failed may well have had smaller capital, but even at a mere £10,000, that would have meant a loss to shareholders of £120,000. In reality, the amount was probably much higher.

For many, their loss would have been severe, even devastating. Many shareholders were people of small means, persons of the middle class, very often officers, widows and country clergymen. The financial suffering of these small investors was contributing to the decline in manufacturing of 'standard' items, mentioned above. Wealthier speculators would probably have been able to invest more capital; their companies would be more likely to survive and thrive. Their wealth would increase and .... You know the rest!

I feel here that Wallace's argument lacked consistency. We know from his writing elsewhere that he considered debts to be the problem of the lender, not of the nation. It was the personal decision of the lender to lend. If the debt was not repaid, that was their problem. They had no right to take up time in the Courts, trying to recover the debt. It was not the nation's business. Now, it matters not whether the investor/shareholder is the Queen of England or the local dustman, the person who buys shares is hoping to make money without making any effort. The actual founders of the companies may have put in countless hours of their own time, making their product in the garden shed, or wherever. They deserved their profit. Wallace was not talking about them. Wallace was talking about shareholders – 'Mum and Dad' shareholders they would be called today. He was personalising them: widows, country clergymen! What was the difference between the money-lender and the shareholder? Nothing, actually. Both were advancing money in exchange for interest. Both either expected repayment of the loan or to hold a certificate which they could sell (possibly at a profit!) to recoup their original investment.

In Wallace's mind, it would seem that he was envisioning the 'money-lender' as rich, the borrower as poor. That was where his sympathy lay. With the shareholder, he had changed sides. The lender, now, was the 'poor', the borrower the 'rich'. It was not the failure of the business itself which seemed to worry him. It was the impoverishing of the shareholders. That they had spare money to invest in the first place, that they had been hoping to be the recipient of money, of an income, which they had not laboured to earn, that did not seem to concern him, even though he had frequently criticised the aristocratic and land-owning classes for this very thing. It is not only the stockbrokers who are gambling; the shareholders are as well. It is completely illogical to criticise the City stockbroker yet sympathise with the country shareholder. Wallace's sympathy for the under-dog and antagonism towards the elite classes was clouding his judgement. Speculation cannot be bad for the country and the morals of the individual when practised by one group of people but acceptable when practised by another.

The countdown now reaches No.2, Wallace's second reason for Britain's economic depression - War - or, at least, preparations for war. Military and naval expenditure had increased enormously, not merely in the second half of the 19th century, but during the previous twelve years - that is, since 1874, which year, Wallace held, had seen the start of the present depression. Nor was increased spending in these areas unique to Britain. It was the same in many, if not most, other European countries. The British Empire might be enjoying a time of peace, *Pax Britannica*, but there were, or had been, plenty of wars in other places. Wallace made special mention of the Franco-German war (1872), but also drew attention to the Ashantee war (1875), the Russo-Turkish war (1878), the Transvaal and Zulu wars (1879 and 1880), the Afghan war (1881), the Egyptian war (1883), the Soudan war (1884-1885), since then the French Tonquin war and the Mahdi war and now the Burmese war. None of these were a direct threat to Britain, yet Britain had increased its war budget by 20%.

There were two reasons for this increase. The first was very simple. Ships were bigger, guns were bigger. Steel was replacing iron. Weaponry was costing more. The situation was further aggravated by the introduction of new science and technology. At times, indeed, it seemed almost as if science had become an art. Torpedoes had been invented "an amount of skill and science was devoted to this one destructive art perhaps greater than has been devoted to any other art in the world" (p. 197). As always, Wallace had done his homework and cited the amount of the increase of expenditure in France, Germany, Austria, Italy and Russia, amounting to £54,000,000 - £54,000,000 which could have been spent on trade for constructive, rather than destructive, purposes.

Britain had benefited to some extent in that it maintained a healthy export trade in iron and steel but Wallace would rather have seen our exported materials put to better use. He argued that, had this large amount of money not been spent on armaments, it could have been spent on something else of far greater benefit to humanity. It was not only material resources which were being wasted. Human resources were being wasted too. The number of men enlisted in the military, both army and navy, had risen across Europe by 630,000 men. It is not clear whether Britain was included in these European figures but the main point Wallace wished to make was that these were young, healthy men who could, and should, have been labouring elsewhere - preferably in the fields! Instead of being gainfully employed, they were wasting their time in drill and preparing to inflict destruction.

Behind the military, there was another army - of people supplying the military. Valuable factory resources were being squandered. So, too, was the effort of the miners who toiled to extract the coal and iron from the earth. As if this were not enough, in those places where war was fought, houses, fields, everything was destroyed. Any money they had was spent on rebuilding. No wonder less and less money was being spent on healthy trade! All of this destructive effort was paid for, eventually, by the tax payer, by the workers. Increased taxation meant less money for spending. Simple.

As if all of the above was not enough, Britain was *selling* arms abroad, with no consideration as to whether those arms might one day be used against her. Surely, reasoned Wallace, if a country evolved a new technology which put it ahead in weaponry, it should keep that technology, that weaponry, to itself, not sell it to all comers?

Since Wallace's time, things have gone from bad to worse. Spending on 'defence' is astronomical - aircraft carriers, submarines, fighter planes - I dread to think what else! The circumstances are the same: the money comes from the tax payer. Government thinking is the same. Governments boast about 'defence' contracts under which they supply armaments to other countries.

This was definitely one battle Wallace fought and lost.

Drum roll! We are about to have revealed the No.1 cause of the depression in trade. Overseas loans!

Of course, Britain was not the only country which had lent huge sums of money to poorer countries overseas, although, with its large Empire, it was among the more generous lenders. At first, all went well. The recipient Governments used the money to build infra-structure, roads, bridges, railways, ships - and don't forget, those all important armaments! Much of the necessary raw material, iron and coal, came from England. Those wonderful export figures: they included a large proportion of England's own money, being given back to her in exchange for goods. In effect, many of those exports included in those export figures were actually being given away - free! Of course, England - and all the other lenders as well - were receiving interest on their loans, most of which was paid out of the capital - no need to remind the reader where that had come from! Now, the money (capital) had gone. The interest was not being paid. Not only Britain, but all of Europe, was experiencing a fall in exports because the recipient countries had no more 'free' money to spend. Some countries (Wallace does not name Britain) were trying to rectify the situation by offering more loans. Money loaned had to come from somewhere - 'the people' of course! Now that many loans had been expended, repayments could only be made by the raising of taxes in recipient countries, which decreased trade even more. While international loans were generally spent on Government projects, Britain (and other countries) had enjoyed good trade with household items, many of which were quite new in some places, and much desired.

All European countries were suffering in a similar way and this was causing a restriction in trade between them, as well as Asia, Africa and America.

Over-generous loans were irresponsible. It was also morally wrong when one generation lent money (without the peoples' consent) upon terms which affected future generations, which a fifty-year loan, for example, did. The Parliamentarians who authorised the loan would, almost certainly, be dead and buried before any problems emerged. Non-repayment of the loan would be a problem, not for them, but for their children/grandchildren.

At the beginning of this century, America experienced a similar situation when over-generous lending on the part of banks resulted in an unusually high number of property foreclosures, which rapidly escalated into a property crash, which caused house prices to fall, in many cases below the amount still owed, which caused more foreclosures, etc. Some acts, which seem generous at the time, can have undesirable consequences and Wallace believed Britain, and Europe, were suffering the results of ill-conceived plans of previous decades. There was no solution. Britain would have to work off the debt herself. All that could be hoped was that politicians would learn the lesson and not make the same mistake again.

Wallace may have abandoned Christianity, but one feels that he still adhered to the biblical dictum: neither a lender nor a borrower be.

Chapter 10

Paper Money

Wallace was concerned about the effect upon wages of the fluctuating price of gold. Chapter IX of *Studies Scientific and Social* (1900; vol. 2) considered the introduction of paper money as the 'standard of value'. Paper money had been introduced in 1797 but the metal, gold, was still the 'standard'.

Prof. W. Stanley Jevons had shown, by noting the average price of some fifty to a hundred 'necessaries of life', that gold had suffered a drop in value of up to 46% from 1789 to 1809, while from 1809 to 1849 its value rose 145%. These were large fluctuations. Since then it had fallen and risen again, although Wallace did not say by how much. Wages and rents may be staying much the same, but clearly purchasing power was not. While Wallace believed that the figures given by Prof. Jevons were exaggerated, he nevertheless supported his basic premise – that fluctuations in the value of currency were not acceptable. Jevons had suggested that a Government official, who might be called the Registrar of Prices, should collect a list of everyday, necessary commodities, such as food, clothing, houses, fuel and literature, which would be published monthly or quarterly. An appropriate adjustment would be made to currency in circulation to force an adjustment in value. If there was more money in circulation, prices would fall; if money was withdrawn from circulation, prices would rise. Because these minor adjustments would be made on a regular basis, almost steady value would be maintained.

Wallace suggested that the easiest way to achieve this goal would be by the use of paper money to establish the standard of value. More could easily be printed if required. Surplus could easily be stored when withdrawal from circulation was deemed necessary.

Wallace's main objective was the prevention of inflation. Nowadays, economists seem to welcome it, at least in moderation.

I am not quite sure why Wallace thought it would be easier to manipulate paper money than coinage. Yes, printing more money would have been easy, but was it not the duty of the Royal Mint to mint money? Since some would have been withdrawn in times of inflation, would that much new money have needed to be minted? Initially, Wallace suggested producing £1 and £5 notes in the form of thin, tough cards, which could easily be slipped into the wallet. No plastic in those days, otherwise one might have thought he was envisioning the bank card!

Minimum wage, Cost of Living Index, abolition of the gold standard. All in place today - but without the hoped for positive results!

Wallace made another reference to paper money in another chapter, in a completely different context. He related how the Channel Island of Guernsey had been much in need of a market, which the Government estimated would cost £4,000. Instead of borrowing the money, the Government issued 4,000 £1, inscribed "Guernsey Market Notes". With these notes, which became legal tender, the Government paid both suppliers and workers. The notes entered general circulation. When the market became operational, it produced revenue. From this revenue, the Government redeemed the

"Market Notes" and in ten years they had completely *disappeared* from circulation. The market had been built, no debt had been incurred, no interest had been paid. It was a 'win-win' situation for both Government and people – although not, of course, for the money-lenders!

Why, asked Wallace, could not this simple strategy, here utilized for a small project, not be extended to apply to far larger projects, such as the building of railways?

The building of railways was proving both a blessing and a curse. Their potential had swiftly been realized, not just for passenger travel, but for the swift carriage of goods. The canals, which had been so labouriously built, were quickly being replaced. The earliest railway lines covered but short distances and were highly successful. Far longer distances were soon to be covered, especially in America. At times, reluctant land owners were forced to make land available. Although Government approval was necessary before work could be commenced, Government funds/tax payers' money, was not used. Private investment footed the bill and this investment was not made by one person, it was made by a group of investors, who expected to reap future rewards. Unfortunately, in many cases it turned out that there were simply not enough goods needing to be transported between the predetermined points to fill enough carriages to make the railway pay. Many went broke – and their investors with them.

Wallace had written his chapter on *Interest Bearing Funds* in response to an article by Bradley Martin, jun., published in December, 1898, in *Nineteenth Century*. In it Bradley Martin had argued that the wealth of a society could be measured by the wealth of its millionaires. Millionaires only spent a small proportion of their money; the rest was saved and, thereby, increased society's wealth. That same amount of money shared among, say, 10,000 people would soon be spent. There would be no savings, no wealth.

Wallace totally disagreed. Money saved, squirrelled away, made the country poorer, not richer. To do good, money needed to circulate. Money spent by one person was earned by another. It put food on another family's table. Although not mentioned by Wallace, Spain had already learned this lesson the hard way. When they conquered much of South America, the Spanish shipped back hordes of gold to Spain. The Government forbade its use in trade with other countries. All the gold was to remain in Spain. Spain was to be wealthy! Spanish ladies may soon have been bedecked with golden jewellery, but gold could not be eaten, it could not be made into ploughshares. Its only *productive* use was as currency. Within Spain, any metal (or paper!) would do. To increase Spain's prosperity, the gold had to be used to acquire items from abroad, from India, from China, from places which could provide materials not available at home. The prohibition had to be cancelled. For a short time, everything had seemed fine. In the long term, the policy's shortcomings were painfully obvious.

Gold, or silver, locked away in a bank vault, was useless. To be productive, money needed to circulate. But was the wealth of those millionaires referred to by Bradley locked in a vault? No, it wasn't. It was being 'invested'. Sufficient people had made their million on the railways to encourage others to try to follow suit, even though the most profitable routes had already been taken, and there were plenty of other business in which to invest.

Borrowing money was not the problem. This problem was paying it back. In times gone by, all loans were fixed term. All were expected to be repaid within a definite period of time. Many a person had come to grief at the hands of money lenders, not only as a result of money lent for business purposes, but for personal as well. Wallace believed, whatever the term of the loan, it should not exceed 30 or 40 years – which he designated as one generation. No person, or generation in the case of municipal works, should commit a future generation to debt. Each person, or community, accepting a loan should be prepared to repay that loan *themselves*. Wallace did not specifically identify that point in time when all had started to go wrong, but it is fairly easily done. It happened in two stages.

Some kind person, a father?, a grandfather?, offered to lend money for some project but was not in any hurry for it to be paid back. "Don't worry about paying me back; I'll probably be dead by then, anyway. Just give me a small share of the profits." Now, if this small share was to terminate when the principal had been repaid, there would have been no problem. The loan may have been informal, with no fixed repayment amount and no fixed repayment term, but the debt would still have been terminated – eventually. When 'grandfather' died and 'grandson' inherited the money he was supposed to be paying back, everything became evened out. The problem only became a problem when there was no termination, when the small annual amount was to be paid in perpetuity. Eternal debt had been created!

The debt did not terminate with the death of the lender (unless there was only one borrower and he was the sole heir to the estate). The debt, the 'share' in the business was passed on as part of the Deceased's Estate. At some point, the current owner of a 'share' needed some money; someone else offered to give him some in exchange for his 'share', and 'eternal' *transferable* debt had been born! The only way in which such a debt could be ended was by the closure of the company – or by the loss or destruction of the paperwork. This led to such paperwork (certificates) being closely guarded, stored in banks. They soon attracted the attention of financiers, who were willing to purchase these certificates, with their promise of perpetual return, rather than lending their own money. By Wallace's time, there was a booming Stock Market, with people growing rich by merely trading in these pieces of paper, as if they were hay, or cattle, or iron or gold. The Stock Market was nothing but legalized gambling.

In Wallace's eyes, these people were contributing nothing to the wealth of the nation. Others toiled in the fields through hail and shine, worked in the mines, sailed the seven seas or hauled loads along the nation's roads, while these people grew rich doing ... ? Nothing much, in Wallace's view. On the contrary, every pound they paid themselves was the result of some other person's labour.

Nor were Stock Exchanges the only injurious result of wealth. Thousands of people worked in factories producing "luxuries, ornaments, nick-knacks, and worthless toys ... permanently occupied as domestic servants to the wealthy, or in connexion with horse-racing, yachting and other amusements of the upper classes ..." (p. 255). I am going to say a word here on behalf of the wealthy. The advantage of a settled existence against that of a hunter-gatherer was that it enabled people to specialize. More work could be accomplished in less time. There is not (and never has been) enough work to go around in a 'civil' (permanent dwelling) society. An evening ball may have seemed like an evening of frivolous entertainment but it provided work for dressmakers, hairdressers, milliners, candle-makers, caterers, wine merchants, coachmen, and many, many more. Money passed from the 'idle rich' to the 'deserving poor'. Over my life time, I have spent nearly twenty years working as a cleaner, first in domestic houses and later in hotels. It amazed me that even young couples could afford to spend hundreds of dollars on one night's accommodation, but I did not begrudge it. Better (some of it) in my pocket than in theirs! If no one had savings, would there be a tourism industry? However, I agree with Wallace there has to be a balance. Some degrees of wealth are obscene. My study of Egyptian archæology was brief - we voted to study Neanderthals instead - but I remember wondering how many of the pyramids and other great works were commissioned by the Pharaohs *solely* for their own aggrandisement? There was no Social Security in those days. Making sure that every man had a job, had an income, would have been a big headache for the Pharaoh. A construction work which would take decades to complete, now that was a very good idea, especially if the men working on its construction were told that their labour was to be an eternal tribute to some God or some Pharaoh. I am sure the Chinese Emperors felt the same way. I heard it suggested in a recent documentary that the Great Wall of China was built for this very reason. A determined invader would simply have gone around it, particularly in its early stages when it was not very long.

Wallace urged that every child should grow up aware that it owed a debt to society for all that it received, all the infrastructure to which that child had contributed nothing but of which it received the benefit. Each child must understand that they needed to work, not merely to earn money for their keep, but to *repay* society for benefits received, including education. No child should grow up feeling itself entitled to benefit from "the evil of all institutions which permit or favour the paying of (nominally) perpetual interest, income or profit, on any invested capital" (p. 255). Wallace suggested that, after a fixed date, transfers (sale) of stock should be banned. All loans were to have a termination.

Wallace reiterated his view that if one chose to lend money to another in expectation of being repaid, that was a choice made by the individual. "There is absolutely no reason whatever for the Government to keep up a costly organization for the purpose of protecting people who choose, with their eyes open, to lend money without security" (pp. 163-164). The Courts were for the administration of justice, not for the settling of private disputes. Lawyers grew rich on these disputes, which they lengthened to the maximum, if they could. This had resulted in the Courts being unable to cope with the cases before them without lengthy delays.

All monies lent were to be at the lender's risk. There were to be no open-ended loans. All loans must have a termination date. All termination dates were to be within the expected life-span of the recipient. Future generations were not to be expected to pay the debts of past generations. Conversely, future generations were not to expect to receive unearned benefits from the labours/investments of past generations. Paper money was to replace coinage, its circulation being more easy to control, thus controlling inflation and preserving its steady value.

Chapter 11

The Revolt of Democracy

Although this was the last book Wallace wrote, being published in September, 1913, two months before his death, I have decided to place it here because in it Wallace returned to the issues of trade, employment, wealth and poverty - our (temporary) physical needs during our stay on this Earth, rather than our spiritual needs, which last for eternity, which were the focus of his other works, covered in the remaining chapters of this book. My copy is the second edition, published in 1915, which included a twenty-eight page biography. This biography had clearly been written by Marchant with Wallace's assistance before he died. I have no idea whether it was amended in any way after Wallace's death I debated using it as a replacement for my own two introductory chapters, but, as the biography progressed, it became more and more about Wallace's ideas and less and less about Wallace as a person. I have, however, included it here as Appendix I.

'*The Revolt of Democracy*' was a strange title for a book published, as it was, at a time when the British had been at peace, both at home and abroad, for nearly a century. That Wallace was using the term 'democracy' in a way which differed from that of today gradually became clear. Wallace returned to the topic of his major concern: the side-by-side increase in wealth and want. Industry had developed in a manner never before known and had brought a marvellous increase in wealth, but this wealth had not been distributed equally among all. What was even worse, many of the recipients of the wealth contributed nothing in labour! While Wallace did acknowledge that mechanisation was replacing human labour, he did not appear to acknowledge that "it was better to have the idle rich than idle the poor"; in other words, if the rich also worked, they would take much needed positions away from the less wealthy, increasing unemployment among the already poor.

Of course, big houses provided employment, but Wallace seemed to be critical of those who took this type of work, 'middlemen' who distributed products from wealthy merchants to wealthy landowners (as well as to the less wealthy, of course). To these had to be added 'innumerable parasites' (p. 4) – builders of the mansions, makers of the furniture and clothing, costly ornaments, children's toys, clerks, domestic servants, grooms, game-keepers, house-keepers, stable boys and kitchen maids, all of whom, Wallace claimed, lived off the product of the true workers - those who laboured on the land and in the mines. I feel Wallace was being illogical here. Surely, the less wealthy sharing the homes, the food, the land, and, even (second hand) the clothes of the wealthy was what he wished – for all! Many benefits were 'free' (the view, for example) but these employees were also paid for their labour. I am sure Wallace did not truly wish to see these people loose their positions. It was *for* the sharing of the riches of the wealthy with the not-so-wealthy that he was campaigning. Surely, what Wallace wanted was to see the employees of the industrialists in the factory treated as well as the employees of the landowners - as *people*, rather than as extensions of machines?

Not only did politicians support the *status quo*, so, too, did the clergy. Again and again, I have to wonder whether

Wallace was suffering from a guilty conscience. During his life-time, he was acknowledged as co-discoverer of the principal of natural selection. It was Herbert Spencer who had introduced the phrase "survival of the fittest' but it was Darwin (1859/1998: 186) who had famously written "... let the strongest live and the weakest die". Many had come to believe that it was God's will that the weak should die. This put the clergy in a difficult position. Giving to the poor had always been considered a Christian duty. Now, some people were not so sure. Wallace had never written such a thing himself, but, nevertheless, as an (co)originator of the doctrine of natural selection, did he feel in some way responsible?

Wallace then embraced a more positive tone, praising the vision and work of a politician! That politician was Sir Henry Campbell-Bannerman, who, when he became Prime Minister in 1905, had declared it to be the duty of government to deal with the problem of unemployment and poverty. (Previously, no one had been responsible for (un)employment and poverty had been the responsibility of the Parish.) He attacked increasingly injurious land monopoly and wished to make the native soil: "a treasure-house for the poor rather than a pleasure-house for the rich" (p. 7). In his Ministry, he enlisted the aid of two notable people: John Burns for his knowledge and administrative experience and David Lloyd George for his energy, ability as a public speaker and enthusiasm for reform. Not surprisingly, Campbell-Bannerman did not last long in his job, Asquith becoming Prime Minister in 1908. Lloyd George became Chancellor of the Exchequer and, in his budget, introduced provision for Old-Age Pensions and other far-reaching measures to benefit the working classes. The budget was rejected by the House of Lords. This had led to a number of strikes, by the Transport Union, Miners and Dock Labourers, which had brought home to the higher classes, and the government, quite how dependent they were on the labour of the working classes.

The current conditions were a disgrace to civilisation, but no one in a position of power had proposed a workable plan to redress the situation, although such a plan had been put forward more than twenty years previously by the Rev. H. Mills in his book: *Poverty and the State*.

The first claim currently being put forward was the paying of a "decent *minimum* wage", sufficient for food, clothing, recreation and housing "fit for human beings" (p. 14). Also demanded was an eight-hour working day. The worker did not want charity; he wanted what was his right as a citizen. The statement by the Union representative had included the words: "Democracy must be its own emancipator" (p. 15). Church, Parliament, the Press, the rich, they would have to make up their own minds as to their attitude towards it. Clearly, 'democracy' is here being equated with the working classes, not with a system of government. It would seem that this book was referring, not so much to the revolt of democracy as to the revolt of the workers.

Wallace cited Mr. Seebohm Rowntree, one of the best and most sympathetic employers, as having said that wage-earners should be regarded as 'necessary partners' (p. 18). Was Rowntree a Quaker, like Cadbury, also a purveyor of confectionery, whose high standard in regard, not only to the treatment of workers within the factory, but provision of a complete village, with recreational facilities, both indoor and outdoor, set a standard rarely equalled anywhere in the world to this day? Cadbury, apparently, chose to manufacture chocolate bars to ensure that these 'treats' were available in a form and at a price affordable by the working people. The consumption of chocolate was no more to be the privilege of the rich.

Wallace's immediate solution for the problem of death by starvation was free bread. Furthermore, he insisted this free bread should be available to all who asked. There must be no test to establish necessity. At the very least, every citizen was entitled to bread to eat. "Better give bread to a hundred loafers than refuse it to a hundred who are starving" (p. 25). Coupons would be handed out by police, clergy, etc., to whoever asked, without question. (When I was growing up in England, greengrocers put a table of slightly over-ripe or damaged fruit/vegetables outside the front of their shops which were free for anyone to take and bakers put yesterday's leftover bread outside their back door, but we all knew that these were for people who needed them. Nobody who could afford to pay took these free goods. At that time, females paid one penny (1d) to use the public lavatory/toilet. Each facility had one free cubicle but, again, anybody who had a penny, paid. That was how it was in those days.)

The Prime Minister had expressed his opposition to the fixing of a minimum wage by Act of Parliament although he had made no positive objection to raising the wages of Government employees above the suggested minimum. However, he did think it unfair to compete against private industry in this way – using tax payers' money to 'outbid' industry – an opinion shared by those Members of Parliament who were also industrialists. Women may not yet have the vote, but all men did and the workers now had far more power at the polls than ever before. Nevertheless, many Government employees were still as badly off as many of those of the lower class of private capitalists – an interesting comment, since it implies that some, at least, of the 'higher class' of capitalists were paying more adequate wages. I found this section a little confusing.

Wallace demanded that the Government declare war on poverty. He also demanded that, except in the case of gross misconduct, no Government employee should be dismissed before retirement age. In this way, the Government would act as an example to other employers. Wallace did not seem to consider that, if employing somebody meant that person was being employed for life, a prospective employer might think twice before offering anybody a job. Wallace also wanted as many factories and workshops as possible to be built in the country, giving workers access to 'open and healthy country' (p. 33) – which would, of course, have become less 'open and healthy' had more factories been built there!

Wallace argued that increased wages would lead to increased spending, which would be of benefit to the manufacturers. Wallace's demand that the Government ensure full employment is somewhat naïve considering he had previously drawn attention to the fact that industrialisation had produced machines which could accomplish the work of several – or many – men, especially upon the farm. In the past, it had been the duty of the landowner to ensure that every person on his estate was gainfully employed. Even the 'village idiot' was paid – for walking around the fields, waving his arms and talking (yelling) out loudly, scaring the crows! Landowners could 'make' work, find jobs, far more easily than could the industrialist – yet he had just criticised such employees as 'parasites'. Once again, Wallace offered as his solution to unemployment, self-employment, working the land, the organization of which was the responsibility of the Government. Wallace was not alone in this idea, recommending other supportive reading. Wallace also held that people should train in more than one type of work, so that they could work on the land in the summer seasons and in the carpenter's shop in the winter, or whatever other combination appealed. There would be psychological benefits, as well as material, 'a change being as good as a rest'.

Wallace also claimed that the best trade was trade within one's own country. Trading overseas necessitated competition with other nations, whose wages and other manufacturing costs might be lower. This continues to be a problem to this day. Indeed, it is probably more of a problem today than at any other time in history. Until all currencies have the same value, there can be no such thing as 'fair trade'.

It had been argued that all should contribute towards taxation because all received the benefit of law at home and protection from invasion from overseas. A beginning had been made with differential taxation, but more needed to be done. The reverse was true of wages where differentiation needed to be reduced. The work of a carpenter or engineer, a bricklayer or a ploughman was not worth intrinsically less than that of a Member of Parliament – or an Army Officer – or a mill owner. The problem lay with the idea that the intrinsic worth of an individual *as a person* could be measured by that person's wealth or position. Wallace deplored the terms "Merchant princes" and "Captains of industry", which encouraged egotism. (Today, some of our highest paid employees are entertainers and sports people, who must have a very high opinion of their own abilities to undertake the work that they do. These qualities are necessary, of course, to be a competitor or to desire to take centre stage and are not a problem in themselves. They only become a problem if developed to excess.)

Wallace suggested advertising should be banned. Advertising increased costs and would be unnecessary if Governments ensured that goods were produced to an acceptable standard. People would buy what they needed, not what they were encouraged to *think* they needed, by advertising. Competitive advertising was forcing manufacturers to produce 'new' goods, which were often inferior, or certainly not any better, than those previously available, but which were advertised in such a way that people were deceived into thinking their present product was inferior, out-of-date, in need of replacement. No advertising would mean cheaper products, which would help those on low incomes. He specifically mentioned some advertised foods and medicines as being actually harmful. The 'changing' of certain items of food from their natural state into one which makes them more appealing to the taste is being increasingly acknowledged today as 'problematic'.

In summary, Wallace called the current situation, in which thousands of people were living in a state of poverty, if not actual starvation, a "crime against humanity" (p. 77):

> Any Government that *will* not abolish starvation in this land of superfluous wealth must be driven from power. The forces of Labour, if united in the demand for this one *primary* object, must and will succeed ...

> This must be the great and noble work of our statesmen of to-day and of to-morrow. May they prove themselves equal to the great opportunity which the justifiable revolt of Labour has now afforded them.

Thus ended the life-time writings of this great man.

Chapter 12

Is Mars Habitable?

Wallace was eighty-four when he published *Is Mars Habitable?* in 1907. The sub-title explained that the book was: *A critical examination of Professor Percival Lowell's book "Mars and its Canals" with an alternative explanation.* The book expanded upon views he had expressed earlier in *Man's Place in the Universe*, which had been published 1903. This was a far more comprehensive work.

Is Mars Habitable? had become necessary, not only due to the publishing of the above-mentioned book, but also of an "elaborate mathematical article" which had appeared in the *Philosophical Magazine* in July, 1906, in which Lowell had claimed that, despite Mars' excessively thin atmosphere and its much greater distance from the sun, Mars possessed a climate "on average equal to that of the south of England", a view which Wallace strongly opposed. Wallace found himself far more in accord with views expressed by his friend, the astronomer Sir George Darwin.

Chapter 1 - Early Observers of Mars

Early Observers of Mars was more about early *observations* on Mars than it was the early observers, although, of course, their names were mentioned. The first point Wallace made was that Mars was the only planet sufficiently near to us for the physical features of its surface to have been determined with any accuracy - and that had only been achieved due to the great improvement which had taken place in the construction of telescopes. These had not only acquired larger lens with improved refraction, but had been placed in much higher positions, as far as practical in mountainous areas, where the atmosphere was considerably more clear. Only the cloudy atmosphere of Venus was visible to us and the low density of both Jupiter and Saturn indicated that only a small proportion of their huge bulk was solid. The rings of Saturn, the satellites of Jupiter, the brilliance and moon-like phases of Venus, although of great beauty, did not invite the speculation that did certain aspects of Mars' surface.

The first of these were its polar snow-caps. These had initially been observed some 250 years previously - mid 1600s - but it had not been until the late eighteenth century that Sir William Herschell had observed that they increased and decreased in the summer/winter of each Martian hemisphere. This gave an instant point of similarity with Earth. Further, the day of Mars was but an hour longer than an Earth day, although Martian seasons were nearly double the length of those of Earth, due to its much longer year - being so much further from the Sun.

Great excitement had been caused when, due to very favourable conditions during 1877 and 1879, Schiaparelli had discovered that in the whole of the temperate and tropical regions of Mars, between 60°N and 60°S, there was a remarkable network of lines, some straight, some curved. Wallace reproduced, as his frontispiece, one of Schiaparelli's maps. These were termed 'canali', meaning 'channels', but, unfortunately in Wallace's opinion, translated into English as 'canals', which immediately inserted into the minds of many the possibility of their artificial construction - by intelligent beings! In 1881, Schiaparelli determined that about twenty of these canals were double, consisting of two parallel lines, some of which stretched for many miles. They were very straight, sometimes close together, sometimes a considerable distance apart.

Dark patches had long been known and had been termed 'seas'. In 1892, Pickering had observed that, in addition to these 'seas', there were numerous small, black 'spots', apparently circular, which occurred at every starting point or intersection of the canals, referred to as 'lakes'. Lowell (1894) claimed that all such 'lakes' had now been observed to be connected to several canals - none were singular.

As the seasons changed, so changes were observed on the Martian landscape. The polar snows melted, alternately, as they do on Earth. The 'seas' turned a distinctly green colour. This supported the idea that these canals had been artificially created for the purposes of irrigation. Conversely, at the same time, Pickering and others, with the help of their continually improving telescopes, were making more accurate observations of the Mars landscape, which clearly showed that over the entire surface there were mountainous regions, ridges, rifts and canyons. These were observed in the so-called 'seas' as well as on the presumed 'dry land'. Clearly the 'seas' were not seas at all. It came to be accepted that there were no permanent bodies of water on Mars.

Chapter 2 – Mr. Percival Lowell's Discoveries and Theories.

Lowell had established an observatory in Arizona, at an elevation of 7,300 ft. above sea level. This had allowed unprecedented observations to be made. In 1905, Lowell published observations taken from 1894-1903. It was these observations, and the conclusions drawn from them, which inspired Wallace to write his book. Wallace had made observations about Mars in his earlier book, *Man's Place in the Universe*, but it was Lowell's observations and theories regarding the possible habitability of Mars by intelligent beings, similar, if not physically, then intellectually, with humans, which now demanded a response.

The book was mainly an account of the 'non-natural' features on Mars - the canals and the 'Oases, as the 'lakes' were now termed. Lowell held that the canals had been constructed to husband the scanty water supply on Mars. He further held that it was possible that there was also animal life on Mars, as well as 'intelligent' life. Vegetation was assumed - what else would cause that green colour which appeared seasonally?

The network of straight lines was indeed quite extraordinary. Many exceeded a thousand, or even two thousand, miles in length. They often started/ended at the polar snow-caps. Some of these lines were now known to be double, "a pair of equally fine lines exactly parallel throughout their whole length" (p. 11). Lowell described them as being like a railway track, although, of course, even the ones close together were far farther apart! Of the more than four hundred canals seen by Lowell, fifty-one (approximately 1/8th) were seen as double, constantly or occasionally. The canals themselves were between about a mile to several miles wide, in one case over twenty. About 180 circular dark spots had by then been observed, the more prominent being estimated to be between 75-100 miles in diameter.

Chapter 3 – The Climate and Physiography of Mars.

Lowell admitted that there were now no permanent bodies of water on Mars, although there may once have been. What had previously been thought to be rain clouds were now known to be dust storms or surface haze. As each pole successively experienced its winter, the polar snow covered about half of the temperate region of that hemisphere. As the snow melted in spring/summer, the darker portions of the surface changed colour, first becoming bluish and then a decided blue-green. More than half of Mars, from its equator outwards, remained permanently a reddish-ochre tint. Unlike the polar regions of Earth, the snow of the polar regions on Mars disappeared each year, leading to the assumption that the snow was not very deep. It was suggested the amount was equivalent to about one or two foot of snow in Europe or America. Because of different atmospheric and gravitational conditions on Mars, the weight of the snow would be about three-times less than on Earth. Miss Agnes Clerke (1896) had described the polar caps as 'snow *soufflé* (p. 21). Lowell had included some coloured plates in his book. These showed that the bluish-green in the south temperate region turned chocolate-brown and then back to bluish-green and that portions furthest from the supposed fertilising overflow were permanently green.

Lowell also claimed that the surface of Mars was 'wonderfully smooth and level' (p. 18). There were no mountains, no hills, no valleys, no plateau. This claim was necessary to support Lowell's other claim, that the straight lines were irrigation canals. Canals cannot travel 'up hill and down dale'. Wallace claimed that Lowell was maintaining conflicting positions. Only if the surface of Mars was almost perfectly level would it have been possible for canals of the length and number claimed to have been constructed by intelligent beings. However, if the surface was as smooth as claimed, the canals would not be needed, since the melt-water would spread across the ground, unaided, irrigating just as much land, but in a more compact, and therefore more convenient, manner. Indeed, it might irrigate even more land, since the long canals would allow much water to evaporate before it could irrigate. Cutting canals to carry water across the Martian equator would, in Wallace's opinion, be the work of madmen, rather than intelligent beings.

Continuing to quote Ms. Clerke, Wallace cited her calculations. If the average depth of the polar snow was 20 ft., that would be equivalent to about one foot of water. The maximum area covered was about 2,400,000 square miles, about the size of the United States. The observed dark-green areas were in the southern hemisphere, extending over "at the very least 17,000,000 square miles," an area approximately seven times that of the snow-cap. This would equate to about two inches of water - not allowing for evaporation - to fertilise the lands. Lowell claimed the surface of Mars to be in "fluid equilibrium", hence its perfect smoothness, which Wallace claimed was not the case. It was known that there were hills on Mars, even 'mountains', although these were not as stark as those on Earth. Lowell did not explain how the canals would hold their form in a surface which was in "fluid equilibrium".

Chapter 4 – Animal Life possible on Mars?

Although the irrigation just spoken of had been suggested principally to allow growth of vegetation, nevertheless the purpose of Lowell's arguments was to prove the existence of 'intelligent beings' on Mars, intelligent enough to construct the canals - i.e. the equivalent of humans, not merely of animal life. Some animals on Earth do construct quite elaborate living quarters. Nevertheless, the constructions of canals for the purpose of irrigation would be outside the mental (and physical) capabilities of any other form of animal life known to us.

It was Wallace's intention to prove the non-existence of intelligent beings on Mars and his task was made easier by the acknowledgement by Lowell of certain conditions which needed to be met before animal life, as we understand it, could exist of any planet. These were the presence of water, an atmosphere containing oxygen, water vapour and carbonic acid (carbon-dioxide) gas, plus, of course, plenty of vegetable matter for food. Also critical was temperature, not only for the comfort of the 'intelligent beings', but to enable water to exist in its liquid form. Then, of course, there was the need for 'atmosphere'.

Lowell had estimated that the atmosphere was scanty: "not more than about four inches of barometric pressure as we reckon it". In a footnote (p. 33), Wallace noted that, in a later paper, Lowell had estimated the density of air at the surface of Mars to be 1/12th that of the Earth. Wallace acknowledged Lowell's right to assume that the atmosphere contained oxygen, nitrogen, water-vapour and carbon dioxide, in approximately the same proportions as upon Earth, until such time as he was proven wrong. Wallace claimed that the water vapour in our atmosphere was derived from liquid water in the oceans, rivers, lakes, as well as from evaporation from the soil under the action of the sun. Some vapour was also derived from foliage of the tropical forests, and other vegetation. Wallace, therefore, denied the existence of water on Mars, believing that the snow-caps were formed not of frozen water but of frozen carbon dioxide (dry ice) or, possibly, some other heavy gas in a frozen state.

To support his contention, Lowell cited the appearance of a blue band which appeared as the 'snow' retreated, accompanying the retreat. This blue band was supposed to be definitive proof that the substance was not carbonic acid (carbon dioxide) but water. Wallace pointed out that, while water may appear blue in large quantities, when it contained impurities, pure water was colourless. Since it was acknowledged that the amount of fluid produced by the melting snow-caps was not great, there would not be sufficient depth for any blue tint to be formed.

Wallace's next argument required greater scientific knowledge. It depended upon "very weighty argument depending on the molecular theory of gases ... The mass and elastic force of the several gases is due to the greater or less rapidity of the vibratory motion of their molecules under identical conditions" (p. 35). The vibratory speed of all the chief gases had been ascertained and in some gases was so great as to enable them to overcome the force of gravity and escape the planet's surface into space. The force of gravity on Earth was sufficient to retain all gases composing our atmosphere, except hydrogen. Hydrogen was released into our atmosphere from volcanoes, and decomposing vegetation, but "no trace of it is found in our atmosphere" (p. 35). By contrast, our Moon, having only one-eightieth the mass of the Earth, could not retain any gas, hence its lack of atmosphere.

It had been ascertained that, in order to retain water vapour within its atmosphere, it would be necessary for a planet to have a mass equal to one-quarter that of Earth. The mass of Mars was only one-ninth; therefore, there could be no water vapour in the Martian atmosphere. Contra Lowell, Sir William Higgins (1893) had determined that "there is no conclusive proof of the presence of aqueous vapour in the atmosphere of Mars" (p. 37). Other observers agreed.

Wallace claimed the absence of water to be conclusive proof that there was no form of animal life on Mars, unless it was conjectured that animal life on Mars had developed by utilising some other form of liquid.

Chapter 5 – The Temperature of Mars – Mr. Lowell's Estimate

Before considering Wallace's arguments in relation to the heat of the Earth, and of other planets, it is necessary to point out that nothing was known in the nineteenth century about nuclear fission and the generation of heat by this means. It was assumed that any heat contained within the body of the planet had been created at the time of the planet's formation or acquired by the direct action of the sun.

It was not only the activity of volcanoes which bore witness to the internal heat of the Earth. This soon becomes perceptible to miners, even at a moderate depth and could become very uncomfortable for those working in deep mines. This heat was not due to any action of the sun. The rocks and soil which form the Earth's crust are exceedingly poor conductors of heat. Little heat from the sun penetrates the soil; little heat from the centre reaches the surface. (Walking on sand in the heat of the day can burn the feet, yet scratch the sand away a few inches, and it is quite cool beneath.) Lava may continue to be red hot a few feet below the surface for years after the surface has reconsolidated. There was a glacier on the south-east side of Mount Etna, underneath a lava stream from which it was separated by a layer of volcanic sand only ten feet thick. This had been visited by Sir Charles Lyell in 1828 and for a second time thirty years later, when the ice remained apparently undiminished. The ice-cold water from the polar regions sinks to the bottom of the ocean, gradually creeping to lower latitudes, yet remaining extremely cold. The constant beating down of the rays of the sun upon the surface of the oceans has little effect below the surface, nor was this water warmed by the Earth's internal heat.

Earth's climate was controlled solely by an external source – the heat of the sun. This affected the upper layer of the land and sea and it also affected the atmosphere. Heat absorbed by land and water was given up during the night, helping to equalize Earth's temperature. The change was greater in the higher latitudes than it was in the equatorial, but, were it not for the heat being released at night, the swing would be far greater. Our dense atmosphere was also a great equaliser. The water vapour, and other gases it contained, allow the sun's warmth to reach the surface of the Earth, but absorbed and retained the "dark or lower grade heat given off by the earth which would otherwise radiate into space much more rapidly" (p. 41).

It was known that under uniform pressure gases expanded 1/273rd of their volume for each 1°C of increased temperature. While there was no known upper limit to the amount of heat which could be applied and volume to which the gas could expand, clearly there was a lower level. Suns were known to burn at extremely high temperatures, but it was understood that -273°C was the lowest temperature to which any substance could be reduced. This was known as 'absolute zero'. Most gases, subjected to a lowering of their temperature, would become first liquid, then solid, at temperatures considerably above absolute zero.

Mars, being so much further away than Earth from the sun, would receive less heat. It also had a far thinner atmosphere, which would allow more heat to reach the surface from the sun, but also allow more to escape. Calculating the probable temperature of Mars was complex. By deducing that the ice-caps on Mars were composed of snow which *melted*, Lowell had assumed the presence of water on the ground and water vapour in the atmosphere. Neither of these things would be possible if the temperature were below zero. Lowell had recently published a paper, *A General Method for Evaluating the Surface Temperature of Mars* (1907), using mathematics to support his conclusion. Wallace was not a mathematician but analysed as best he could Lowell's reasoning, which had been based on formula worked out by others (pp. 47-50). Wallace concluded that Lowell's reasoning was erroneous, at least in some places, for example, his claim that water-vapour and carbon-dioxide were among the heavier of the gases, while Wallace believed science had shown them to be among the lightest.

Wallace finished the chapter by citing material from an article by Poynting (1907), also disputing Lowell's calculations, concluding that the temperature on Mars was far lower than Lowell claimed.

Chapter 6 – A New Estimate of the Temperature of Mars

Before tackling the difficult problem of the temperature on Mars, Wallace identified areas in which Mars, the Moon and Earth were either similar or different. (I noticed here that Wallace used a capital letter for both 'Earth' and 'Moon', something which he rarely did.)

Firstly, Wallace noted that Mars had a scanty atmosphere, the Moon either none at all, or one so scanty that it had not yet been detected. Next, he pointed out that the Moon's mean distance from the Sun was the same as that of Earth. The Moon travelled with us around the Sun. Circling us at the same time that it was circling the Sun meant that at times the Moon was closer to the Sun than us but that at others it was further away – by the same amount. The two distances, measured over a whole year, are the same. Because the Moon did not revolve on its axis as did we, it always maintained the same position in relation to us, i.e. with the one facet (face) always turned towards us. This resulted in the Moon experiencing but one day and one night over the course of its annual journey around the sun. Over the course of the year, the amount of heat reaching the Moon must be the same as that reaching the Earth, not one-quarter, as claimed by Lowell. However, the heat accumulated during the Moon's day was lost by radiation during the Moon's night. A Mr. Langley, with the aid of his 'Bolometer', had estimated that the temperature on the surface of the Moon facing towards the sun would gradually rise to as much as 491°F [255°C], but that during the Moon's long night, all that heat would be lost by radiation and the temperature would fall to almost, if not quite, absolute zero. A mathematician friend of Wallace's had calculated that during the Lunar night, the temperature on the Moon would fall as low as -258°F.

As his comparison with Earth, Wallace considered the arid dessert, the place where there was the greatest rise and fall in temperature within the space of twenty-four hours. Wallace cited geographers who had estimated that the surface temperature in some parts of the Sahara Desert could reach as high as 150°F [65.5°C], while it could drop almost to freezing point over night, a difference of 118°F in about twelve hours. It had been claimed that the difference was even greater in some high desert regions of Central Asia. Wallace felt it safe to assume that differences of 100°F were not uncommon. It had been calculated that the Moon's temperature fell quite dramatically during a full eclipse, even though the Sun's rays were only obscured for less than two hours. This had come as somewhat of a surprise.

Even in the desert regions of Earth, where the atmosphere was dry and clear, Earth's atmosphere was considerably heavier than that of either the Moon or Mars. The denser atmosphere provided a blanket, protecting the Earth from receiving too much heat during the day and from loosing too much at night.

Next, Wallace considered the origin of the Moon. The surface of the Moon was known to be covered by craters of extinct volcanoes. There were "very lofty cones and craters, as well as thousands of smaller ones, which, owing to the absence of any degrading or denuding agencies, have remained piled up as they were first formed" (p. 60).

And how was that? Wallace subscribed to the theory of the Moon's origin put forward by Sir George Darwin, also endorsed by Sir Robert Ball. These astronomers held that, at one time, the Earth rotated on its axis at a far higher speed than it does today. This caused the equator to bulge to breaking point. A large portion of this equatorial protuberance broke away at its weakest point. The energy released at this time was sufficient for this new body to be flung some distance from the Earth but was not sufficient for the body to fly into space as an independent entity. It was captured by the Earth's gravity field and has been circling around us ever since. Not only was a large portion of the Earth's crust torn away but with it went quantities of liquid/semi-liquid matter and gases from Earth's interior. As the new body spun itself into the spherical shape of all heavenly bodies, the crust once again rose to the surface. Wallace believed this to have been lighter than the interior, presumably because the interior was assumed to contain molten metals. Over time, imprisoned gases would have escaped through points of weakness, be they but small fissures or large volcanoes. The Moon's gravity being only one-sixth that of the Earth, the height of the volcanic eruptions would have been great. The craters had remained. What had not remained were the gases, some of which Wallace suggested might have been recaptured by the Earth, since they, like the Moon itself, would have felt the effect of the Earth's gravitational pull.

If the origin of the Moon, above described, was correct, Wallace felt it logical to assume that the surface of the Moon, to considerable depth, would be made of loose, porous material. The entire surface of the Moon had been subjected to volcanic eruptions and lava flows are far more friable than, say, granite. Gases, too, were presumed to have escaped through cracks and fissures. Such a condition of the surface would enable it to absorb a large amount of heat, which would be conducted downwards to a greater depth than on the surface of Earth. However, such absence of atmosphere would allow the heat to be lost more quickly than on Earth. Temperatures would rise and fall more rapidly.

Wallace gave over two more pages to the consideration of other people's estimates, which confirmed these conclusions. The purpose, explained Wallace, of spending such time considering temperatures of the Moon, was to show how different could be the temperatures on two bodies situated the same distance from the sun. The principal reasons for these differences Wallace stated as being: the dense, compacted surface of Earth, compared with the more porous one of the Moon, due to the greater gravitational force, the covering of vegetation on Earth and Earth's dense, vapour-laden atmosphere. These three circumstances had resulted in the Earth having a mean temperature of about 60°F [15.5°C], variability rarely exceeding 40°F above or below that figure. Over more than half the land-mass of our globe, the temperature rarely fell below freezing point. This compared with another globe, the same distance from the sun, made from the same materials, which had a maximum temperature of about freezing point and a minimum close to absolute zero.

Now it was time to consider the temperature on Mars. This Lowell had estimated to be -35°F. Poynting had estimated -38°F, a wonderfully close approximation. Poynting had added a ryder to his calculations: they had been based on the assumption that Mars was Earth-like in all its conditions, something which Wallace denied. Of course, Mars was subject to the same laws of physics as Earth, but it was not that which Wallace believed Poynting was claiming. Comparing conditions on Mars with those on Earth and the Moon, Mars was more similar to the Moon in less favourable conditions. Like the Moon, the surface of Mars was less compact than that of Earth. Like the Moon, it had no covering of vegetation. The force of gravity on Mars was similarly closer to that of the Moon than that of Earth, neither of the former being able to retain water-vapour in their atmosphere – or the atoms of which water/water vapour was made. Wallace had already disputed Lowell's assertion that the surface of Mars was smooth, being in a state of liquid equilibrium. Telescopes had revealed the surface of Mars to be similar to that of the Moon, apparently having been moulded by some form of volcanic activity. Since the force of gravity on Mars was closer to the force of gravity on the Moon than that on Earth, Wallace felt it safe to assume that its surface would also be light and porous, which would aid the loss of surface heat by radiation.

There was either no vegetation (Wallace's opinion) or very little, if it was accepted that the colouration which appeared and disappeared with the Martian seasons indicated some, temporary, vegetable growth. Lowell had estimated air-pressure on Mars to be but one-twelfth that of Earth, which would not support water-vapour. The temperature on Mars, Wallace maintained, would be closer to that of the Moon than that of the Earth. At this point, Wallace did not directly remind his reader that Mars was much further away from the Sun and would not, therefore, receive as much heat, although in the first paragraph of the following section he does make reference to "small amount of solar heat received by Mars" (p. 71).

Wallace criticised Lowell for not taking into account the *cumulative* effect of continuous reflection and radiation from clouds and water-vapour in our atmosphere. He likened Earth to a huge glass-house, its surface temperature being much higher than that of its outer (less dense) atmosphere. Temperatures in our polar regions were well below freezing point during their respective winters. The Mars full year being double that of ours, Wallace held that temperatures at the poles of Mars during their winters would be far lower than those registered at our poles. It would take all of the (extended) Martian Spring, receiving its scanty supply of heat from the sun, for temperatures on Mars to rise to that of our poles during their winter. Despite all of this, Lowell was proposing that the temperature on Mars was "almost exactly the same as that of mild and equable southern England, and a disappearance of the vast snowfields of its polar regions as rapid and complete as what occurs with us" (p. 75). Wallace continued: "Mr. Lowell ... accounts for the supposed mild climate of the polar regions of Mars by the absence of water on its surface and in its atmosphere. He concludes his fifth chapter with the following words: 'Could our earth but get rid of its oceans, we too might have temperate regions stretching to the poles.' " (p. 75). Lowell ignored the equalising effects of warm ocean currents and the storehouse of heat held in water-vapour derived from these self-same oceans.

Chapter 7 – A Suggestion as to the 'Canals' of Mars

At last! After 77 pages of preparatory explanation, Wallace is finally ready to set out his own theory as to the origin of the famous 'canals' on the surface of Mars! He recapitulates the important point made earlier that, not only are these 'canals' extremely long, they are extraordinarily straight. Furthermore, there was surprising uniformity in regard to their width. It was the straightness, rather than the length, which had led Lowell (and others) to assume that they must be an artificial contrivance.

The American astronomer, Mr. W. Pickering, had suggested that the 'canals' were cracks in the volcanic crust, caused by internal stresses due to the action of the heated interior. Pickering further proposed that water and carbon dioxide also issued from these cracks, under the influence of sunlight promoting the growth of vegetation. Contrary to other thinkers, Pickering suggested that the low atmospheric pressure on Mars would *inhibit* the rise of the gases, rather causing them to roll down the craters, including along their borders, promoting growth of vegetation.

While Wallace found (parts of) Pickering's explanation more acceptable than that of Lowell; he criticised Pickering for not providing any scientific facts to support his ideas, to explain why such lengthy cracks had not occurred on either Earth or the Moon. To solve this problem, it was necessary first to consider the origin of the three bodies. That of the Moon had already been discussed. Now it was time to consider the origin of the Earth and Mars. There had been a great increase in knowledge with regard to the stellar universe, the comets, meteor-streams and meteoric dust. Current opinion supported the Meteoritic Theory, that planets had formed by the slow aggregation of solid particles around centres of greatest condensation. Of course, no one knew from where the primary particles had come. Wallace quoted from a presidential address by Professor Gregory given to the Geological Section of the British Association (pp. 82-83). Although originally cold and dark, repeated collisions created heat, and, if repeated often enough to form a large enough body, eventually also light. Gravity gradually condensed the meteoritic swarm into a single globe. There were many swarms in the solar system - let alone the stellar system! These swarms were orbiting, some as massive nebulæ far out in space, others closer to home, around our Sun. "These groups, already as dense as a swarm of bees, were then packed closer by the influence of gravity and the contracting mass was heated by the pressure, even above the normal melting point of the material ..." (p. 83).

Wallace proposed that there was scope for great diversity of result, depending on the *amount* of material available and the *rate* at which it became available (p. 84; italics in original). Earth and Mars had been formed by different combinations. When small swarms crossed paths, small collisions might occur. When large swarms crossed paths, not only were more collisions likely, but the greater gravitational pull exerted by the larger bodies being formed, would attract more meteorites, causing more collisions, more heat, and, possibly, more light. The effect would be cumulative. The swarms which had collided when Mars was formed were less dense than those which collided when Earth was formed. Mars had only one-ninth the mass of Earth. Wallace felt it possible, probable even, that the heat resulting from the collisions involved would not have been sufficient to liquefy or permanently heat the centre of Mars. Being of small mass, any heat generated would quickly have risen to the surface and been dissipated into space before the surface had become hardened. The inner space of the planet would thus have been enabled to become cool, cool enough to harden before the upper surface, which had received its heat. As the new planet continued its way through the swarm, attracting more meteorites, the heat of the impact would liquefy the small meteorites, resulting in the *outer* layer of Mars being hotter than the inner – the reverse of Earth. The larger meteorites from the larger swarm, when they collided to form Earth, did so with sufficient force that their masses merged, the one mass penetrating the other. Heat became trapped within the body of the mass. The outer circumference, being many times that of Mars, cooled more quickly as its large surface surrendered its heat to space. The cooling layers which now form the Earth's crust, were surprisingly insulating, as Wallace had already mentioned. Heat from those collisions was still trapped within the centre of our globe, being gradually released via volcanoes and hot springs.

As the Earth gradually cooled, its surface layer contracted, causing the formation of mountains, etc. The surface of the Moon and of Mars are pocked marked with the remnants of volcanic craters. Earth had some such craters, but it had mountain ranges not found on either Moon or Mars because they had been formed by different circumstances. Earth did have some fault lines, which were quite straight. Wallace mentioned several whose lengths ranged from 30–120 miles. These were insignificant compared with those of Mars, in number and in both comparative and absolute length.

As Mars cooled after its creation, being comparatively small with a lower gravitational force, its surface would remain more loosely packed than that on Earth. Gases would be able to escape through cracks and fissures, some (the heavier ones) remaining to form the scanty atmosphere which Mars now possessed. The lighter gases would have returned to space. The temperature on Mars being below freezing, the cooling surface would contract. However, the inner core of Mars was already solid, unlike the core of Earth. The surface was contracting on a non-contractible nucleus. Great superficial tensions would have been produced which could only be released by the weaker portions giving way forming cracks and fissures. These would radiate outwards from this weaker point - the so-called 'lakes' or 'oases'. They could extend for considerable distances, although Wallace also suggested that, as cooling continued, further contractions, further cracks and fissures, were likely to have occurred at the termination of previously formed cracks and fissures, extending them to their present great lengths. It was along these cracks and fissures that the heavy gases, including those of the annually melting snow-caps, would naturally flow. As they spread out, they would evaporate, after the same manner as water-vapour on Earth, recirculating in the atmosphere, the carbon-dioxide (or possibly other heavy gas) re-freezing the next polar winter.

The gases would spread out along the edges of the 'canals' and it was this which caused the bluish-green tinge which had been observed.

Wallace was reluctant to give a definitive explanation for the double canals but suggested that two cracks/fissures occurred at two close points of weakness at the periphery of the central weak point, the 'lake' or 'oasis'.

Documentary

As fate would have it, I was just completing this chapter when I happened across a documentary entited: *A Traveller's Guide to the Planets - Mars*. Participants were all involved with space exploration, associated with NASA or other organizations investigating space travel. One was involved in the design of the robots, generally known as 'Martian Rovers', several of which had successfully landed on Mars and were sending back incredible images. Unfortunately, that was all they were sending back. No 'Rover' had yet made the return journey, no samples from Mars had made the journey to Earth.

The main thrust of the documentary revolved around the question of whether there was water beneath the surface of Mars. It was acknowledged that the surface of Mars today is completely barren. No drop of rain had fallen there for millions, possibly billions, of years. It was explained that Mars had probably been formed at around the same time (4.5 billion years) as the Earth, and in the same way. Strangely, the length of day on Mars was very similar to that on Earth, 24 hours, 39 minutes, 35 seconds. However, because Mars was further from the Sun, it had a larger orbit. The Martian year was 697 Earth days, nearly twice as long. The average temperature on Mars was given as -80°F (-60°C), the minimum as -195°F (-125°C) and the maximum as +70°F (+20°C). Perhaps the most important statistic was the diameter: 4214 miles (6780 kilometres). It was this diameter, so much smaller than that of Earth, which determined the gravitational pull, which was 0.38 times that of Earth, almost one-third.

The amount of dry land was about the same as that of Earth, the difference being that dry land was all there was on Mars. There was not one drop of water. There was a high proportion of iron oxide on the surface, which gave it its reddish tinge. There was much red dust in the atmosphere, dust storms being quite common and at times quite severe. The atmosphere contained approximately 95.3% carbon dioxide.

The surface of Mars was 'pock marked', as was that of the Moon, bearing evidence to ongoing strikes by meteors. These were estimated at about 200 a year, although it was not clear whether this was one Earth year or one Mars year. It was not made clear, either, whether this constant bombardment would increase the size/mass? If billions of years' of meteor strikes had increased the mass, then gravity on Mars would have been less in times gone by.

We were treated to pictures of Mars' landscape. Stretches of desert, peppered with rocks, bearing a striking resemblance to Death Valley and other desert regions. These were shown, identified, not only by name but also by latitude/longitude. We were shown 'mounds' which were actually mountains, miles high, although they did not look it. They were smooth, not craggy as Earth mountains. In other places there were ravines, many times deeper than the Grand Canyon. These, it was assumed, had been gouged out by water - torrents of water. To me, it seemed that the argument was tautological. "We know the ravines were gouged out by water. Therefore we know that there was water."

It was acknowledged that, for water to have been present, the atmosphere would have needed to be denser than it is today and the temperature would have needed to have been warmer. It was not yet known when, or why, the atmosphere had disappeared, causing the temperature to plummet. There was no acknowledgement that, for the temperature on Mars once to have been approximately the same as that on Earth today, it would have been necessary for Mars' atmosphere to have been far denser than that of Earth. Mars is much further from the Sun. It receives less heat. To retain an amount of heat equal to that retained by Earth, it would need a denser atmosphere. For that, it would needed greater gravity and for that it would need a mass *greater* than that of Earth.

These issues were not addressed in the documentary. Instead, the viewer saw torrents of water cascading down some, unidentified, large riverine floor.

The last fifteen minutes contained 'evidence' of water beneath the surface of Mars. A Rover had been landed as near as feasible to an Arctic region. As it landed, it straddled a hard, white piece of earth/rock. This, it was declared, was frozen water. It proved that just beneath the surface of the entire planet there was a layer of ice - likened to an ice hockey ground! On more than one occasion, we saw a Rover extend an arm, which was lowered to ground level, and a long 'trowel' like extension ruffled the surface. Nothing was actually picked up; what was shown was that the surface of Mars was friable, as Wallace (and others) had predicted it would be, the lower gravitational pull not compacting the surface material as firmly as on Earth. We had also been shown pictures of a small bulldozer, which extended its bucket, clearing away a patch of soil, exposing another piece of white 'rock'. There was no identification of locality - Earth? Mars? Had a Rover truly taken a bulldozer to Mars? If there was a bulldozer on Mars, what need of the small Rover arm with its long trowel? The surface was shown in the dusty-red colour used at every other time to indicate Mars. The commentary claimed evidence of frozen water on Mars, beneath the surface, but was the commentator making that claim in relation to the patch exposed by the bulldozer or that beneath the parked Rover? Of course, I replayed this section several times. It could be taken either way, but I felt this small section had been deliberately obfuscational.

In view of the cold temperature on Mars and the fact that its atmosphere was composed of more than 95% carbon dioxide, should not at least some consideration have been given to the possibility that the solid white substance was dry ice (frozen carbon dioxide)?

I had chanced upon the above documentary while searching for *Mars: The Ultimate Traveller's Guide*, which had recently been aired on television.

What had taken my attention was a brief segment in which a Professor triumphantly announced that we now had proof that there had once been water on Mars, not just a little, but plenty. His proof was a close up picture of a segment of the Martian landscape, taken by one of the Rovers. It showed a small, smooth rock, which the Professor claimed must have been made smooth by subjection to the wearing-away effect of running water. Acknowledgement was made that the atmosphere would have needed to have been more dense, the temperature warmer.

In a one hour documentary, there is only so much information which can be given. The viewer saw only a small part of what I am sure had been a much more lengthy talk with the Professor. During the small segment we were shown, there was no mention by the Professor of Mars' distance from the Sun, the planet's smaller mass, its lower gravity. In a manner similar to that of the experts interviewed in the former documentary, geological features which resembled water erosion on Earth were assumed to have been caused by water erosion on Mars. No alternative explanation was considered.

As luck would have it, a few days later another documentary was shown, a repeat (holiday season - lots of re-runs) of a documentary first aired some years ago recording the meteor strike in Russia in 2013. Not only had mobile phones been invented, they had become cameras! For the first time ever, there was an ample record of the meteor's passage through the sky, the results of its crash to Earth. Because the meteorite had exploded, recovered pieces were mostly fragmentary. However, we were shown larger fragments which had been found over the years. Apparently, *tons* of material enters our atmosphere every year. There are pieces everywhere, which most of us mistake for pebbles, as well as plenty of dust. The expert recognizes these treasures and they find their way into a collection. The chunks we saw were maybe a foot or two in length, heavy, because they were predominantly iron, but able to be lifted by the female scientist. She drew particular attention to the smooth surface of one rock, which was not perfectly round, having smooth grooves, about the width of a finger. The smoothness, she explained, was not because the meteorite had had any contact with water; it had been in a molten state during its entry into the atmosphere. The smoothness was due solely to its passage through the atmosphere. Mars may have a lighter atmosphere than Earth's, but it has one. Could not passage through Mars' atmosphere be the explanation for the smoothness of the rock on Mars' surface which so fascinated the Professor?

The above documentaries were followed by yet another – this time produced by Professor Brian Cox, the well known astrophysicist. He also claimed that Mars had once sustained great quantities of water, but his reasoning was somewhat different. He agreed with Wallace that, being smaller than Earth and further from the Sun, Mars had solidified more quickly, the centre of the planet hardening before the surface area, the opposite of that which had happened with Earth. However, both Mars and Earth had electro-magetic fields, the result of friction between the solid and molten portions of the planets. Mars solidified first, loosing its electro-magetic field and, thus, its atmosphere. Hydrogen, being light, was one of the first gasses to leave. Thereafter, there has been no water on Mars.

It should be noted that Wallace based his calculations of the assumption that it was gravity, not the magnetic field, which held the atmosphere in place.

Chapter 13

Man's Place in the Universe

In 1903, Wallace published *Man's Place in the Universe*. In his *Preface*, he explained that he had originally planned to write an extra four chapters on astronomy for a new edition of *The Wonderful Century*, but his attention had been taken by articles written by Sir John Herschell, Professor Simon Newcomb and Sir Norman Lockyer, which claimed, not only that our Sun was situated in the plane of the great ring of the Milky Way, but that it was very nearly in the centre of that ring. They also stated that recent research had shown there was little or no proof of their being any stars or nebulæ very far beyond the Milky Way. Wallace also stressed that none of the facts presented in the book, nor obvious conclusions drawn from them, were the result of his own research but were drawn from the work of the best astronomers, mathematicians and scientists.

The first portion of the book discussed Man's physical place in the Universe - or, rather, that of the Earth upon which we live. The second part discussed the far harder question of Man's place (relevance) in the 'greater scheme of things'. Wallace was eighty when this book was published. He may have started out life as a nominal Christian, become agnostic, but, with age, his belief in a Supreme Being, in there being some plan, some purpose, for the existence of the Universe in all its aspects, had become compelling.

Early ideas as to the Universe and its relation to Man

There had been an early understanding that the stars were ever present, only being invisible during the day due to the bright light of the sun, which Wallace assumed had come about due to the stars having been observed from the darkness of the bottom of a well, or some such. He then reminded his readers that since ancient times it had been supposed that the stars were suspended upon a crystal ball which enclosed the heavens. Empedocles (444 B.C.) was believed to have been the first to separate the (moving) planets from the (fixed) stars, while Pythagoras and his followers worked out the succession of planets outwards from the Sun, from Mercury to Saturn. Later astronomers calculated the movement of the heavenly bodies on the theory that they revolved around the Earth, which was at the centre of the Universe. Early astronomers had accepted that the Earth was round, the concept of a flat Earth being a product of the Dark Ages.

After the discoveries of Copernicus and Galileo, rapid progress had been made. The size of our globe had been estimated, the distance and the size of the Moon were determined. The Greek astronomer, Posidonius, had estimated the circumference of the Earth to be 28,600 miles, which Wallace acknowledged as being remarkably close, considering the imperfect data with which he had to work. The size of the Sun and its distance from the Earth had not been accurately determined until much more recently. The Earth was believed to be the dwelling place of the Gods and their gift to Man. It was at the centre of the Universe because the Universe existed solely for the benefit of Man (and the Gods?).

Distance from the Stars

Early astronomers, such as Copernicus, Kepler and Galileo, had argued that the Sun was many millions of miles distant from Earth. Their calculations suggested 13.5 million miles. Other Suns, seen by us as stars, were also moving but their distance from us was so great that it could not be measured and they appeared to us as 'fixed'.

It was not until the latter part of the eighteenth century that a transit of Venus had been able to be used to make an accurate mathematical calculation of the distance between the Earth and the Sun, which was determined to be 92,780,000 miles. The Sun was now believed to be moving at the rate of 12½ miles per second. (Think for a moment. Imagine one second. The sun, and all of its accompanying galaxy, just moved 12½ miles! Did you feel it? Perhaps the simultaneous rotation of the Earth on its axis, and movement around the Sun, distracted you?) By taking measurements six months apart, it was possible to use the difference in distance from the Sun to make further calculations of the comparative positions of other stars. The distance of about forty stars had by then been measured. Alpha Centauri, for example, was now believed to be 275,000 times as far from the Sun as us (about 25 million million miles). Its light would take 4½ years to reach us. This compared with 8 minutes 13⅓ seconds for the light of the sun to reach Earth. Distances in 'light years' had become the most convenient method of measurement. 61 Cygni, the star next nearest to us, was about 7¼ light years away. 61 Cygni, despite being the second nearest star to us, was only fifth magnitude in regard to brightness, teaching that brightness was no guide to distance.

The distance of Mars, when nearest to us, had been determined to be 36 million miles, about four thousand times the Earth's diameter. There followed half a dozen pages of explanation about measurements before Wallace asked a novel question: *What is a million?*

Wallace believed that few people had a clear conception of what constituted a million. It had been suggested that a large wall in every school should be devoted to showing a million at one view. This would need a hundred large sheets of paper, each about 4 ft. 6 ins. square, ruled in quarter-inch squares. In each alternate square a round black dot should be placed, slightly over lapping the edges, so that the overlap exactly equalled the white space around the dot. (I confess I am not sure why Wallace did not merely suggest that alternate squares be coloured black.) A space should be left every ten squares x ten squares (100 squares). Each sheet would then hold ten thousand spots. One hundred such sheets would contain a million spots.

Governments regularly dealt in millions – not just populations but budgets! Science also dealt regularly in millions, especially astronomers. Having some appreciation of the magnitude of one million would help in the appreciation of several million, or tens of millions, or hundreds of millions, or thousands of millions, or millions of millions! Wallace suggested that such walls should not only be found in schools but in public buildings, such as libraries or Town Halls.

Wallace could not resist having a dig at the Government. He had estimated the number of *letters* which would be contained in his book. It came to 420,000, less than half a million. "Try and realise when reading it, that if every letter was a dollar, we waste as many dollars as there are letters in *ten* such volumes whenever we build a battleship" (p. 83).

The problem astronomers faced was that Earth was so small that, even taking two measurements as far apart as possible, did not provide much by way of comparative angular measurement. The instruments themselves, greatly improved as they had been within the last century or so, were inaccurate inasmuch as they were subject to expansion and contraction with temperature. Another source of error was atmospheric refraction, which was subject to change both from hour to hour and also with the seasons. Accurate measurements (with the help of photography) were now being made over periods of time, a year, ten years, fifty years. The movement of distant stars could be measured over these amounts of time.

I have 'cherry picked' snippets of information from this chapter, which is twenty-five pages long. Near its conclusion Wallace asks us once again to view in our imagination the million-dot-wall. Imagine those dots spread out in a line a mile long. Imagine another million dot line spread out beyond it, and another, and another. It would take a *million* times a *million* of these dots, repeated *twenty-six more times*, to reach the nearest 'fixed' star!

The Unity and Evolution of the Star System

Wallace started by advising his reader that this thirty-five page chapter was but a very condensed sketch of recent discoveries in this area which he hoped would give some idea of the work which had already been done and of the number of interesting problems yet to be solved (p. 90):

> As Darwin solved the problem of the origin of organic species from other species, and thus enabled us to understand how the whole of the existing forms of life have been developed out of pre-existing forms, so astronomers hope to be able to solve the problem of the evolution of suns from some earlier stellar types.

It should be noted that neither Darwin, nor the astronomers, purported to offer any explanation for the *origin* of anything, only subsequent development.

There was general agreement that the whole of the visible universe consisted of one complete system. Nebulæ were now accepted as being faint clusters of stars, some appearing to be formed like a small version of the Milky Way. Herschel had discovered "thousands of telescopic nebulæ" which he spoke of as "so many distinct universes scattered through the immeasurable depths of space" (p. 101). Herschel revised his views later in life, coming more into line with those of Herbert Spencer who, in 1858, in an essay titled *The Nebular Hypothesis* published in the *Westminster Review*, had argued that the nebulæ formed part of our own Galaxy and of our own stellar universe. Spencer was a philosopher, not an astronomer. The *Westminster Review* was a little read periodical. Spencer's work was little read. It was not until Proctor published a series of articles between 1869 and 1878 that the essential unity of the stellar universe came to be accepted.

It was also now accepted that stars were suns - or, alternatively, our Sun was a star. The density of our Sun was one-fourth that of Earth, less than one-and-a-half times that of water. This showed that the Sun could not be solid, but must be gaseous. The force of gravity at the surface of the Sun was twenty-six-and-a-half times that at the Earth's surface. Were the Sun comprised of solid material, its density would be twenty times, rather than four times, that of Earth. Its gravitational force would give its gases somewhat of a liquid behaviour.

Professor Langley had shown by experiment that the Sun was 5,300 times brighter and eighty-seven times hotter than the white-hot metal in a Bessemer converter. Unfortunately, Wallace did not say of what metal the Bessemer converter was made. The size of the Sun was so great that, were the Earth at its centre, not only would there be room for the Moon to orbit, but another satellite 190,000 miles beyond the Moon could also orbit. The mass of the Sun was 746 times greater than that of all the planets combined. It will be noted that, throughout his explanations, Wallace did everything he could to create meaningful pictures in his reader's mind to enhance understanding.

The outer layer of the Sun was the photosphere, a layer of gaseous or partially liquid matter. Sometimes eruptions would occur, which were termed sun spots. Sometimes they were numerous, sometimes but a few; they could be seen with the naked eye, when protected by smoked glass. They were cyclic, increasing and decreasing in number and strength over a period of nine to eleven years. Disruptions in the Sun's outer layers were always accompanied by variation in Earth's magnetism. Above the luminous surface of the Sun, was the 'reversing layer', or absorbing layer, consisting of dense metallic vapours a few hundred miles thick, somewhat cooler than the photosphere. Above the reversing layer came the chromosphere, surrounding the sun to a depth of about 4,000 miles. Sometimes there were eruptions: "which shoot out in towering tree-like flames or geyser-like eruptions, and while doing so have been shown to reach velocities of over 300 miles a second and which subside again with almost equal rapidity" (p. 107). The chromosphere appeared to be gaseous, consisting of hydrogen, helium and coronium, while the eruptive prominences always showed the presence of metallic vapours, especially calcium.

Beyond the red chromosphere and prominences, there was the marvellous white glory of the corona, which was subject to periodic change in form and size. A minimum of sun spots co-incided with the maximum extension of the corona. During the total eclipse of 1878: "a pair of enormous equatorial streamers stretched east and west of the sun to a distance of ten millions of of miles" (p. 108).

It was evident that the substances of which the Sun was composed were in constant motion. The puzzle was: if the Sun was constantly burning itself as fuel, from where was this fuel being replaced? It was suggested that the movement of the Sun might bring it into contact with material in space which would become part of its mass. After all, small pieces of material from space were continually being found on Earth, particularly noticeable in the snowy areas of the Arctic and the Alps. The constant movement on the surface was the result of internal agitation, uprushes and explosions. The outer envelopes of the Sun were only visible to us during a total eclipse, evidence of their very low density.

There was a growing body of opinion that the nebulæ consisted, not of gases, but of solid particles – cosmic dust. Particles were constantly colliding; gradually bodies grew in size. More than ten thousand nebulæ were known and more were constantly being discovered. All seemed to be of spiral formation. All appeared to be moving through space, although how these motions originated, or were now regulated, was not known. No theory can take us to the origin of things, only a step or two at a time into the distant past.

Are the Stars Infinite in Number?

Debated was whether or not our 'Universe' was the only one or whether there were other Universes beyond our knowledge. Wallace considered it established fact that, as our telescopes penetrated the distant space beyond our Milky Way, there was an apparent diminution in the number of stars. There were stars beyond the Milky Way, but their density became less and less, until, some assumed, they ceased altogether. There was, of course, the possibility that, beyond what appeared to be that empty space, more stars appeared, became denser until they formed another Universe. As to whether or not that was the case, Wallace professed to have no opinion. He deemed such speculation to be utterly useless. If such another Universe, or Universes, did exist, they were too far distant to exert any influence on ours, certainly not upon our Earth. His argument regarding the infinity, or otherwise, of stars related solely to the Universe as we know it. Others, for example the late Richard Proctor, had extended their arguments to infinite matter and infinite space. This was beyond Wallace's capabilities and, he argued, beyond the capabilities of any human.

Wallace cited both Miss Clerke and Professor Newcomb as stating that the sideral system was finite. Central to the argument was the amount of light received from the stars, compared with that known to be emitted by our Sun. The amount of light received by Earth was variously estimated to be one fortieth, one twentieth, one tenth, that of moonlight, while that received from the sun was 300,000 times that received at full moon. Then followed a discussion about magnitude of stars as estimated by their light, the fact that magnitude was no indication of distance, discussions about parallaxes, light lost (or not) due to absorption by the ether, by the interference of dark stars, which some held to be more numerous than those we can see, etc., which I dutifully read more than once. The only illumination I received was an understanding of why my interest in astronomy had waned after I left primary school!

When first telescopes were used, and improved, more and more stars became visible. That was no longer the case. Improved telescopes (aided by photographic plates) were revealing little new. It would seem that what appeared to be space between the stars, *was* truly space between the stars. Mr. Gore had concluded that: "... if the whole heavens were as rich in stars as the Pleiades, there would be only thirty-three millions in each hemisphere" (p. 146). It was argued by Herschell that the spaces between the distant stars seemed to be perfectly dark, which they would not be if there were stars beyond the reach of our telescopes, emitting light, whose soft glow, it was argued, would be discernible, however faintly. Wallace accepted Herschell's argument (p. 148):

> But as not a particle of evidence can be adduced to prove infinity, and as all the facts and indications point, as here shown, in a directly opposite direction, we must, if we are to trust to evidence at all in this matter, arrive at the conclusion that the universe of stars is limited in extent.

Wallace explained 'magnitude'. The scale then in use gave nearly two and a half times as much light as one of the next lower magnitude. Down to sixth magnitude, stars were visible to the human eye and were termed lucid stars. Beyond that, stars were telescopic. Seventeenth magnitude was the greatest magnitude at which any star had been identified by the telescope. From first to sixth magnitude, stars increased in number at the rate of about three and a half times those of the preceding magnitude. The total number of stars down to the sixth magnitude was given by Professor Newcomb as 7647. To the tenth magnitude, the estimate was 2,311,000 stars, an approximate ratio of 3.5 compared with lucid stars. Counting stars beyond this magnitude was not easy. It was estimated that their number did not exceed one hundred million. Another estimate was 1,400 million. There was a very real and very rapid diminution in the number of the fainter as compared with the brighter stars.

After more discussion Wallace stated his conclusion (and that of others, of course) that the stars of our universe were limited in number. He repeated that this conclusion did not imply that there were not any number of other universes in space of which we knew nothing. However, it was his conclusion that the stellar universe of which our solar system formed a part, had definite limits - in other words, was finite.

Our Relation to the Milky Way

Wallace commenced this chapter with a recapitulation of information given in his Chapter 4 on the distribution of stars (p. 156):

> ... the Milky Way ... contains a greater number of stars of the higher magnitudes than any other part of the heavens of equal extent, but it also comprises a great preponderance of star-clusters, and a great extent of diffused nebulous matter, besides the

innumerable myriads of minute stars which produce its characteristic cloud-like appearance. It is also the region of those strange outbursts forming new stars; while gaseous stars of enormous bulk – some probably a thousand or even ten thousand times that of our sun, and of intense heat and brilliancy – are more abundant there than in any other part of the heavens ...

Among its millions of minute telescopic stars, hundreds or thousands may appear or disappear yearly.

Although the Galaxy formed a great circle in the heavens, from our point of view, that did not mean that it was, in fact, circular. It could be elliptic or angular in shape. The general opinion seemed to be that the stellar universe was spherical, the Milky Way being its 'equator'. It was also presumed to be rotating. Newcomb considered that because the number of stars in the Milky Way seemed to be about the same when viewed from Earth in any direction, Earth must be near the centre. There was no claim that Earth was in the precise centre, merely somewhere near the centre. After several pages of further explanation, Wallace summarised his conclusions as follows (p. 168):

1. that the stellar universe is not of infinite extent;

2. that our sun is situated in the central plane of the Milky Way;

3. that it is also situated near to the centre of that plane;

4. that we are surrounded by a group or cluster of stars of unknown extent, which occupy a place not far removed from the centre of the galactic plane, and therefore, near to the centre of our universe of stars.

Critics had claimed that it was immaterial whether or not our Solar system was near the centre, because it was in constant motion. Five million years ago, we would have been somewhere else by comparison, and in another five million years we will be somewhere else again. After several pages of citing other experts and debating their views, Wallace pointed out that if the Sun was moving in a circular manner, rather than in a straight line as implied by his critics, then it could retain its comparative position among the stellar system, which, itself, was also in constant motion, probably also in a circular motion. It was not being suggested that the 'centre' was virtually stationary, that the outer stars were moving far faster. It was being suggested that the Sun, and its planets. during its time of existence, which was less than that of the Universe, had maintained the same approximate position in relation to the other stars, which were, in any case, appearing and disappearing. Our Solar system had always been within a certain 'region'.

The Uniformity of Matter

Of great importance, following the introduction of the spectroscope, was the confirmation of uniformity throughout the Universe. The Sun, the stars, the nebulæ, all were composed of the same elements and compounds. The same laws of physics and chemistry appeared to be everywhere in operation. In addition to that provided by the spectroscope, information was also obtained more directly by the analysis of the numerous meteorites which fell upon the Earth. It was assumed that many of these belonged to the streams of meteors which circulated around the Sun but others were now believed to have originated from the débris of passing comets. Still others may have come from stellar space – through which the solar system was travelling – bringing matter from remoter regions of space. None of these meteorites had been found to contain a single non-terrestrial element. Of particular interest was the fact that, while none of the meteorites had supplied any new *elements*, they had provided some new *combinations* of elements forming minerals not found in any of our rocks.

It was suggested that some smaller meteors might be torn apart while they were passing close by a larger body – that collision was not necessary. Meteor(ite)s were thus seen to be in a constant state of flux, sometimes colliding and fusing to form a larger body, at others fragmenting to provide particulate matter. The Laws of gravity were fundamental throughout the Universe, as were the Laws of light. The whole Universe was essentially one.

The Laws governing the Universe being the same throughout its extent, Wallace felt it was reasonable to argue, in the absence of any proof to the contrary, that the laws governing the appearance of life would also be universal. The outward forms may differ, as they differed on Earth, but *all* forms of life on Earth, flora, fauna, fungii, had a fundamental unity of substance and structure. Growth, movement, development, all had an underlying similarity. Wallace did not specifically mention the cell, which was then the subject of study but, despite Mendel's theory having been resurrected in 1900, there was, as yet, no understanding of DNA, of how cells reproduced, individually or to form a complete new being. On Earth, there were certain requirements which had to be fulfilled for life to exist. Wallace held that these requirements would be the same throughout the Universe, since the same laws operated everywhere in the Universe.

The Essential Character of the Living Organism

Defining 'life' was not easy. De Blainville had offered 'continuous composition and decomposition', Spencer 'continuous adjustment of internal relations to external relations', but neither of these, or anything else suggested, were any improvement upon Aristotle's suggestion of (p. 190): "Life is the assemblage of the operations of nutrition, growth, and destruction". Professor Burden claimed the most distinctive peculiarity of living matter was its ability to be ever changing while ever remaining the same – or almost the same, since we definitely change as we become older! This ability of renewal was brought about by the permeation of the body with vessels which allowed the twin processes of nutrition and excretion to be carried out. These twin processes occurred in every cell, in every organization of cells. Another writer had referred to living processes as 'energy trafficking'. Wallace wrote that the matter absorbed or appropriated was 'dead matter' but this is not correct. Plants are able to absorb non-living matter from the soil but animals must eat living matter. A lion might kill its prey before consuming it but the tissues of the 'dead' carcass are still living, making even the definition of 'death' difficult, something with which our medical profession daily struggles. Organs being transplanted from a 'dead' body must be kept 'alive' if they are to be of any use for transplant purposes. Sperm may appear 'dead' when frozen, sometimes for years, yet come alive again, when thawed. Wallace would not have been aware of this but, a century earlier, Lamarck (1809) had pointed out that plant seeds could be completely dried out, desiccated, but come back to life when in contact with water. Wallace referred to the extraordinary ability of trees to raise (nutritious) materials, sometimes hundreds of feet, into the air.

Most extraordinary of all was the ability of all living things to reproduce. In lower forms, this was simply by cell division but in higher forms cells, which in their earlier stages might not appear any different from other cells, somehow became capable of reproducing another entity similar to itself – many entities, in fact. Every living form had the ability to (re)produce more entities than needed simply to maintain numbers. These entities were usually exact resemblances of form, colour, hair or feathers, teeth or claw, even in metamorphic change which took place during the entity's life span. If these occurrences were not so familiar to us, we would consider them as incredible and as impossible as the tales of Sinbad the Sailor.

A large number of chemical atoms were combined in an endless variety of ways.

Wallace attributed to Huxley the term 'protoplasm' for the substance commonly made up of three gases: nitrogen, hydrogen and oxygen, with one non-metallic solid, carbon, which formed the basic substance of which living things were made. He should have referred to Lamarck (1809), who identified mucilaginous material as the basic substance from which vegetable matter was made and gelatinous material as the basic substance from which animal matter was made. Today, these two are jointly referred to as protoplasm, but Lamarck's differentiation was important – and interesting. All animal (gelatinous) life is ultimately dependent upon plant (mucilaginous) life. – at least, in the case of that living on the surface of the Earth. I have read that, in the oceans, fish, etc., may have preceded seaweed, and other plant life, which is remarkably scanty, due, no doubt, to lack of light. On the surface of the Earth, carnivores were the end of a food chain which commenced with the devouring by some form of animal life, however small, of vegetable matter. Plants absorbed nitrogen through their roots. Without this ability, nothing, plant nor animal, could live. Ammonia was produced in the atmosphere by electricity (lightning), carried to the soil by rain, constituting the first step in the long chain of operations which enabled the existence of living matter. Water was essential for life, not just because water was a constituent of all cells, but because it was necessary to bring nitrogen from the atmosphere, in the form of ammonia, to the soil.

Carbon-based substances were very complex. They were far more numerous than those of all other chemical compounds combined. Other substances may be incorporated into the living body, such as sulphur, phosphorus, silica, and so on, but those four elements were always present, and combined in the many miraculous ways that they were, were the basic elements of all our tissues, be they bone or muscle, hair or skin. A constant proportion of carbonic acid gas (carbon dioxide) was the source from which the whole of the carbon in the vegetable and animal kingdoms was derived. Wallace remarked that the leaves of plants were able to decompose carbonic acid at 'ordinary' temperatures, something which no other agency in nature could achieve, humans in the laboratory needing to apply heat to achieve this end.

Wallace did not feel sufficient notice had been taken of the fact suitable conditions not only needed to exist, they needed to exist, within narrow limits, for millions and millions of years, for life to evolve to the extent that it had on earth.

Most people were unaware of the miraculous processes by which they lived their daily life, even more so today than in the past, because of city living. Country people came more into contact with nature. Instead of quiet contemplation, such as when walking through the countryside, people were cramming themselves into theatres and music halls – or taverns.

The Physical Conditions Essential for Life

Wallace commenced this chapter by recapitulating the conditions which were essential for life:

1. Regularity of heat supply, resulting in a limited range of temperature;

2. A sufficient amount of solar heat and light;

3. Water in great abundance, and evenly distributed;

4. An atmosphere of sufficient density, and consisting of the gases which are essential for vegetable and animal life. These are Oxygen, Carbonic-acid gas, Aqueous vapour, Nitrogen and Ammonia. These must all be present in suitable proportions;

5. Alternations of day and night.

Most vital phenomenon occurred at temperatures between the freezing point of water and 104°F (40°C), mainly due to the properties of nitrogen and its compounds. (Creatures do survive in dessert regions with higher temperatures but, from what I have seen in documentaries, bury themselves in the sand or under an outcrop during the heat of the day, being active at dawn and dusk, when the temperatures are within the range suggested by Wallace.) Despite fluctuating temperatures during the course of a day, warm blooded animals maintain a remarkably stable internal heat, 98°F in the case of humans. No land animal passed its whole life in a place where temperatures did not rise above freezing point.

Plants extract carbon from the carbonic acid in the air solely by the agency of solar light. Wallace suggested that just *any* sun might not do. Suns differed in their spectra and, therefore, in the nature of the light they emitted. Water must be plentiful and readily available. The atmosphere must not only be sufficiently light to allow sufficient heat to reach the Earth from the Sun, but must also be sufficiently dense to store heat received on its surface, which could be released back into the atmosphere at night, helping to maintain some uniformity of temperature. The atmosphere needed also to be sufficiently dense to incorporate, in sufficient quantity, all the gases necessary for life.

The atmosphere becomes less dense with elevation. Even in the tropics, mountain tops are covered in snow. At about 1,800 ft., the atmosphere is about half the density of sea level. This is higher than the snow-line, showing that if our Earth's atmosphere were half the density that it is, the Earth's temperature would be below freezing point. Carbonic acid was essential for plant life, and therefore for animal life, but in high concentrations it was poisonous to animal life. In cities where the concentration rose, this had been shown to be detrimental to health.

Uniquely, water was found in three forms, solid, liquid, gas, at temperatures found on Earth. While a temperature of 212°F (100°C) was necessary for water to boil, water would evaporate at almost any temperature, ensuring that water vapour was always present in the air anywhere water was present on the Earth. This helped to prevent loss through the leaves of plants and the skins of animals. Harder to prove was the necessity for the alternation of night and day. Everything on this Earth had evolved to accommodate this change, a change which occurred regularly in the tropics but in a more extended manner with rising latitude. Life was more abundant in the tropics. How essential to life was rhythmic movement? Could life have evolved without it? It was difficult to be certain but Wallace inclined to the belief that it was necessary, partly because the whole Universe seemed to operate in a rhythmic manner.

The Earth in its Relation to the Development and Maintenance of Life

The first essential factor for the development of life was distance from the Sun. A planet too close would be too hot; a planet too far away would be too cold, for which reason we are now sometimes referred to as the 'Goldilocks' planet, although that nick-name had not been thought of in Wallace's time (p. 216):

> The heat derived from the sun is inversely as the square of the distance, so that at half the distance we should have four times as much heat, and at twice the distance only one-fourth of the heat. Even at two-thirds of the distance we should receive more than twice as much heat.

Heat received was but the first part of the equation. The second was distribution. This was influenced by the density of the atmosphere and its composition, particularly the presence of water vapour. The presence of water, from rain drops to massive oceans, was also a great equalising force, absorbing heat during the day and releasing it at night. Ocean currents redistributed heat, but very gently. Water was not a very good conductor. The heat did not pass into the depths of the ocean and it was released from the upper layers but gradually. The less dense atmosphere at higher elevations (mountains) failed to retain heat, making mountain tops inimical to life. The specific heat of water being greater than that of air, one pound of water cooling one degree would heat four pounds of air one degree. Air being 770 times lighter than water, the heat from one cubic foot of water would heat 3,000 cubic feet of air by the amount it cooled itself. Wallace cited these figures (p. 236) to help his reader appreciate the importance of the vast stretches of ocean surface to our welfare. Little of the Sun's heat reached the ocean depths. It was its absorption by the surface layers of the ocean, and its steady release, which moderated and maintained our climate. Ocean currents carried warm air from the more tropical regions to the higher latitudes, the English people being well aware that their winters were far warmer than those of their Continental neighbours, thanks to the Gulf Stream Drift.

These factors were readily demonstrable upon our own Earth. We did not need to speculate. Simple calculations were enough to tell scientists that no other planet in our solar system could support what we know as life - nor could it ever have done, nor would it ever in the future.

There was more - our axis. Were our axis directly in line with the Sun, the result would have been a tremendous contrast between seasons. There would be far greater differences between mid-summer and mid-winter, with the sun beating down from overhead for about a month at mid-summer and a commensurate lack of heat at mid-winter. Were the axis to be at right angles, that would be more favourable, the whole surface would enjoy equal day and night, an equal amount of heat year round. There would be virtually no seasons, although heat received would vary with latitude. The tropics would be hotter, the poles would be colder. This would create a greater circulation of air. There would be strong winds. It seemed to Wallace that our slightly slanted axis was the most favourable. It was known that, in times past, far larger areas of the Earth's surface had been covered in vegetation. From the presence of coal beds, it was known that the Arctic Circle was once home to luxuriant vegetation, as was the whole of Australia, where now most was dessert, and the Sahara, although Wallace did not mention these places. This vegetation had lasted for epochs. There was far more carbonic acid gas in the atmosphere than now.

Of interest was the preservation of much vegetation. Often trunks of trees, cycads and tree-ferns were found standing erect, their roots still embedded in the soil. Leaves were often perfectly preserved, even ripple marks were found solidified in mud or sand. Wallace made no mention of footprints, either human or dinosaur, some of which have been most remarkably preserved, but he did mention something else. Rain-drops! Preserved in rocks! Now, *that* I do not believe! Sir Charles Lyell had given illustrations of impressions of rain-drops in mud-flats of Nova Scotia and on a slab of shale from a carboniferous formation in the same country. Living in the tropics, I have seen plenty of rain-drops, some pelting down with great force, but I have yet to see one leave a lasting impression on a *rock*. Hale stones, maybe? Fine debris from a volcano or a meteorite? Rain, no!

Although for life to have evolved there must have been a continuity of favourable climatic conditions, yet these were not absolutely stable. There was evidence of considerable changes in climate at certain times, the Eocene and the remote Permian. There was evidence of ancient glaciation. More than half a century had passed since the existence of a past Ice Age was first mooted, and accepted. Now scientists were becoming accepting of the notion that there may have been several such events. Fossil evidence showed that life forms came and went, but there was never a time when all life became extinct. When one form died out, it was replaced by another and the general trend was towards greater complexity.

Land occupied 28% of the surface of the Earth, the remaining 72% being ocean. The mean height of land above sea level was 2,250 ft. The mean depth of the ocean was 13,860 ft. The bulk of the ocean was about thirteen times that of land above sea level. If land was levelled out, it would fall below the surface of the sea, being covered by about two miles depth of water. Great ocean depths were a permanent feature of the Earth's surface. There was no fossil evidence to indicate that the large land masses had ever sunk beneath the surface; all land masses had preserved fossils from *all* geological Ages (Wallace's italics, p. 228). All the great oceans were scattered with islands, none of which bore evidence of ancient stratified rocks, or ancient fossils. These islands had emerged from the ocean as a result of volcanic action or coraline growth.

The laying of telegraph lines beneath the ocean had given scientists a knowledge of the ocean floor never held before. Wallace claimed that the ocean floor had been found to consist of vast plains, with no evidence of the mountains and valleys which characterised so much of the surface of the land. I believe this is not now considered to be the case. There was a lot of ocean floor and not many telegraph lines!

Wallace discussed Professor George Darwin's theory of the separation of the Moon from the Earth, which was covered in the previous chapter. The Pacific Ocean was formed from the large chasm left when the Moon parted from the Earth. No other planet had a satellite so proportionately large as the Moon was to us. Whether or not the Moon had been torn from the Earth's surface in the manner suggested by Professor Darwin, or not, was to some extent irrelevant. The Moon was there, its gravitational pull had a profound effect upon our tides and the movement of the oceans' waters in general. Its (reflected) light was of great benefit to many animal forms of life. It appeared to be unique, as did so many other aspects of Earth and its position in the Universe. To this uniqueness, Wallace believed Earth owed its ability to support life, an ability which Wallace had come to believe was unique in itself.

The Earth in Relation to Life – Atmospheric Conditions

It was impossible to say whether some other form of life would have developed on Earth if its atmosphere had been composed of a different mixture of gases. What seemed plain to Wallace was that some atmosphere of some sort was necessary and the presence of an atmosphere around a planet was dependent upon the planet's mass and its temperature.

Mass (size) determined gravitational force. Earth's gravitational pull was sufficient to retain most gases, the exceptions being hydrogen and helium, which may be released into the atmosphere via vents from the centre of the Earth – large vents in the case of volcanoes – but which would gradually drift upwards and outwards into space. Hotter air in the tropical zones, rose. Cooler air, from the temperate zone, was pulled in. These currents were the base of the winds which circulated air around the globe, helping the distribution of heat. Either side of the equator, this movement could, at times, build up into winds of hurricane force, which were destructive, but not lethal. Life continued. However, if our atmosphere were much denser, more heat would be retained, especially in tropical zones, and it was possible that winds of far greater destructive force would be frequent, making at least some portions of the Earth's surface virtually uninhabitable. Once again, it was a case of 'Goldilocks' - not too little, not too much.

Currents of wind alone were not sufficient. Also necessary were currents of water. Wallace postulated that had the land mass of the Earth been congregated in one place, depriving it of the equalising effect of the ocean currents, parts of the land mass would have been very hot, while other parts would have been very cold. (He seemed to have been envisioning something long and narrow, possibly north and south America, with everything else stuck on, making the land mass fatter and hotter in the tropical zones.) We now know that a large land mass did once exist - Gwandanaland - the explosion of life does seem to have followed its splitting into smaller sections, so perhaps Wallace was on to something there.

Rainfall was less over the oceans than on the land, the air cooling as it hit higher ground, hills and mountains, giving rise to rivers and streams which continued to flow and "moisten and beautify the earth" (p. 245) before rejoining the seas from which they originally derived. Wallace then wrote of the importance of dust, the information being the same as that contained in Chapter 3 of this book.

Wallace completed his chapter by drawing his reader's attention to the importance of natural electricity. Nitrogen was a vital element in the composition of all living bodies, both plant and animal, along with carbon, hydrogen and oxygen. Nitrogen was found in the atmosphere in the form of ammonia, produced by electrical discharge in the atmosphere, known as lightning. Clouds performed an important function by assisting the accumulation of electricity. Vegetable life drew nitrogen from the soil. Animal life acquired nitrogen from plant life. Dust was important in the atmosphere, in the clouds, all playing their part in the production of the final result. Without lightning, there would be no life on Earth.

Wallace deplored the fact that it was among the so-called 'enlightened' peoples that the most ignorance was shown in regard to the need for clean air to breathe and clean water to drink. The 'primitive' people would be appalled at the smoky, polluted air breathed by so many 'civilized' people. The importance of clean water had (belatedly) been recognized by the middle of the nineteenth century. The importance of clean air was not officially recognized for a further century, the famous 'Clean Air Act' being passed in Britain in 1956.

> In this beautiful land there is ample space and a superabundance of pure air for every individual. Yet our wealthy and our learned classes, our rulers and law-makers, our religious teachers and our men of science, all alike devote their lives and energies to anything or everything but this. Yet this is the one great and primary essential of a people's health and well-being, to which everything should, for the time, be subordinate. Till this is done, and done thoroughly and completely, our civilisation is naught, our science is naught, our religion is naught, and our politics are less than naught – are utterly despicable; are below contempt.

> It has been the consideration of our wonderful atmosphere in its various relations to human life, and to all life, which has compelled me to this cry for the children and for outraged humanity. Will no body of human men and women band themselves together, and take no rest till this crying evil is abolished, and with it nine-tenths of all the other evils that now affects us? Let *everything* give way to this. (p. 256. Italics in original)

The Earth is the only habitable planet in the Universe

In many ways, this chapter is scarcely necessary, since it is largely a recapitulation of points previously made. Wallace commenced by re-iterating the correlation between the mass of the planet and its atmosphere. Only planets with a mass at least one quarter of that of Earth would be able to retain water vapour in their atmosphere but at that size it was unlikely that such a planet would be able to retain enough for the purposes of sustaining life. For that, the size of our Earth was probably about the minimum.

Wallace re-iterated the fact that, although some free hydrogen does find its way into our atmosphere from vents in the surface, as well as from decaying vegetation, it is not retained in any appreciable quantity in our atmosphere. Had more free hydrogen been available to combine with free oxygen at some indeterminate time in the past, there would have been so much water that all the land would be covered. Wallace seemed to consider that this would have made the Earth unsuitable for life, but we now believe that living forms occupied the oceans long, long before they made their way onto dry land. We also now know that some sea creatures, such as the octopus, are highly intelligent. How far life could have evolved within the oceans is for others to contemplate. Wallace found himself wonder-struck by how fine was the adjustment between enough hydrogen to provide the water we have and too much, which would have resulted in inundation. After the necessary water had been formed, there was enough free oxygen left in the atmosphere to support life on land.

What if our planet had been slightly bigger - say, had a diameter of 9,500 miles instead of 8,000? Even this small increase in diameter would increase the bulk of the planet by two-thirds, because the extra bulk would be found at the outer circumference. This would increase gravity, causing the retention of more hydrogen, the production of more water and the entire globe would probably be covered in water several miles deep. The smaller planets of our solar system are too small to have sufficient atmosphere to support life; the larger planets had little solid matter, their gaseous nature being shown by their very low density. The only other planet upon which life might be possible was Venus. However,

Venus received from the Sun about double the amount of heat that did we. Furthermore, Venus rotated on its axis at the same time that it revolved around the Sun - or, as Wallace expressed it, its day was the same length as its year. It always presented the same face to the Sun. The side which never received any heat from the Sun must be very cold, while the side which always faces the Sun must be very hot.

Mercury, also, always presented the same face to the Sun. It was only about one-thirtieth the mass of Earth and possessed very little atmosphere.

It was now acknowledged that the highest mountains in every part of our globe exhibited on their loftiest summits stratified rocks which contained marine organisms. Geologists had been forced to come to grips with the notion that, not only were the mountains and valleys of this Earth far older than had ever before been contemplated, but that they had been the subject of great upheavals, upheavals that were almost unimaginable. Yet there was no evidence that, once life had taken hold upon Earth, there had ever been a time when it had failed to support life of one form or another. It was known that certain forms had become extinct, but following extinctions came the arrival of new forms, presumably evolved from the old, but changed to adapt to their new environment. It was understood that there had been constant changes in climate; at times global temperatures were quite cold, the Ice Ages; at others, the temperature rose, but never so far as to extinguish life.

It was accepted that the Earth was cooling. Heat was continually being lost from the interior, chiefly by volcanoes, but also by hot springs. At that time, nuclear fission being unknown, it was thought that there was no way in which new heat could be generated. The same was true of the Sun. The length of time calculated by Lord Kelvin for the Sun to have been in existence, a mere 50 million years, was insufficient to accommodate theories of the evolution of life, as they were now being understood. In his book, *Island Life*, Wallace had given reasons for thinking that stratigraphical and biological changes may have gone on more quickly than supposed, and this fascinating book will be considered next.

In summation, Wallace concluded that man's place in the solar system was altogether unique. No other planet had, or could, host life as had the Earth.

The Stars – Have they planetary systems? Are they beneficial to us?

It had been argued that, since the multitude of stars (suns) of the universe were of no use to us, providing little light or heat, they must have been created to be of use to others. Therefore, there must be others for them to be of use to.

Wallace pointed out that many of the stars were smaller than our Sun. They would cool quicker than our Sun. He questioned whether their possible length of existence would be sufficient for the development of life, at least of higher life, on any of their planets, assuming that they had planets. Other stars were bigger and would emit too much heat. The Milky Way was a "theatre of extreme activity and motion" (p. 280). It was crowded. There were many collisions, evidenced by the appearance of new stars. Wallace concluded that if we were to search for other planetary life, our search must be directed either to inside the circle of the Milky Way or far removed from it. Scientists had concluded it to be "almost certain that it is only when the growth of a sun is nearly completed, and it has attained a maximum, that the epoch of life-development is likely to begin upon any planets it may possess at the most suitable distance" (p. 281). Many stars were binary - double stars which rotated around each other. The presence of the second sun would be detrimental to the development of life upon any planet of the first. "The tidal disturbances mutually produced must be enormous" (p. 280).

The more astronomers searched for suns and planets which fulfilled all the necessary qualifications, the harder it seemed to be to find any. Rather than the odds being in favour of life existing on other planets, the odds were growing that it did not.

Wallace devoted several pages to discussion regarding any possible benefit the Earth may receive from other suns. He concluded that some benefit could not be ruled out on the grounds that our instruments were able to detect distinct chemical changes, indicating that some heat-effects, however minute, must be reaching our Earth. Considering the vast number of stars whose light was reaching us, there must be a possibility that the sum total of all their energies, however minute, reaching us did have some effect, even though that effect had not yet been identified.

Wallace could not make a definite determination as to the usefulness to us of the stars. He made no attempt to suggest another reason for their creation, any more than he did for Creation at all. However, he did conclude that the onus of proof lay with those who proposed other life on other planets. Life (as we know it) could not simply be presumed to exist elsewhere. Those who proposed that it did should provide evidence for the possibility.

Stability of the Star System – Importance of our Central Position

There were differences of opinion between astronomers as to the importance of gravity. Professor George Darwin, was of the opinion that it would be possible for a system of bodies to travel in a circular motion without a central body for a period of time, but would be unstable, their different gravitational pull upon each other eventually having a destabilising effect. Another astronomer denied that gravity was a factor at all, claiming an electro-dynamic force rather than a gravitational force as being fundamental. There were debates about how much gravity was responsible for the speed of suns of various mass at various distances, hundreds of millions of miles apart. Wallace's ten pages covering these questions included two diagrams of the stellar universe, "to help readers understand'. I hope his readers of the nineteenth century had a greater understanding than one particular reader of the twenty-first!

However, Wallace concluded that as far as the development of life was concerned, the crucial factor was a source of heat which would maintain a "wonderful uniformity" of temperature (p. 301). It was accepted that there had been a considerable amount of climate change over the millions of years during which life had existed on this Earth, at times dropping, resulting in what were now termed 'Ice Ages', at other times rising, so that even areas near today's Arctic region enjoyed tropical climate; nevertheless, these changes were moderate enough for life to be sustained. We owed this uniformity to our central position. Over immeasurable extents of time, our Sun had taken up a position in the central portion of the vast oval ring which formed the Milky Way. Our Earth had taken up its position, not too close, not too far away from the Sun. This incredible double positioning had produced the miracle of Earth's consistent temperature, low, but not too low, warm, but not too warm. Matter was continually entering the Milky Way from the outer reaches of space; some would collide with other bodies, increasing their size and creating heat.

We now know that this is constantly happening. Early this century (2013) a meteor crashed in Russia. Another meteor had crashed about a century earlier (1908), also in Russia, flattening vast expanses of forest, but not that time 'caught on camera'. Our Earth's surface bears witness to other, earlier, collisions, as do the surfaces of the Moon and Mars. It is now accepted that *every day* matter is entering our atmosphere. Some reaches the ground, unperceived, as small stones or rocks. Most, it is believed, is powdered into dust before it reaches the surface of the Earth. Most has an iron base.

> I have shown that, owing to the highly complex nature of the adjustments required to render a world habitable and to retain its habitability during the aeons of time requisite for life-development, it is in the highest degree improbable that the required conditions and adaptations should have occurred in any other planets of any other suns, which *might* occupy an equally favourable position as our own ...

> ... our Earth is almost certainly the only inhabited planet in our solar system ... in order to produce a world that should be precisely adapted in every detail for the orderly development of organic life culminating in man, such a vast and complex universe as that which we know exists around us, may have been absolutely required. (p. 306. Italics in original.)

Wallace's summary of his findings covered several pages. The conclusions reached were brief, but potent. This globe could well be the *only* one sustaining life as we know it, yet it sustains an incredible quantity of life, both as to type (species) and number of individuals. There were a hundred thousand distinct species of living beetle and, in some parts of sub-Arctic America, mosquitoes were so abundant that they obscured the sun.

No two stars, no two clusters, no two nebulæ were alike. Everywhere, Nature tells the same strange, mysterious story of the exuberance of life, of endless variety, of unimaginable quantity (pp. 328-329):

> However vast it may seem to our faculties, it is as a mere nothing in the ocean of the infinite. In infinite space there may be infinite universes, but I hardly think they would be all universes of matter. That would indeed be a low conception of infinite power!

Of infinity in any of its aspects we can really know nothing; but that it exists and is inconceivable.

The Bible taught that the Earth had been created by God for the use of Man. Many, including Wallace, had rejected this idea. Wallace was now having second thoughts. Had the material Universe been created to allow the non-material (spiritual) a new avenue for existence and development? When simple plant, and then animal, life came into existence, were more advanced forms already held in the Mind of the Creator? Was Mankind? How much (if any) of the Creator's plan had been carried out with humans in view? Wallace did not know - but he could not help but wonder.

Chapter 14

Snowed Under

I had not expected to read a book entitled *Island Life* when I embarked upon this project. Why should I? Would not a book entitled *Island Life* be about life on islands? Would it not be but an extension of Wallace's first book, *The Malay Archipelago*? Would it not be about evolution/natural selection rather than Wallace's other interests? Why, than, in *The World of Life*, did Wallace refer his reader to this book if they wanted more information about Ice Ages? True, there is an island made solely of ice, and island so large and so important that it is called a continent – the Arctic.

To my surprise, *Island Life* turned out to be a substantial book. Wallace discussed a number of different types of island: the island which had arisen from the ocean as a result of major underwater geological activity (the South Sea Island of our imagination), the island which formed from coral, the island which had once been part of a continent, but was now separated by sea, an island near a major land mass to which it had never been joined.

Wallace did, indeed, discuss (with his usual thoroughness) the various ways in which these different types of island had come to be invaded and colonised by plant and animal life. When I say 'thorough', I mean 'thorough', pages and pages of classification of plant and animal genera, species and variety. Undoubtedly, he had much reference material at his disposal, but only someone with an extensive knowledge could have re-interpreted that which was available, presenting it in a new manner which, Wallace claimed, would make the establishment and evolution of life on islands more clear to his reader.

Not this reader! It was all beyond me, so no more about that.

It soon became clear that this book was as much about *geological* evolution as it was about biological evolution and the Ice Ages were a major contributor.

It was not until the middle of the nineteenth century that the concept of a former Ice Age had been accepted and Wallace adhered to the notion that there had been but one extended period of time (between 200,000 B.C. and 100,000 B.C.) which deserved the application of this term. However, it was becoming increasingly clear that temperatures had fluctuated considerably throughout, there having been "a long succession of climate changes ... cold or even glacial epochs in the Temperate zones on the one hand, and mild or even warm periods extending into the Arctic regions on the other" (p. 87). It was the latter occurrence which may have come as a surprise to some readers.

There were many proofs of past ice activity – striated rocks, some fine scratches, others deep grooves, which might be many yards long, present on hills and mountainsides as well as in their valleys. Had the grooves been formed by ice 'sliding' down the mountain/hillside during Spring and Summer, the striations would have followed the direction of the slope, but they did not. They followed the direction of the valley, which was (more or less) at right angles to that of the mountain/hillside. They could only have been formed by glaciers.

Also left behind by glaciers were the isolated rocks so often found dotted around the countryside, looking like some dead person (or strange animal) which had been turned to stone by the Gods, presumably as some form of punishment. Even more strange were the 'perched' rocks, where one rock was balanced precariously atop another. Forget giants, think glaciers. In every case, geologists were able to trace the origin of the rock to terrain further up the mountain, some times many miles away, even as much as a hundred. 'Moraine' was the term applied to that which most lay people would term 'débris' - small rocks, stone, soil, plant and animal matter, dragged along for the ride, often in great masses, which was found along the sides of valleys and at the mouth of rivers, sometimes reaching quite a distance out into the sea.

Very sensibly, Wallace gave first illustrations from Scotland, Wales and the north of England, of which his reader may have some knowledge. He then named other places exhibiting the same phenomena, Canada and North America, Scandinavia and northern Europe, Greenland and, of course, the Arctic. He never made specific mention of the Islands north of Scotland, the Orkneys, Shetlands and Hebrides, but, of course, these were contained within that area. Some of the ice sheets were of enormous thickness. What was interesting was the uncovering of ancient fossils which showed that times of great coldness had been interspersed with temperate ones - even sub-tropical. Remains had been found of ox, elk, horse, reindeer, hippopotamus, mammoth and "other great pachyderms" - as well as the hyena (p. 93). Undoubtedly, there had been a host of smaller animals, whose remains had not fossilized. All of these creatures (including dinosaurs in more ancient times) would have needed vast amounts of vegetable matter to sustain their life, especially since most of those named roamed in vast herds. The more southern limits of past ice ages had supported a wide range of animals during their temperate times. The hippopotamus, the reindeer, and, in some cases, the woolly rhinoceros and mammoth, had been found *associated* in caves of North Wales and Bristol.

What was more, there was enough vegetable matter *left over* to form the coal deposits which had been found in the Arctic region, as well, of course, further south, as in Britain, under land which had once been covered in sheets of ice. Stop and think about that for a moment. Pause your mind and let it visualize this landscape, adding to your visualisation the knowledge of the oil fields now known to exist in these regions, of which Wallace was unaware, but which are also of vegetable origin. That was some mass of 'left over' vegetation!

There was clear evidence, not merely of one change of climate, but of several. Indeed, Wallace was coming to understand that perhaps the only 'constant' was 'constant change'. It was also clear that as the environment changed, so did the flora and fauna. There were extinctions – followed by the appearance of new life forms. While to the end of his life, Wallace publicly upheld evolution by natural selection, I cannot help but wonder how much Wallace may have privately pondered upon the emergence of new forms. Did his increasing belief in a Higher Power allow him to accept some measure of divine intervention? Today that would be termed 'Guided Evolution' or 'Intelligent Design'. Anybody interested in past Ice Ages and their effect on evolution can do no better than to study some of the many books and articles written by Niles Eldredge. He wrote a century after Wallace but, in this respect at least, their thinking was much alike.

In his next chapter, Wallace tackled the thorny question of 'What caused glacial epochs?' There were two contributing factors which Wallace believed were established beyond question: a decrease in the original heat of the Earth and changes in the obliquity of the ecliptic. He dismissed as 'theoretical' three other possible causes: changes in the position of the Earth's axis of rotation, changes in the amount of heat radiated from the Sun and variation in the temperature of Space. That left two possible conditions which he needed to address: the combined effect of the precession of the equinoxes and of the excentricity of the Earth's orbit and changes in the distribution of land and water.

The Earth moves in an ecliptical orbit around the Sun, but not in an equal one. Our distance from the Sun varies. Wallace stated that, at the time he was writing, the northern hemisphere was three million miles nearer the Sun in summer than the southern hemisphere. Hence, its summers were warmer than those of the southern hemisphere; there was more ice in Antarctica than in the Arctic. Over a period of time, stated by Wallace to be 10,500 years, the relative positions reversed. As one hemisphere cooled, the other warmed.

Two things were necessary for the formation of ice/snow: cold and moisture. As all skiers know, no fresh snow will fall, no matter how low the temperature, if the sky is a clear blue – and it is when the sky is clear, and the Earth is loosing heat, that the temperature falls at night. How infuriating! The most important factor in the establishment of an Ice Age was not either the coldness or the dampness, but the properties of water itself.

There are not many lessons I remember from my school days but there is one which I shall never forget. The science teacher asked us whether, if heat were applied to water, the temperature would rise? "Yes", we all responded in unison. No dissenters – except, of course, the teacher, who asked if the temperature would rise if the water was already boiling? Silence. The boiling point of water had been last week's lesson! The heat/energy was being used to convert the water into steam and, apparently, this required quite a lot of energy, which was why it took but a few minutes for the saucepan to boil but, once the potatoes had been added, the water in the saucepan could continue to boil for another twenty or thirty minutes with very little lowering of its level. New respect for our evening meal!

It takes a lot of heat energy from the sun to convert ice/snow into water, which is why the skier can enjoy a full day's skiing down the slopes with very little loss of snow cover, despite the heat radiating down from the sun, shining through that clear blue sky! (Even non-existent clouds have silver linings, it seems!)

> The great aerial ocean which surrounds us has the wonderful property of allowing the heat-rays from the sun to pass through it without its being warmed by them, but when the earth is heated the air gets warmer by contact with it ... although pure dry air allows such dark heat-rays to pass freely, yet the aqueous vapour and carbonic acid in the air intercept and absorb them. But the air thus warmed by the earth is in continual motion owing to changes of density. It rises up and flows off, owing to the greater weight of the cooler air which forces it up and takes its place and this heat can never accumulate in the atmosphere beyond a very moderate degree.
>
> ... there is no such thing as an accumulation of earth-heat from year to year. But, though heat cannot, cold can be stored up to an almost unlimited amount, owing to the peculiar property water possesses of becoming solid at a moderately low temperature.
>
> Rain - no matter how much of it may fall, runs off rapidly ... it produces no permanent effect on temperature ... but if snow falls for a long time, the effect ... is very different, because it has no mobility. It remains where it fell and becomes compacted into a mass, and it then keeps the earth below it and

the air above, at or near the freezing point till it is all melted ... the warmth of the whole succeeding summer may not be able to melt it.

In order to melt one cubic foot of ice, as much heat is required as would heat a cubic foot of water from the freezing point to 176°F, or two cubic feet to 88°F. To melt a layer of ice a foot thick will therefore use up as much heat as would raise a layer of ice-cold water two feet thick to the temperature of 88°F ... to melt a layer of ice only 1½ inches thick would require as much heat as would raise a stratum of air 800 feet thick from the freezing point to the tropical heat of 88°F (pp. 102-104).

Nor was ice on land the only ice to be considered. Antarctic icebergs could be miles in length and were but fragments of the ice sheet from which they had become detached. It was estimated that the thickness of the ice at the edge of the Antarctic could be a mile or more thick. If that was the case, then how much deeper must the ice be closer to the Pole? (Wallace definitely wrote 'Antarctic', not 'Arctic', although I would imagine the ice in the Arctic would be even thicker, there being no land beneath it?) All this snow and ice was 'imprisoning' warmth which would otherwise be being distributed by wind and water across the globe. It would seem that, once the process was started, ice ages would form quite quickly as global air temperatures fell but their termination would take far longer. The perpetuation of the ice cover would be assisted by the properties of ice itself. Ice/snow reflected heat. Without heat near the surface of the Earth, there would be little formation of moisture, or the clouds necessary to produce rain, which might help wash away some snow.

There was another way in which the presence of ice might affect the climate: its weight! Wallace suggested that the sheer weight of so much ice would have the effect of depressing the land beneath it, causing an apparent rise in sea levels, although, of course, there would, in fact, be less water in rivers and oceans because it was trapped as ice. Was it possible that there could be a compensatory lift in land towards the equator? A tilt of the land mass? There was clear evidence of great shifts of land mass, ancient sea shells having been found on hill and mountain tops. Wallace was not suggesting that ice caused these major shifts but he thought it possible that other, smaller but significant, changes might have occurred. For example, it would seem that there had been times in the past when the neck of land joining North and South America had been submerged, allowing the Pacific and Atlantic oceans to be linked. The Gulf Stream Drift might not then have drifted northward, bringing its blessed warmth to the British Isles. The flow of water might have been more east/west than north/south. The blocking of currents around islands, be it directly by the ice itself, as with Greenland, or indirectly, due to change in elevation, could have a profound effect on land far distant. Changes of elevation, the scouring out of a valley, such things would also change the currents of wind which constantly redistributed heat all over the Earth.

It was clear that Ice Ages were the exception, seemingly a more modern phenomena, taking into account the great age of the Earth, having occurred only in the last few hundred thousand years. The further back geologists were able to delve, the more evidence there was that the higher latitudes of the Northern Hemisphere had enjoyed a temperate climate, if not a sub-tropical one. Bear Island, in the extreme north of Eastern Siberia, provided evidence of "abundance of large stony corals" (p. 148). "Everywhere we have abundant floras and faunas indicating warmer conditions than such as now prevail" (p. 149). Wallace did not mention the salt mines of Siberia, of which he may have been unaware. These give evidence of past vast areas of sea where there is now mostly ice and snow. Scientists were coming to understand the vastness of life forms which had existed in the past, not just numerical but also individual size. There were far more huge animals in the past than there were now. Some ancient vegetation was also huge by today's standards, although it was acknowledged that the larger flora and fauna were more likely to fossilize, so that an abundance of small life forms should not be discounted. Vast amounts of carbon which had been in the atmosphere were now locked up in deposits of coal, which would have contributed to a fall in temperatures, to the Ice Ages, with their extreme loss of plant and animal life.

Somehow, the Earth recovered. Life adjusted. New forms appeared. Life went on.

Chapter 15

Vaccination: Proved Useless and Dangerous

Vaccination broke upon European consciousness towards the end of the eighteenth century, thanks to the pioneering work of Edward Jenner. The concept was not new. It had long been recognized that milk maids owed their proverbial beautiful complexions to cows with whom they daily came into contact. The cows gave them cow-pox - a disease somewhat similar to small-pox, but much milder. It was not considered fatal and, most importantly, the residual pock marks quickly faded. Those who had had cow-pox, rarely contracted small-pox. As Wallace pointed out, there were many other fatal diseases, then known as zymotic diseases, believed "to be due to the agency of minute organisms ... Such diseases are: plague, small-pox, measles, whooping cough, yellow fever, typhus and enteric fevers, scarlet fever and diphtheria, and cholera" (p. 5). These diseases were thought to be attributable to "foul air and water, decaying organic matter, overcrowding, and other unwholesome surroundings" (p. 5). What people dreaded most about small-pox was not its fatality rate, which was not any worse than any other major disease. It was the unsightly pock marks, which could be quite deep and which could last a life time, producing disfigurement among survivors. The disease occasionally resulted in blindness (p. 6).

It is hardly surprising that the idea of deliberately acquiring cow-pox, or a mild form of small pox, with the intention of avoiding a severe small-pox outbreak, had occurred to people from areas as widely separated as China and Ireland, but the practice was sporadic. In Turkey, it had been the practice to use small pox fluid from a person very mildly affected, rather than cow pox fluid, as was the practice in other places. The method had not been adopted by the medical profession, at least not in Europe.

For hundreds of years, although London had never been entirely free from small-pox, some country villages had never recorded a case. The precise method of contagion was unknown but it was assumed to be via some form of bodily/personal contact – hence the term 'contagion'. Breathing the same air is not today considered 'contact' but then the boundaries were less clear. London was a cosmopolitan city, with people from around the world constantly coming and going. Anything was possible. Country villages may never receive a visitor from overseas, let alone one 'carrying' small-pox. This was considered by many to be sufficient to account for the difference in rates of infection. The beneficial effects for health of a permanent supply of clean water had been recognized during the nineteenth century and, by the time Wallace wrote his book (1889), every household in Britain had access to clean water, yet small-pox persisted. Clearly, water *alone* was not the answer, but exactly what was, was as yet an unanswered question.

Although the term used almost exclusively throughout Wallace's book, when referring to Jenner's claimed method of preventing small-pox, was 'vaccination', Wallace does make occasional reference to 'inoculation'. The word 'vaccination' came from the Latin word for 'cow' (*vac*) and referred to the deliberate infection of a person with matter from a cow-pox pustule. Quite how the body fought disease was not known but it was clear that it did. No disease had a 100% infection rate, even among those who nursed the sick. No disease had a 100% fatality rate among those who did become sick. There were always some people who recovered. Skin complaints, such as rashes, boils, pimples, pustules, etc., were accepted as being the body's means of eliminating unwanted matter.

Jenner studied the writings and experience of others before undertaking and promoting his own experiments. During the second half of the eighteenth century, Lady Mary Wortley Montagu, whose husband was Ambassador to the Ottoman Empire (Turkey), wrote home to England of the Turkish practice; Princess Caroline, Princess of Wales had her children inoculated. The Russian Empress, Catherine the Great, was inoculated, along with her children. Inoculation was also practised by a few in America but incidence was rare and sporadic. By his campaign Jenner brought the practice to general awareness.

Jenner inoculated using pus from a small-pox pustule (which he euphemistically called 'lymph') rather than vaccinate with pus from a cow-pox pustule. He thus inoculated several older people who had had cow-pox in their younger days. None developed small-pox. He then vaccinated (with cow-pox pus) several young boys, whom he had 'rescued' from an orphanage. They developed cow pox, but recovered. A short time later, he inoculated them with small-pox 'lymph'. None went down with the disease. Upon these two small (personal) experiments, Jenner built his empire.

Wallace argued that it was a well-known fact that older people were nothing like as susceptible to various infections as were younger people, which may have been the reason why Jenner selected them. It was also known that people did not take two diseases at the same time, or even closely one after the other. Jenner must have known this too. Wallace believed these facts alone would have protected the older people in the first instance and the boys in the second, in the same way that any other disease would have prevented the development of small-pox within that short time frame. Wallace also complained that Jenner had used pus/lymph from the *last* of a series of patients with small-pox, someone in whom the disease had not been very severe. I agree with Wallace inasmuch as I am sure that this was done deliberately, but I am prepared to give Jenner the credit for having worked out that such a pustule would have the most preventative effect, that there would be enough infective material to produce a mild case of the disease and enough of the protective material to enable the disease to be overcome with all swiftness.

What Jenner could not, and never did, claim was that the procedure gave life-long protection. That would have taken decades to establish. Jenner relied on the general perception that those who had once suffered small-pox were unlikely to suffer from it again – the implication being that they were in some way protected. The whole concept of immunisation rested upon this belief, which was the case with a number of other infectious diseases, such as measles, mumps, chicken pox, etc. Wallace (p. 76) pointed out that very few people suffered the same major incident twice in their life-time, be that incident a ship wreck, a road or rail accident, a house fire, or whatever. The previous incident had not conferred any special immunity. Occasionally, a person was unlucky enough to be struck by tragedy more than once, but the statistical probability, taking into account the size of the population and the infrequency of 'incidents' was sufficient to ensure that these were experienced at a minimum. The very fact that they happened, that anybody at all contracted small-pox more than once, showed that it was possible.

Jenner travelled extensively around Europe, including Britain, demonstrating the success of his vaccinations/ inoculations with the help of the boys. Quite how often each one was subjected to the procedure, I am unsure. One would think that, if the same boy was used again too soon, the vaccination would not take? It was necessary for the boy(s) to produce at least one pustule each time for the procedure to have been deemed successful. As stated, there was never any claim by Jenner, or anybody else, that vaccination ensured life-long protection. On the contrary, revaccination was recommended, especially if there was an outbreak nearby. Quite how frequently revaccination should be performed was difficult to estimate, but, while some thought after five years, there was a general feelings that eight-to-ten years was sufficient.

This uncertainty caused problems. Who should be considered to have been vaccinated, and who not? For the first half of the 19th century, the Public Vaccinator kept records of those whom he had vaccinated. Some private doctors also performed the procedure but no public record was kept. Thus, there was no central record of *all* vaccinations. The public health officials were obliged to trust the word of the patient about whether or not they had been vaccinated. It was the opinion of many of these that patients would lie rather than admit that they had not undergone the procedure. Some officials, with the permission of the patient, did attempt to ascertain the true position from the patient's physician. But how reliable was the word of the doctor? Some patients continued to insist they had been vaccinated, despite their doctor's denial, which they believed was made because the doctor did not want to admit that the procedure he had administered had been ineffective.

One of the perceived advantages of the procedure was that, the illness being less severe after vaccination than when contracted 'naturally, the marks were less deep and tended to fade with time, but the amount of time varied considerably from person to person. When a patient was admitted to a small-pox hospital with the disease, had they been vaccinated or not? How was the attending physician to distinguish between residual vaccination marks and those of the present sickness, bearing in mind that admission to a hospital often took some time to accomplish, particularly in country areas. If there were no discernible pock marks, was that because the patient had not been vaccinated, or because the marks had faded? If it was accepted that they had undergone the procedure, how long ago was allowable?

There was a general consensus among the medical profession that the onus was upon the patient to *prove* that they had been vaccinated; their word alone was not enough. For those in London, reference would have been made to the records of the Public Vaccinator, but, in the early days, the telephone not yet having been invented, this process was lengthy. Even in the second half of the century, the telephone was very new and not readily available. Checks would have been made by mail, and, of course, in person, by calling upon the doctor. The special infectious diseases hospitals were in the towns; even checking the records of country doctors would not have been easy. By the time these processes had been carried out, the patients were either recovered or dead. Either way, they had left the hospital.

Wallace believed that, not just hundreds, but thousands, of people who had been vaccinated were entered into the figures as unvaccinated, due to these very difficult problems.

Support for Jenner's method was swift and universal – across the countries of Europe and across the bounds of class. In 1804, Dr. B. Moseley, Physician at the Chelsea Hospital, had published a small book on cow-pox, detailing many cases of persons who had been vaccinated and who had subsequently developed small-pox. He also reported cases of sickness, injury and death following vaccination, which failures had been admitted by the Royal Jennerian Society in their Annual Report of 1806. In 1805, Dr. William Rowley, Physician at the St. Marylebone Infirmary, in his book, *Cow-Pox Inoculation*, gave details of 504 cases of small-pox and injury after vaccination, with 75 deaths. These early dates show how quickly Jenner's new method was accepted by the King, how early the Royal Warrant had been issued. The Royal Warrant was not lightly given and this overt approval by King George III would have made a deep impression, not only on the public, but upon the medical profession itself. It will be remembered that the King's daughter-in-law, the Princes of Wales, had herself been inoculated, along with her children, with no reported side effects and no subsequent infection.

Support for Jennerian vaccination had been too swift, according to Wallace (p. 12). In 1802, a mere five years after Jenner had published the results of his experiments, the House of Commons, based on the findings of its Committee and the evidence of leading physicians and surgeons, awarded Jenner £10,000 – a huge sum of money for that time. In 1807, despite the findings cited above, Jenner received a further £20,000 and in 1808 was awarded an annual sum of £3,000. In 1840, vaccination was made free and in 1855, compulsory, remaining compulsory until 1867, by which time it had achieved a compliance rate of approximately 95%. The male head of households who refused to comply were fined and/or imprisoned.

Government grants necessitated Government Reports, which were delivered 'periodically' (p. 13). The two reports of 1812 and 1818 both gave the number of deaths from small-pox prior to the discovery of vaccination, as given in the London Bills of Mortality, as 2,000. Wallace confirmed that the average number of deaths from small-pox in London over the previous century had been approximately 2,000 per annum, although this number had fallen during the last two decades of the century to an average of 1,751 and 1,786. The report of 1826 changed these figures. It stated that an annual pre-vaccination death rate reported in the Bills of Morality had been 4,000, a figure repeated in the 1834 report. The 1836 report raised the figure to 5,000.

In 1802, Dr. Lettsom, giving evidence before the Parliamentary Committee, had estimated the annual pre-vaccination death rate of Great Britain and Ireland as having been 36,000. He arrived at this figure by taking 3,000 as the death rate for London, which he multiplied by twelve on the grounds that London's population was one-twelfth of that of the whole United Kingdom. In fact, small-pox was ever present in over-crowded London but had never been present in many parts of the less-populated countryside. Things became no better. In 1884, The National Health Society, with the approval of the Local Government Board, issued a tract which included the statement (p. 16): *"Before the introduction of vaccination, small-pox killed 40,000 persons yearly in this country"* (italics in original). Wallace went on to say that in later issues of this tract, that statement was replaced with another: "Before its discovery (vaccination) *the mortality from small-pox in London was forty times greater than it is now"* (italics in original).

With figures like these, it was not hard for pro-vaccinators to claim improvement following the introduction of vaccination, an improvement which Wallace staunchly denied existed in reality. In fact, mortality rates varied widely, depending upon whether or not there was a current epidemic. Some years, the mortality rate in the whole country, or in a specific place such a London, may well have been forty-times that of the previous year, but this had nothing to do with vaccination, which, as previously stated, had been compulsory from 1855-1867, yet major outbreaks were still happening. Indeed, the outbreak of 1871 had been among the most severe ever recorded. (Vaccination was no longer compulsory but the carry-over effect of compulsory vaccination, which had ceased only a few years previously, should still have prevented this outbreak, if vaccination was the preventative its supporters claimed it to be.)

Wallace wrote his book in response to the "recent Royal Commission" (p. 31) which had spent "more than six years ... occupied in hearing evidence and cross-examining witnesses ... the majority came to the enquiry more or less in favour of vaccination" (p. 24). The Commission was composed of medical men, lawyers, politicians and country gentlemen, few of whom, claimed Wallace, had the ability (or desire?) to interpret the many tables of statistics which were presented to them. Wallace claimed that in no other area would experts from that being investigated be employed as the investigators. This had happened because of a perception that only medical men could understand a medical problem. Wallace claimed that this was not a medical problem; it was a statistical problem. Did the statistics support vaccination by showing a decrease in infection rates/fatality rates, or did they not?

Not all submissions were made by medical people. Wallace, himself, had made a submission (p. 57).

The amount of material submitted to the Commission was vast. Most included statistics, either in the form of tables or diagrams, or both, all of which were virtually ignored in the Majority Report laid before Parliament, although some were mentioned in the Minority Report.

Wallace bemoaned the fact that no effort had been made to ascertain the effectiveness of vaccination by means of a controlled study, a comparison of a town or area which had been heavily vaccinated, either voluntarily or by compulsion, with another which had remained free from vaccination. Such a place need not necessarily have been in England, since small-pox was a universal problem across Europe and not all countries had embraced vaccination with an equal enthusiasm. Wallace struck lucky!

The most heavily vaccinated people in Britain were the armed forces. Even after vaccination was no longer compulsory for the rest of the population, it remained so for the Army and Navy – and it was 100%. Furthermore, every person in the Army or Navy had been required to pass a basic health test. Poor nutrition, unsanitary living condition, poor health, none of these things could be cited as contributory factors for any case of small-pox within the Armed Forces – that is, if there were any, which there should not be, but, of course, there were.

Wallace appended a Table showing the overall mortality rate for the Army and the Navy, and the small-pox mortality rate for each service, for the years 1860-1894. The first point of interest, looking at the overall mortality rate for the two Services, was the steady reduction in both. The second point of interest was the difference between the two. Initially, the Navy had a higher mortality rate than the Army. This changed. The general mortality rate for the Navy, as well as the small-pox death rate, fell. By the end of the time under scrutiny, soldiers had a higher mortality rate than sailors. The first difference Wallace attributed to the general improvement in health which had occurred throughout the nation as the result of better living conditions – clean water, sanitation, etc. He had given other Tables elsewhere to show this. The decline in small-pox mortality closely followed that of general mortality – as did the mortality rate for other diseases. The second difference, that between the two Forces, he attributed to sailors spending much of their time in the fresh air – if not on the open sea, then at least in Port, near the seaside, with its clean air. Soldiers spent most of their lives in barracks, barracks which were generally located in large towns, where the air – and everything else – was less pure. Wallace was convinced that overcrowding was the major contributing factor, although quite exactly in what way he could not say. The Navy Staff Surgeon had proudly attributed the improved health of the Naval personnel to (p. 64): "Shorter sea voyages, greater care not to overcrowd, plentiful and frequent supplies of fresh food, the introduction of condensed water, and the care that is now taken in the general economy and hygiene of the vessels." (Condensed milk - with that I am happily familiar - but condensed water? What on earth was that? Presumably, he was referring to water which had been boiled and then 'condensed'?)

Wallace now compared the small-pox death rate of the Army and Navy with that of Leicester. He chose Leicester for two reasons. The first was that there were a little over 200,000 men in the Forces and about 220,000 people in Leicester, close enough to provide a fair comparison. The epidemic of 1871 had been a great shock to the whole country. The death rate was extremely high, despite vaccination. The people of Leicester had given up on vaccination. From 95% under compulsory vaccination, the rate had fallen to just 5%. Wallace cited the figures for all three groups for the years 1873-1894, which were:

Army	37 per million
Navy	36.8 per million
Leicester	14.4 per million

Because the figures covered twenty years, the later improvement in Navy health was balanced by the earlier poorer health, so that the two Services returned a surprisingly similar average. What was of interest was the far lower mortality rate in Leicester. It was a disturbing result because it seemed to indicate that, far from providing protection against small-pox, if anything vaccination encouraged it. This was the sad conclusion to which Wallace came. Not only had vaccination not saved a single life, he came to believe that it had been the cause of death for thousands, many of them innocent children, who died in the first few months of their lives.

Both the Government and the Medical Profession had committed themselves too quickly to the support of Jenner's views. Having committed, as early as 1802, a sizeable amount of public money, £10,000, to its promotion, it was difficult for either the Government or the physicians to admit a mistake. Many people had accepted vaccination upon the recommendation of their doctor, they had paid their doctor to perform the procedure. To admit, not only that the procedure had failed, but that it may have caused serious injury, even death, to their patient, would leave the medical fraternity in a very difficult position. People did not sue their doctors then, as they do now, but that payment had been made for a service not received would have been tacitly understood by all. The best that could be hoped for would be to maintain that vaccination had made no difference. It had not caused any damage; it simply had not prevented it.

For decades, no admission was ever made that vaccination was responsible for any 'side effects' - including death. In support of his contention that some other cause of death, such as erysipelas, was given on the death certificate, Wallace cited a letter by Mr. Henry May, Medical Officer of Health, which had been published in the *Medical Observer*, in 1810: "Very few deaths from cowpox appear in the Bills of Mortality, owing to the means which have been used to suppress a knowledge of them. Neither were deaths, diseases, and failures transmitted in great abundance from the country, not because they did not happen, but because some practitioners were interested in not seeing them, and others who did see them were afraid of announcing what they knew."

Every page of Wallace's book is full of cases, accounts from doctors who had abandoned vaccination after disastrous results, as well as reports and tables. Wallace appended a number of tables, including some from overseas. Wallace had access to the same material as the Royal Commission and the

Royal Commission had access to the same material as Wallace, yet the two had come to such different conclusions. The Royal Commission threw its support behind vaccination.

Was it *unqualified* support? Wallace did not think so. The findings were not supported by statements containing such words or phrases as: "We are convinced ..., It has been proved to us ..., The statistics ... demonstrate ..."; rather the Report used such words as "We think ..., it appears ..." (p. 74). The Commission cannot have been ignorant of the facts, not after spending six years studying them. It was rather that the medical profession had 'painted itself into a corner' and could see no way out.

When reading *Island Life,* I had been amazed at the amount of material Wallace had studied, assimilated and re-arranged for the benefit of his fellow naturalists, but this had been a field of interest to him since his youth. Wallace had never before shown an interest in medical matters *per se*, his interest in health being from the view point of social conditions, inadequate housing, inadequate nutrition, unsafe/unhygienic working conditions, and so on. This was the first expression of an interest he had shown in infectious diseases and he threw himself into the study of this new area with his customary enthusiasm and dedication. How many members of the general public read complete government reports? Wallace not only did this, he read the minority report as well. Nor was this all. He also read all of the submissions. That he, himself, made a submission shows that his interest had been aroused, if not before the Report was commissioned, then by its very commission and that he had gathered enough information to make his submission acceptable. This was in a time when there was no internet, no world wide web of information, no photo-copying machines, and very little communication by telephone. Some information may have been available at the local Town Hall or library; some may have been available from the local hospital.

Anything provided in print form, Wallace almost certainly needed to purchase and print form he must have had to be able to reproduce the statistics, tables and diagrams that he did.

Unlike *Island Life*, it was not Wallace's aim to produce new arrangements of the available information. Rather he sought to simplify by careful selection, offering the information to his reader in a more readily understandable form. He did produce one new 'table', a very simple one of only three items, that comparing the Army, Navy and Leicester. Its very simplicity made it compelling.

The more I studied Wallace and his work, the more impressed I became.

Chapter 16

Social Environment and Moral Progress

This book is one of the last Wallace published. It was first printed in 1913, just before Wallace died, presumably achieving some measure of success, since it was republished in April, June and July, 1914. In it, Wallace tackled the thorny problem of whether humanity had actually made any moral – or intellectual – progress over the thousands of years of recorded history.

Some changes which had occurred could, indeed, be considered progress and of many of the more recent *material* changes Wallace had written, with approval, in his *Wonderful Century*. However, there were other changes which Wallace considered to be retrograde. These were *social* changes, not material inventions. How close was the link between material and social change? Did both always move in the same direction? For some, the answer may be 'Yes' - but for others it was a distinct and definite 'No'.

Wallace defined 'moral behaviour' as 'right conduct' - but what was 'right conduct'? In times past, it had generally been believed that every person was born with an innate knowledge of the difference between right and wrong and that wrong doing could, and should, be punished. The problem with this position was that, what was considered 'right' in some communities and at some periods of history, was considered 'wrong' at another. 'Right' and 'wrong' were, to some extent at least, a matter of convention. The purpose of his present volume was to try to distinguish between that which was permanent and inherited and that which was superficial and variable.

'Character' was a term used to described the aggregate of an individual's moral faculties and emotions. There was a general assumption that some characteristics, at least, were inherited, and it was with inherited characteristics that evolution was concerned. "There can be no progressive improvement in character without some selective agency tending to such improvement" (p. 7). Wallace held that there was no proof of any real advance in the inherited characteristics of human beings throughout history.

In reverse order, Wallace mentioned great moral teachers of the past: Socrates and Plato (~ 400 B. C.), Confucius and Buddha (~ 600 B. C.), Homer (still earlier), the great Indian Epic, the Maha-Bharata (~ 1500 B. C.), all of whom/which showed intellectual and moral character equal to any today, while less desirable characteristics, such as the love of war and gambling, were no worse than today. Wallace cited some passages to prove his point. The teachings of the Ancient Indian Vedas were as pure and lofty as anything found in the Hebrew scriptures, this point supported, once again, by the citing of passages.

The ruins of grand temples, forts, palaces, weapons, instruments, jewellery and exquisite fabrics gave evidence that ancient Eastern civilizations in India and China were advanced materially as well as socially. More recent were the great empires of Egypt and Mesopotamia, the magnificent pyramids never having been equalled to this day.

Archæological digs had unearthed ruins from Nineveh and Babylon, with statues and reliefs. Along with 'reliefs' were 'inscriptions', which gradually evolved into writing and 'brick-books', libraries of which had been discovered, which were being translated.

Wallace had made a careful study of writings about the Great Pyramid of King Cheops (or Khufi), the pyramid having been dated to 3700 B.C. Wallace cited evidence that the pyramid was not merely a tomb, but an astronomical observatory. I cannot here repeat all the interesting facts he gave of the ways in which it was believed the Egyptians had made their calculations. I will but mention a few of the most simple. The pyramid, which covered 13½ acres, was sited north-south, east-west. In the days before the discovery of the compass, this was no simple task. It was claimed that a hollow had been dug from which observations of the movement of the sun, and other heavenly bodies, could be made over a period of time. This, apparently simple, task had been quite complicated. The pyramid formed a perfect square, its sides were all equal and the four faces of the pyramid, were they to be detached and lain down, would have formed a perfect square – due to the accurate calculation of the pyramid's exact height. These were just the start.

It was Wallace's assertion that the people who accomplished these ancient feats had intellects every bit as sharp as ours today. We had the advantage of an *accumulation* of knowledge but they, were they to be transported in time to the modern day, Wallace believed, would be able to perform as well as any modern architect or scientist.

Articulate speech, although possessed by no animal, was possessed by every race of mankind. There must have been some accompanying cerebral development, although we had no way of knowing how quick, or how slow, the process of acquiring speech had been. Only one thing was known for certain: all human beings possessed it in approximately the same degree of sophistication. Not all humans possessed writing. However, among those that did, there was a large degree of diversity, suggesting that different cultures had developed different forms of writing at about the same time, rather than writing having been copied. 'Writing' came under the heading of 'accumulated knowledge'. Those cultures without it were able to acquire it, once taught, in the same way as the next generation of one which possessed this skill.

So extraordinary did Wallace believe the acquisition of fully articulate speech to be that he introduced a new term to describe its advent: spiritual influx. For Wallace, the likelihood of one animal, and one animal only, acquiring this skill, acquiring it separately, but virtually simultaneously, over scattered populations, could be explained in no way other than that this animal had reached the required degree of perfection in its evolution over millions of years to permit its being able to receive this modification, which must have occurred as the result of an influx of spiritual energy.

Darwin, observing a meeting between the captain of *The Beagle*, Captain Fitzroy, and the chief of a small island near Tahiti regarding compensation for damage to an English ship, had commented: "I cannot sufficiently express our surprise at the extreme good sense, the reasoning powers, moderation, candour, and prompt resolution which were displayed on all sides" (p. 32). Captain Cook, speaking of the natives of the Friendly Isles, had described them as: "liberal, brave, open and candid without either suspicion or treachery, cruelty, or revenge" (pp. 32-33) and Admiral Erskine had remarked that "they carry their habit of cleanliness and decency to a higher point than the most civilised nations; while all the Polynesian races are kind and attentive to the sick and aged and unlimited hospitality is everywhere practised by them" (p. 33). Mr. Curr, for forty years protector of Australian aborigines in Victoria, described them as "polite, gay, fond of laughter ... very strict in obeying their laws and customs, even under great temptation" (p. 33). The popular story-teller might like to portray natives as uncouth, but in reality, they were equal to, or superior to, many civilised people. Human beings were the same all over the world, and probably always had been. That which had, at first sight, appeared to be substantial differences, were merely the results of accumulated knowledge, thanks to the invention first of writing and later of printing.

There had been no advance in morality from age to age. This accorded with the doctrine that our essential nature was inherited at birth but its *manifestation* could be modified by teaching (and experience?) as taught by Robert Owen (1771-1859). Not all people were the same and some seemed to manifest certain qualities or abilities in a manner superior to most others – or inferior, as the case may be – but there was always a tendency to regression to the mean (average), or "regression to mediocrity" as Wallace expressed it. Over the centuries, the average had been maintained, in its physical and mental manifestations.

It was the ability for the expression of our inherent nature to be influenced by external circumstances to which Wallace now turned his attention.

The nineteenth century had been one of change to a degree never before experienced in human history. The earth had been ransacked for its treasures, both vegetable and mineral, bringing wealth never before imagined. Civilisation was unprepared for the upheaval, at least, not a civilisation led by what Wallace termed 'superficial Christianity'. 'Superficial Christians' may have polished their halos by abolishing slavery, but they employed, not only men, but women and children, in their factories at the lowest wage they could, for the longest hours which could be extracted, in appalling conditions. "It was not until 1819 that the age of children employed in factories was raised to nine years, while in 1825 the working hours were *limited* to seventy-two a week!" (p. 42. Italics in original). These dates show that the problems had manifested quite early, almost certainly by the end of the previous century, with increasing industrialisation, the building of canals and railways, as well as the building of larger ships for the exporting of goods, seeing the problem escalate with every passing year.

Efforts were made to ameliorate these problems but the passing of the necessary legislation was in the hands of the Members of Parliament, all of whom came from the Middle/Upper classes, the very people who were creating the problem. By the time legislation was passed, it had been watered down to such an extent that it served little purpose. Women and children were working in the mines where there was an enormous loss of life due to poor ventilation. Wallace believed employers should be held responsible for injury to workers, both by paying wages while the worker was laid off and by paying the necessary medical bills. The injured worker should also be entitled to compensation for pain and suffering. Wallace was appalled that death due to preventable causes *"in any profit-making business"* (p.43, italics in original) were not criminal offences. Despite various Acts of Parliament and numerous Inspectors, underground explosions and accidents were increasing, 1910 having been a record year with 1,775 deaths. No one was held responsible for these deaths.

Parliament was doubly culpable. Not only was Parliament not enforcing appropriate legislation to protect the workers, it allowed mines to be privately owned. This was a crime against posterity. It allowed private individuals to acquire and sell as much of these limited resources as they wished, often overseas. Wallace held that ownership of land had never been intended to extend deep under ground. Wealth below cultivation level belonged to the State, to the people. Any profit should be shared among the people and no mined wealth should be sold overseas - an act which was, in effect, stealing from future generations.

Chapter 17

Spiritualism

In 1866, not long after his return to England in 1862, Wallace wrote a little book entitled *The Scientific Aspect of the Supernatural* (SAS). In 1874, he wrote another, longer book, *Miracles and Modern Spiritualism* (MMS), which incorporated much of the material of the earlier book and which went to three editions, the third being published in 1896. Other books describe Wallace's physical travels, his wanderings. These two books describe his far move important travels, his spiritual questioning, his wanderings, his final arrival 'home'.

Wallace was not brought up in a Christian family. Any Church attendance was purely formal. Wallace described himself as a young man as "a philosophical sceptic, rejoicing in the works of Voltaire, Strauss and Carl Vogt, and an ardent admirer (as I still am) of Herbert Spencer" (MMS, 1896/2015: vi).

Wallace went on to say that, so thorough and confirmed a materialist was he, he could find no place in his mind for any agencies in the universe other than matter and force (energy). His curiosity was eventually aroused by inexplicable phenomena occurring in a friend's family. These appear to have happened very early in the emergence of such phenomena since Wallace (MSS: pp. 131-132) wrote that during his twelve years of tropical wandering, he occasionally heard of "table-turning" and "spirit-rapping", occurring in America and Europe, implying that first reports reached him while he was in the Amazon, during the late 1840s: "... from my own knowledge of Mesmerism, that there were mysteries connected with the human mind which modern science ignored because it could not explain, I determined to seize the first opportunity on my return home to examine into these matters".

Wallace (MSS: p. 152) dated 'Modern Spiritualism' from March, 1848: " ... the first time intelligent communications were held with the unknown cause of the mysterious knockings and other sounds similar to those which had disturbed the Mompesson and Wesley families in the seventeenth and eighteenth centuries." From this we learn that certain 'mysterious' phenomena had been known in earlier times, but it was only then that a concerted and organized effort was made to understand and interpret the phenomena, which, astoundingly, did not merely indicate that 'spirits' were responsible, but that they were imparting specific information. In this particular case, the 'receiver' was a nine-year-old girl, Miss Kate Fox, who, with her younger sister, continued to act as a medium for several more decades. And the information imparted? There was a dead body buried in the cellar! It turned out that a man had visited the house five years earlier and had never been heard of since. The 'rapper' (signaller) was the murdered man. This was no parlour game; this was serious business. What Wallace did not say, probably because he did not know, was how the information was conveyed. Were the signals given in Morse Code, or one rap for 'A, two for 'B, and so on? As kids we loved semaphore and Morse Code and spent hours messaging each other in these and other codes which we invented. Somehow, it seems to make a sort of sense that it was a nine-year-old kid who realized that the rapping was not random, but code!

Not all messages were coded; some were received via the spoken word. Mediums were usually in some form of trance state. They may, or may not, be conscious of the words they were speaking. Mediums today do not bother with the darkened room, the trance, but in the nineteenth century, these ingredients were part of the mystery. There was another phenomenon sweeping Victorian Europe – Mesmerism – and this, too, involved a trance state and other 'unexplained' happenings.

Known today as hypnotism, this trance-like state had been presented to the nineteenth century (European) world by Anton Mesmer. Promoted mostly as an entertainment, it soon became clear that its application could have profound effects. Some were troubled by the apparent surrender of the 'will' of the individual to the control of another; others were excited by its power to relieve pain. Operations were being performed under mesmeric influence, without anethæsia. Wallace first watched, then tried the practice himself and found that he could mesmerise with varying degrees of success. He made no mention of any 'operation' being performed while one of his patients was in a trance state, but he found no difficulty in inducing the state of insensibility to pain (MSS: pp. x–xi):

> I thus learnt my first lesson in the inquiry into these obscure fields of knowledge, never to accept the disbelief of great men, or their accusations of imposture or of imbecility, as of any weight when opposed to the repeated observations of facts by other men admittedly sane and honest. The whole history of science shows us that, whenever the educated and scientific men of any age have denied the facts of other investigators on *a priori* grounds of absurdity or impossibility, the deniers have always been wrong.

It was not until three years after his return to England, the summer of 1865, that Wallace witnessed Spiritualism for himself (MSS: p. 132). The following year, he began a series of observations in his own house. These were to continue for a long time. Not only did Wallace become convinced of the reality of the phenomena, of their occurrence, the teaching communicated via mediums completely transformed his outlook, not just on life, but on death, on the reality and purpose of our existence in the Universe, on the purpose for our presence here on Earth.

Wallace's second book on Spiritualism, *Miracles and Modern Spiritualism*, repeated much of the information contained in his first, smaller book, *The Scientific Aspect of the Supernatural*. Both books contained some degree of duplication because more than one of the papers Wallace cited extensively contained reports of the same event, and many events were very similar. For this reason, I will not give specific references unless there is good reason to do so, for example, direct quotes. All material cited is from one or other, or both, of these books, except where I have cited my own experience, and that is clearly indicated.

Wallace's logical mind insisted that one could not discuss the 'Supernatural' without first defining the meaning of the term. Also in need of a definition was the word 'miracle'. The great philosopher, Hume, had defined a miracle as "a violation of the laws of nature ... A miracle is a violation of a law of nature by a particular volition of the Deity, or by the interposition of some invisible agent." (MSS: p. 4).

Wallace argued that claiming that a certain phenomena violated some law or laws of nature implied that humans knew everything about all natural law(s). Since Wallace's time, much more has been learnt. Do scientists of today know everything there is to be known about natural law? Some may like to think so - not the young scientist, starting out on his career, who would be wasting his time if everything were already known. Wallace argued that, so long as there was so much as a single event which had occurred, which could not be explained by the application of known law, then the conclusion had to be drawn that we do not know everything. *Nothing* can be above natural law, not even an Act of God, because God had created all natural law and no law could be above/beyond that which God had ordained. If God changed the law, that was his prerogative, but the simple continuation of the Universe, which the people of Wallace's time were beginning to comprehend in its immensity of time and space, was evidence of the enduring nature of God's Law. It was us who were ignorant, not God who was fickle.

An apparent miracle might be due to some as yet unknown law of nature – in which case it was not really a miracle at all. The first human being(s) who saw a solid piece of metal being moved, raised (?) through the agency of a magnet may well have thought they were witnessing a miracle. Now, we understand the laws governing magnetism. Well, some of us do! The whole thing is a complete and utter mystery to me, but the phenomena is constantly occurring in a predictable manner and is, to some extent, controllable, so I agree that it is no more of a miracle than, for example, the birth of a baby.

Wallace (MMS: p. 5) offered as his definition of a miracle: "Any act or event necessarily implying the existence and agency of superhuman intelligences".

So, who were these 'superhuman intelligences' and what were the 'miracles' they were causing to occur?

Most of us hearing the word 'miracle' will think of a miracle of healing, such as those recorded in the New Testament as having been performed by Jesus, his Apostles and followers, although other miracles, such as the Feeding of the Four/Five Thousand, when a small amount of bread and fish was multiplied to enable thousands of people to eat, also occurred. Walking on water, turning water into wine, disappearing from the midst of a crowd and turning up somewhere else, these, too, were miracles of a different nature and they more resembled the phenomena witnessed and experienced by the Spiritualists.

Many of the phenomena were similar, session to session, house to house, country to country. They involved 'rapping' or 'tapping', which was described as: "the noise which the ends of knitting needles would make if dropped from a small distance upon a marble slab" (SAS: p. 58). There were many, many reports of furniture (mostly tables) being lifted off the ground, of them being moved, even when laid with glasses, decanters and dessert, and even when their movement was resisted by all persons present in the room, who were pulling with all their might in the opposite direction.

There were many reports of writing, sometimes automatically while the pencil was held by human hand, at other times a 'spirit' hand which manifested, holding the pencil and writing by itself. This resembled the writing recorded in the Old Testament as having occurred during Belshazzar's feast. Also resembling an Old Testament account were frequent records of people picking up hot coals, putting them on other peoples' heads, wrapping hair around them, all without any evidence of burning, which called to mind the three men who remained unhurt when thrown into Nebuchadnezzar's fiery furnace.

Other phenomena Wallace reported were the tying of knots in cords or strips of leather, whose ends were fastened together, the removal of solid wooden rings from a piece of looped cat gut: "secured and held in the same manner, to the pillar of a small table from which they could not be removed without taking the table to pieces, and where they remained till Zöllner's death" (MSS: p.105); removal of coins from sealed boxes, their replacement by pieces of slate-pencil and, perhaps most fascinating of all, the removal of a man's coat while he was securely fastened hand and foot, the coat being seen in the air on its way to the other side of the room. "Under precisely similar circumstances, another gentleman's coat was placed upon him" (SAS: p. 76).

These occurrences may not seem to be as *purposeful* as miracles of healing, but they are 'miraculous' inasmuch as they occurred without human agency in accordance with no known scientific law. Wallace (MSS: p. 5) had offered as his definition of a miracle: "Any act or event necessarily implying the existence and agency of superhuman intelligences". Critics of Spiritualism tended to assume that these 'superhuman intelligences' were angelic or divine – or, indeed, interventions by the Supreme Being – God – himself. To counter this misunderstanding, Wallace added a ryder to his definition: "considering the human soul or spirit, if manifested out of the body, as one of these superhuman intelligences".

It was understandable that disbelievers should ask why God should trouble himself with manifesting a phenomenon such as raising a table a couple of feet of the ground? Why, indeed? But Spiritualists made no such claim. They never claimed 'Divine' intervention, or even angelic. They merely claimed that the phenomena were caused by departed relatives and friends.

Quite why these departed souls should be making what appeared to be a concerted effort to convince incarnate humans of their continued existence after death at that particular time, Wallace does not say. I suspect it was because faith, not just Christian faith, but any faith, was being questioned then as never before. Of course, there had always been 'heretics'. Sometimes they were ignored; at other times they were persecuted. Now they were being believed.

As science increased its hold upon the minds of the Victorian public, more and more people questioned the truth of the Scriptures. Not believing in the literal truth of Adam and Eve and Noah's Ark, interpreting them as allegories, that was not too great a problem. Some New Testament miracles could be seen as exaggerations. Things became serious when questions were asked about the Virgin Birth, the physical Ascension of Jesus into Heaven. Darwin's close friend, Thomas Huxley, invented the term 'agnostic' for those who did not *know*, who were not complete atheists, did not deny the existence of some Supreme Being, but who did not accept 'God' as present in the daily lives of humans. 'God' was increasingly being portrayed as a distant, unknowable, force, which, having set the Universe in motion, allowed it to run its course, never interfering with the Laws set down at the beginning of time. People were beginning to question not only Heaven and Hell but whether there was any life after death at all.

Growing rejection of Christianity had led the Rev. William Paley, in 1794, to write *Evidence of Christianity*. A few years later, in 1802, he felt compelled to write *Natural Theology*, directed, not at those who did not believe in Christianity, but at those who did not believe in God at all. The apparently trivial phenomena evidenced during Spiritualistic sessions would seem to have been an attempt by loved ones, now passed over, to convince those whom they had left behind that they were not only still alive, but still *present*, still close by, still watching, still caring. The way in which they chose to achieve their end may have been 'simple' but it was effective.

Those coins taken from the sealed boxes – were they ever returned? Wallace did not say. Do the spirits ever take things without our knowledge? My mother used to complain at times of the gremlins, who took things. I remember one incident. She was doing some mending one evening, cut a thread, put the scissors down beside her hip, went to pick them up again a few minutes later and they were gone. She removed the cushions, moved the chair, looked everywhere she could think of, but those scissors were nowhere to be found. A few months later, Christmas Eve to be precise, she took down the box of Christmas decorations from the top shelf of the hall cupboard, and when she opened the box, there they were! Sitting on top of the Christmas decorations. Something even more bizarre happened to me once. When I first retired to Port Douglas, I lived in a caravan for a couple of years, making do with hand washing between visits to the launderette. Sards Wonder Soap was being heavily advertised at the time, so I bought a bar. I had only used it a couple of times when my daughter, struggling to pay her rent alone, asked me to move in with her. Next batch of hand washing, I commented that I didn't think much of the Sards, because the marks were not coming out. She responded, in that tired, patronizing tone of voice that only a child can use to its parent: "That's because you are not using your Sards. You are using my Lux Beauty Soap". So I was! Where was my Sards? We both hunted. Under the sink? In the laundry? In the fridge? The washing machine? In the frying pan? We tried all the obvious places - and a few others besides - without success. After about a year, we moved to another place. A further year later, we parted. I moved into a small unit some twenty kilometres north. There was a shortage of cupboard space, so while I was saving up to have some new cupboards installed, some boxes had to wait outside in the car port. I had been living at my new place for about four months, when I drew up in the car one day and there was the bar of Sards Wonder Soap, sitting on top of one of the boxes, the name clearly visible through the dried soap bubbles. I don't think the gremlins had even used it, so why did they take it? More than two years, and three moves later, they returned it. If they did not return stuff, how would we know they had taken it in the first place? Would we not chastise ourselves for being careless? - or, possibly, chastise our spouse, our children, our elderly parents, whoever was available to take the blame.

There were reports of bells ringing, sometimes for days – not continuously, I hope! Musical instruments played, pianos, stringed instruments, sometimes picked up and placed in the hands, upon the lap, of one of the persons present. Flowers were given, sometimes by a visible, sometimes by an invisible, hand. Most faded and died, or disappeared, but one plant, presented in a pot, planted in the garden, grew and flourished. All of these activities were *human* activities, and this, Wallace came to understand, was the point. These phenomena were not being produced by angels, or gods, or some other heavenly creation. They were being produced by humans, albeit humans in another stage of their ongoing existence.

There are people on this Earth who appear very knowledgeable about one or more matters. We listen to them, we learn from them, but what if their knowledge is not as great, or as perfect, as we think it is? What if it is not as great, or as perfect, as *they* think it is? It is up to each one of us to think over what we are told, what we read, what we discover, for ourselves. It is up to each of us to decide what to accept, what to reject and what to put on 'hold' for further consideration at another time. The information passed on to us via any medium, be it the spoken word, the written word, or rapping, had come from another human being, albeit not necessarily one currently in physical form. At death, there was no magical transformation. As we were at the time of our last breath, our last heartbeat, so we were upon the other side. Our knowledge was the same, but, more importantly, so was our character. Daily, hourly, every minute, souls all around the world were passing to the next stage of existence. Some were educated, honourable, hardworking. Some were uneducated, through no fault of their own; others were lazy, because they chose to be that way. Some were honest, some were not. Every possible variety of human character and behaviour which existed on this Earthly plane, existed in the hereafter. Some had enjoyed activities which were no longer available for them: drinking, gambling, crime, habitual sin. Such souls would hover where they could hope still to enjoy these pleasures vicariously, helping to 'lower the tone' of an establishment. "... these spirits too, in time, lose their fierce passions, and learn how to begin the upward path of knowledge and virtue" (MSS: p. 119). It was important not to accept 'information' received without question. The spirit giver might be just as mistaken as a person on Earth - or just as mischievous in spreading falsehood.

Communication with these beings had taught that they were no further advanced than anyone on Earth in their understanding of the origin of the Universe, of the nature of God, although they all believed that there was a 'Divine' purpose for our existence, that we were on a journey, with much to learn. They told that there was no Heaven or Hell, no reward or punishment, except that which we awarded to ourself as we reviewed our life, our progress, or lack thereof. Our guilt was our punishment, and that was punishment enough. Our joy was our reward when we came to full understanding of how some word or action of ours had lifted another soul. Every moment of our Earthly life was meaningful and it was the meaning we had put into our life which determined our future state, not some death-bed confession and absolution. This was the great gift of Spiritualism - not the promise of some Heavenly existence at an indeterminate time in the future, but meaning and purpose to Now.

Spiritualists naturally took great interest in apparitions but Wallace reported nothing which had not been recorded before, throughout history. There were tales of hauntings following sudden deaths, whether by accident or murder. There were reports of appearances to relatives/friends at the time of death, usually sudden and unexpected, sometimes the deceased person appearing to more than one person, in widely separated places, at what seemed to have been the same time. There were reports of persons continuing to haunt the place at which they had once lived. Wallace recorded the case of one Mr. Richard Children, who, with his wife was often seen by various people at Ramhurst Manor House. One of the occupants (Miss S.) "had many conversations with the apparitions" (MMS: p. 77) who told her that they had once lived at Ramhurst and were saddened that the property had passed away from the Children family, being now in the possession of strangers. Search of historical documents confirmed that the Childrens had formerly lived in Tunbridge. It was not possible to determine the exact year in which they had purchased Ramhurst, but it was noted that Richard Children and his family had lived there for many years, he dying in 1753 at the age of eighty-three.

Wallace having no uncommon or unusual personal incident to report at this point, I thought I would add an anecdote of my own, which I heard when I was sixteen years old. I was attending a Bible Study course, which kept about twenty teenagers occupied and out of their parents' hair for two weeks of the August school holidays. Our spiritual care was in the keeping of a delightful priest, just returned from Africa, where he had spent the last thirty years or so trying to persuade African villagers that Christianity was a better option than Voodoo. I knew very little about Voodoo at the time – still don't – but there was one story he told us that I will never forget.

There was one lass in the village (late teens, maybe twenty?) who would induce in herself a trance state by whirling and dancing, and 'singing'. One evening, while in this trance state, she ran up a palm tree – *ran* up it – she did not climb, she *ran* up it. When she reached the top, she disappeared. She was never seen again! "I didn't believe in Voodoo when I first arrived in Africa," the priest told us, "but I certainly did by the time I left!"

Another phenomenon of great interest was that of miracles. Once again, this phenomenon was not unique to Spiritualism, miraculous occurrences having been reported throughout history all over the globe. Some miracles involved healing, but many did not. Some of the phenomena reported as having occurred during the seances, such as the removal of a jacket from a person bound to a chair, no doubt seemed 'miraculous' to the witnesses but failed to exhibit the one thing which was deemed necessary for a 'miracle' to qualify as such: a benefit to someone. Being able to pass from a crowd to a place of quietness undoubtedly benefited Jesus. Whether it benefited anybody else, the occurrence was still deemed to be miraculous, as was walking on water, quieting the storm and turning water into wine. Thousands were fed with a few loaves and small fish. Nor was the provision of unlimited food unique to Jesus. Elisha (2 Kings 4: 38-44) also fed 'hundreds' from twenty barley loaves, made a small amount of oil sufficient to fill many large vessels, which a widow was able to sell to settle her late husband's debts. Elijah (1 Kings 17: 8-15) did a similar thing for another widow, who shared what she thought was the last of her 'meal' with Elijah during a famine. She, her son and Elijah 'ate for many days'.

Most readily remembered, no doubt, are the miracles of healing, not only those recorded in the Bible as having been performed by Prophets, by Jesus, by his disciples and followers, but later by Saints. Indeed, the Catholic Church requires a minimum of two miracles for Sainthood. Wallace took issue with the great philosophic sceptic, David Hume, who quite clearly contradicted himself. In one place, Hume had written (MMS: p. 8):

> For, first, there is *not to be found*, in *all history*, any miracle attested by a *sufficient number* of men, of such unquestioned *good sense, education,* and *learning,* as to secure us against all delusion in

themselves; of such undoubted *integrity*, as to place them beyond all suspicion of any design to deceive others; of such credit and reputation in the eyes of mankind, as to have a great deal to lose in case of their being detected by any falsehood; and at the same time attesting facts performed in such a *public manner*, and in so *celebrated a part of the world*, as to render the detection unavoidable; all of which circumstances are requisite to give us a full assurance in the testimony of men. (Italics in original)

A few pages further on, Hume had written of miracles regularly performed at the tomb of Abbé Paris, which had been proved upon the spot before judges of unquestioned integrity. Later Hume was to recount a most extraordinary miracle which had occurred to the niece of the famous Pascal and which had been witnessed by many eminent persons, including the Queen-Regent of France (MMS: p. 11):

Mademoiselle Coirin was afflicted, amongst other ailments, with a cancer in the left breast, for twelve years. The breast was destroyed by it and came away in a mass; the effluvia from the cancer was horrible, and the whole blood of the system was pronounced infected by it. Every physician pronounced the case utterly incurable, yet, by a visit to the tomb, she was perfectly cured; and, what was more astonishing, the breast and nipple were wholly restored, with the skin pure and fresh, and free from any trace of scar. This case was known to the highest people in the realm."

Hume went on to argue that miracles had been attested to by followers of many religions which, of itself, was evidence that most of them could not have happened. He appeared to Wallace to be arguing that miracles could only be performed by God "and must therefore support the true religion" (MMS: p. 13). Wallace agreed with anybody who argued that no miracle could be 'supernatural', i.e. performed in some manner by some force which was above nature, beyond nature, contrary to nature. He disagreed when persons, such as 'scientists', claimed to know every Law which existed in Nature, when they claimed that this knowledge enabled them to state with absolute authority what could, and what could not, occur. "... how small a portion of the great cosmos our senses give us cognisance" (MMS: p. 43); "... our five senses are but clumsy instruments to investigate the imponderable" (MMS: p. 48).

In Volume II of *My Life*, covered in Chapter 2 of this book, Wallace gave further examples of miracles. He had become friends with St. George Mivart, an ardent critic of Darwin but a good friend of Wallace through their common interest in Spiritualism. Mivart had visited Lourdes at a time when Bernadette Soubirons (better known as St. Bernadette) was receiving her apparitions of the Blessed Virgin. In April, 1874, Mivart wrote Wallace a long letter, part of which Wallace reproduced (pp. 302-305). I here reproduce a small part thereof:

> A woman named Blaisette Soupevue of this place, about fifty, had had an affection (blepharitis) of the eyes for several years. Both eyelids were partially everted, lashless, and the lower lids had numerous fleshy excrescences. Dr. Dozens attended this case himself, as also a Dr. Vergez. It was pronounced chronic, all idea of cure abandoned. She washed her eyes with the water [from Lourdes] on two successive days; on the second her sight was completely restored, her eyelids righted themselves, and the excrescences vanished ...

> Justin Bontisharts, also of this place, had a rickety child two years old, which had much atrophied limbs, and had never been able to walk. It got worse, and was thought to be near its death. Dr. Dozens tells me he attended it, and was present when the mother placed it under the stream of the Lourdes water. It was motionless while so held, and the

bystanders therefore fancied it was dead already. The mother took it home, placed it in its bed, and noticed that it seemed to be in a tranquil sleep. Next day it woke with a quite different expression of face, craved for food, ate freely, and wanted to get up, but its parents were afraid to let it. The following morning, while they were out to work, it got up, and when they returned was walking about the room, walking quite well, and has done so ever since.

Despite all the new understanding revealed by science since the time of Wallace, especially that related to computers, have we any more right now, than we did then, to claim that we humans, on our little planet, know all that there is to know about the Universe, how it was formed, why, of what it is capable, what it might become, how it might end, what (if anything) there may be to follow? We are told our Universe is 'expanding'. Into what? What exists beyond our Universe. What was there before time? What will there be when time ceases to exist?

Wallace did not offer evidence of any miracle which he had personally witnessed. I hope he will not be angry with me if I finish this chapter with one of my own.

Every Sunday evening, I took the kids roller skating. While they performed all sorts of manoeuvres, I skated round and round, using the hypnotic motion to prepare in my mind the assignments I needed to complete that week. (I was undertaking my studies in psychology.) While thus engaged, a young lass, about eight-years-old, leaning up against the outside barrier, spotted a friend in the centre. She pushed off rapidly to meet her, catching her skate in mine. I spun round, flung out my right arm which smashed to the ground as I fell. Both my ulna and my radius were broken, but that was by no means the whole of it. The doctors told me it was a bad break, that they had set it as best they could, but it would not be perfect. I nodded, not really taking anything in, went home to bed, where I stayed for two weeks. One does not usually need to stay in bed with a broken arm, but I was in such pain, I just lay there and concentrated on drawing the next breath. I could not move my arm; I thought that was because of the plaster, which was above my elbow. When the plaster was removed, I found out how wrong I was.

Apparently, the radius had 'jumped' the notch in which it usually rested against the ulna. This made the thumb side of my arm shorter than it should have been. My hand was twisted markedly inwards. It was also bent forwards in the 'dropped' position as far as it could go. My wrist was also twisted on its axis. The radius, in its new position, had displaced some of the wrist bones, which were now heaped up towards the outer side of the wrist. I was in a mess! The ulna and radius being out of position meant that my elbow would not move. My arm was fixed in a bent position a few inches out from my body. Apparently, the humerus was also slightly out of position, so I could not move my shoulder either. I suppose if I had had private insurance, an operation may have been possible? Or if I had been in a road accident and had been covered by compulsory third party insurance? But that was not the case, and, this being 1988, the Skating Rink had a small sign over the cashier's window announcing that they carried no Public Liability Insurance and that we skated at our own risk! I don't suppose that would be allowed today, but this is now and that was then!

I attended a few sessions of physiotherapy, which did no good at all. Apparently, I had 1° of movement in my wrist – I could lift it 1°. Nothing sideways; nothing to 'untwist'. The specialist pronounced that there was no point in my continuing physiotherapy; I must get on with life as best I could. Of course, I could not drive, I could not write, I could not even lift the tea bag out of my mug, with that hand, although I tried and tried. By leaning over the kitchen bench, I could bring my middle finger into contact with the string, but I could not move my finger at all, I could not hook it beneath the string to lift it up.

It was Wednesday, 21st December, 1988, Midsummer Day 'Down Under'! I received a call from a patient whom I had only seen once. She was hesitant because she did not know how I would react when she told me that she had a 'message' for me. Apparently, she did automatic writing. The next day, Thursday, 22nd December, we met and she gave me the message: "Denise will be helped by a therapy with which she is very well acquainted. She will regain full use of her hand." The 'therapy' had to be homœopathy, in which I specialized. I thought and thought. The picture which kept coming into my mind was that of the field of wheat, with its stalks standing straight and tall, glistening in the sun, because of the silica they contained. Nature uses silica when it needs straightness and strength. If I wanted to straighten my wrist, to give it back its lost strength, then I needed to take *Silica*.

The next day, Friday, 23rd December, I took a one hour bus ride to my, now deserted, Clinic. Homœopathic remedies are taken in very small doses. I took one globule (the size of a 'hundreds and thousands' cake decoration). It was 1M strength, for those who know about these things - it had been diluted 1:99 one thousand times, so the amount of silica present was infinitesimal. That night, before I went to bed, I said a little 'prayer': "I know that if my wrist is healed while I am asleep, it will hurt. Whatever the pain, I accept it."

I lay down to sleep and the next thing I knew, dawn was breaking on Christmas Eve. It was 4.30 a.m. Nothing had happened! My heart fell. I had been so sure. But wait! I realized I was lying on my left side. My right arm was lying along my thigh. It was straight! I did not dare to look. I climbed carefully out of bed, walked across to my dressing table, held out my arm and looked at it in the mirror. My wrist and arm had straightened in the night and I had never felt a thing!

The straightening was not perfect. One of the wrist bones was still slightly out of place which prevented me from completely rotating my wrist. I could write. I could drive a car. I could hand money over at the check-out with my right hand, but I had to use my left to receive the change! Did I not take quite the right remedy? Did I not take quite the right strength? Whatever the reason, I still have a slight kink in my wrist, about which I am very happy because, if it was perfect, who would believe me?

Tuesday, 27th December, I went back to see my doctor. His chin would have hit his boots if his desk had not been in the way. "I do not understand what has happened", he said, "but I am very happy for you." I don't understand it either, but, then, who are we to presume to understand?

Chapter 18

The World of Life

Wallace continued to write until the end of his life, being 87 years of age when *The World of Life* was published in 1910. It was a comprehensive work and, undoubtedly, one of his most important. Its importance was indicted by its subtitle: *A Manifestation of Creative Power, Directive Mind and Ultimate Purpose.*

In his younger day, Wallace had been fascinated and intrigued by the physical world around him. Initially, his interest was in plants and animals, and it was to study these that he left his homeland, to travel to the, still largely unstudied, land of South America. Here he met a mixture of native, European and Black people, the last being mostly run-away slaves. Human beings, their evolution, their path in life, were not of particular interest to him at that time. This was to change during his subsequent visit to the Malay Archipelago, where he met with Europeans, mostly Dutch and English, as well as people from India and China, mainly immigrants of the past two centuries, and an assortment of true native tribes, some of whom had had extensive contact with Europeans and were living increasingly Westernised lives, and others who had had little - or even no - contact with White Man. Wallace was exposed to the working of many different societies, some of which he believed to be superior, at least in some respects, to society back home. This conviction led to his writing many books and articles on social issues, as has been discussed.

By the turn of the century, the market in plants and animals from around the world may have become saturated, but a new and greedy market had opened up concentrated upon the study of fossils. The discovery of Neanderthal Man had raised the possibility of a far more ancient history for the human race than had been allowed by the story of Creation as told in *Genesis*. Some were untroubled by the philosophical implications, others rejected the Old Testament, yet others rejected Christianity and others still rejected the concept of God altogether. Wallace belonged to none of these groups. He belonged to the smallest group, that of people who were previously atheist, or agnostic, but who, as a result of their growing understanding of the evolution of the physical world, had come to an increasing awareness of the spiritual world. His previous book, *Man's Place in Nature*, had concentrated on the place of Man and of the Earth within the *material* universe. This book was concerned, not only with Man's place on this Earth, or this Earth's place within the Universe, but of the Universe's place in the world of *life* – that life for which Wallace could comprehend no beginning and no end.

Reading this book, I was once again overawed by the breadth and depth of Wallace's knowledge. Many people have expertise in one area, some in two, but there can be few who have studied so deeply such a wide range of subjects. We have already seen the lengths to which Wallace was prepared to go to acquire accurate information in relation to the issue he was addressing, be that housing, parliamentary reform, defence spending, health, or anything else, not an easy undertaking before the time of the world wide web, of photocopiers, or even of telephones.

By this stage of his life, Wallace had abandoned his attempts to reform society. He had had some success. Fire hoses were being used instead of guns for crowd control. Not much reward for years of work! Wallace reverted to his first love, the study of nature. No longer did his interests lie only with the evolution of living plants and animals, but with those long extinct. He acquired an extensive knowledge of fossils. His appreciation of the role played by the environment led him to acquire an equally extensive knowledge of geology and climate, both of which, he had come to understand, were constantly changing. He studied astronomy, upon which subject he published articles in relevant journals. He studied chemistry – the atomic table was rapidly taking shape. He was interested in the substances, such as oxygen, hydrogen and carbon, which played such an important role in the development of life, along with others, such as nitrogen, chlorine, magnesium, potassium, sulphur, all of which played roles of differing importance, as did the trace elements. He was interested in substances, such as gold and silver, which seemed to play no active role at all, but remained, virtually inert, in the crust of the Earth, as countless millions of years came and went. Why had they been created?

This book was not an account of Wallace's physical journey through life. It was an account of the journey of his thinking. It was the journey of a life-time.

The Plan

In the Preface to this great work, Wallace explained that approximately the first quarter of the book, Chapters 2-6 contained material of interest to plant lovers. Chapters 7-9 were devoted to further discussions regarding Natural Selection, with particular reference to birds and butterflies. Chapters 10-13 concentrated on the Geological record, with extensive discussion of the fossil record of extinct animals, especially the dinosaurs and other mega fauna, which had lived all over the world, disappearing, Wallace concluded, with the arrival of humans.

It was, however, the final chapters, 14-20, that Wallace considered to be the most important (p. vi):

> ... the most prominent feature of my book is that I enter into a popular yet critical examination of those underlying fundamental problems which Darwin purposely excluded from his works ... Such are, the nature and causes of Life itself; and more especially of its most fundamental and mysterious powers – growth and reproduction.

What is Life, and Whence it Comes

You may have noticed that, in his Preface, Wallace made no mention of Chapter 1. Perhaps he did not want to risk intimidating his reader by admitting that Chapter 1 addressed one of the deepest issues confronting mankind, the nature of the force responsible for the creation and manifestation of the Universe, a problem which had puzzled the human mind ever since human's evolved minds capable of being puzzled.

Wallace suggested that early humans would have recognized animals as living beings, but not plants. He acknowledged that there were people who vaguely believed that all matter was alive - some even believed that stones could grow - but rejected this idea as being without 'a particle of scientific justification' (p. 4). While rejecting the notion that all matter was alive, many men of science agreed that life was a product of matter, among which circle Wallace included the German scientist/philosopher, Ernest Hækel, whose philosophy of 'monism' Wallace then criticised.

Wallace's criticism commenced with the citing of two passages from Hæckel's *The Riddle of the Universe* (pp. 4-5):

> The peculiar phenomenon of consciousness is not, as ... the dualistic school would have us believe, a completely transcendental problem; it is ... a

physiological problem, and, as such, must be reduced to the phenomena of physics and chemistry.

The two fundamental forms of substance, ponderable matter and ether, are not dead, and moved only by extreme force, but they are endowed with sensation and will ... they experience an inclination for condensation, a dislike of strain; they strive after the one and struggle against the other.

Wallace saw these two passages as being self-contradictory; in the first consciousness had been reduced to a phenomena of physics and chemistry while in the second matter and ether possessed both sensation and will. Wallace cites a further passage from Hæckel's book (p. 8):

We hold ... that matter cannot exist and be operative without spirit, nor spirit without matter. We adhere to the pure, unequivocal monism of Spinoza: Matter ... and Spirit (or Energy), or sensitive and thinking substance, are the two fundamental attributes ... of all-embracing essence of the world, the universal substance.

This, deduced Wallace, led to the theory of the "cell-soul", the origin of consciousness, which was itself unconscious. Hæckel also claimed that there was no spirit world independent of matter; universes came into existence, developed and were destroyed, in a continual cycle.

I do not claim to have made a deep study of Hæckel's work, but I read have some of it. It is my understanding that Haeckel rejected Christianity as being dualistic. It postulated *two* eternal spiritual forces, one 'good' (God) and the other 'evil' (Satan or the Devil). If God were perceived to be the greater because He had created the Universe, Satan was seen to be the more successful: he was winning the battle for souls. Far more people went to Hell than to Heaven! In the early Christian Church, conversion and baptism had been sufficient to attain an eternal heavenly existence, but over the centuries, mostly at the instigation of successive Popes, not only was regular attendance at Church necessary, with the taking of the Sacrament, but also regular confession of sins, with absolution. Death bed confessions were a necessity. Any person dying without receiving final absolution was in very real danger of going to Hell – as was a new-born baby, clearly without sin, if it were not baptised before it died, which happened to many new-born babies in those times. Happily, there was a solution. For the payment of a (small?) sum of money, advanced absolution for sins not yet committed could be obtained. These were known as 'favours' – great for the wealthy, but not so great for the poor!

Haeckel acknowledged but one 'force/energy/spirit', hence the term 'monism'. He gave this entity no name, attributed to it no qualities, such as omnipresence or omnipotence. However, he did recommend his followers not to attend Church on Sunday but rather to go out into the countryside, breathe the fresh air, feel the sun on their skin, walk bare-foot through the meadows so that they could truly connect with the Earth. Hæckel also urged the eating of healthy foods and exercise, since the body was the manifestation of the spirit.

Within this context, Hæckel was correct. The phenomena of consciousness was dependent upon the physics and chemistry of the brain. It was these which controlled our loss of consciousness when we fell asleep at night, or when we lost consciousness following an injury. 'Unconsciousness' was a state endured only by the living. Once the brain stopped working, it was not only 'consciousness' which was lost, but life (on this Earth). If it is accepted that this was the context in which Haeckel was speaking, then Wallace's counter-arguments loose credibility. However, many people, Wallace included, held that life and consciousness continued after death and were independent of physical form. There were many reports of the sighting of those who had 'passed over'. Such people were claimed to have been seen in their 'astral' body. If Wallace was referring to an astral body, then he was correct.

Wallace claimed that Hæckel's theory (p. 8):

> ... concealed his real ignorance of the nature of life itself. He evades altogether any attempt to solve the various difficult problems of nutrition, assimilation and growth ...

It was Wallace's intention to tackle such problems.

In contrast, Wallace cited the well-known agnostic, if not atheist, Thomas Huxley, who, in *The Classification of Animals* (1869) had stated that (p. 8):

> ... *life is the cause and not the consequence of organisation;* for in these lower forms of animal life there is absolutely nothing worthy of the name of organisation to be discovered by the microscope ... it is structureless and organless. and without definitely formed parts. (Italics in original.)

Elsewhere Huxley had spoken of "preexisting living protoplasm" and referred to "that matter of life which is the source of our other vital phenomena", which statements Wallace considered "vague and unsatisfactory" (p. 9).

Species – Their Number, Variety and Distribution

Some people thought that Darwin's theory proved there were no such things as species. This Wallace denied. There existed definite, easily recognisable, easily definable species, but they were now known not to be immutable, although very stable. Wallace believed that only then, after fifty years of careful observation, were scientists beginning to discover a very few cases of real change - "the actual production of new species - appears to be going on before our eyes" (p. 12). Wallace gave no details.

Some species occupied very limited areas, others were widespread. In relation to plants, Wallace cited de Candolle's observation that "about 200 species (out of the total then known of about 120,000) have areas equal to *one-third* of the entire land surface" (p. 17. Italics in original). He wrote of the influence of the (ever-changing) environment, both geological and biological.

Wallace discussed, at length, the distribution of British plants, comparing this with that in other temperate climates around the world.

In Chapter 4, Wallace reviewed the tropical flora of the world. This was the first chapter to contain illustrations. Wallace had lived in the tropics on both sides of the world and knew them well. The length of this chapter is testament as much to his interest as it is to the complexity of the subject. Writing of adaptation to drought, Wallace gave an account, accompanied by an illustration, which is, undoubtedly, the most extraordinary which I have ever come across. It is reproduced below.

What look like surface are the upper branches of a tree, the trunk of which and often a large part of the limbs and branches are buried in the earth. The stems shown are the root-like branches, which are 4-5 inches diameter, while growing shoots are from 2 to 3 feet high. The whole plant (or tree) is from 30 to 40 feet diameter. As the branches approach the centre they descend into the earth and form a central trunk. A French botanist, M. Emm. Liais, says of this species: "If we dig we find how all these small shurbs, apparently distinct, are joined together underground and form the extremities of the branches of a large subterranean tree which at length unite to form a single trunk. M. Renault of Barbacena told me that he had dug about 20 feet deep to obtain one of these trunks" The large subterranean trees with a trunk hidden in the soil form one of the most singular features of the flora of these campos of Central Brazil.

On page 77, Wallace stressed the need for the provision of suitable 'reserves' to protect native flora and fauna from destruction. He considered this a duty to posterity. It was also necessary to prevent further deterioration of the climate (!) and fertility of the soil.

Having considered plants, Wallace moved on to a discussion of the distribution of animal species. To this subject, he devoted two chapters, the second of which concentrated upon distribution in relation to evolution. Although, as was to be expected, these two chapters were packed with information, yet their combined length was less than half that of the one chapter on tropical flora. In polar regions there may be more animals than plants, but in the tropics and temperate regions, plants far outnumber animals.

Heredity, Variation, Increase

In the past, there had been no understanding that species changed over time. Even after it became understood (through the fossil record) that species had undergone redistribution and/or extinction, "we have obtained no clue to the *method* by which new species arise to replace them" (p. 101). This, Wallace continued, had been the state of opinion before Darwin, as shown by Sir Charles Lyell in his *Principles of Geology*, the 9th edition of which had been published in 1853, six years before the publication of Darwin's work. The 11th edition, published in 1868, nine years after *The Origin*, maintained this position, despite the close friendship between Lyell and Darwin. Wallace argued that an enormous advance had taken place with the publication of Darwin's theory of natural selection in 1859, which was dependent upon three factors: heredity, variation, and enormous powers of increase.

Once again, Wallace made no reference to Lamarck, which was surprising since Lamarck attributed creation and life to the will and action of a 'First Cause', which he declined to attempt to explain, such things being beyond human understanding. His thorough extrapolation of evolution, from the simple cell to bimanus (humans), which took three volumes of detailed explanation, was based upon a presumption of oversight by a 'Supreme Being', the same position to which Wallace had now come, yet nowhere in his book does Wallace mention Lamarck's name, which greatly puzzles me. Unlike Darwin, who never acknowledged anybody else's work if he could avoid it (for which he was roundly criticised), Wallace constantly cited writers and thinkers in the field he was then discussing. It is almost as if he had an understanding with his good friend, Darwin, not to promote Lamarck's ideas - a pretty weak explanation, but I can think of no other.

Natural 'law' dictated that 'like produces like' - without exception. Not only did each reproduce its own species, it reproduced its own variety. Chinese produced Chinese, Negro produced Negro, never white, even though all three varieties belonged to the same species. Some held that mental qualities were not inherited. Wallace conceded that there may be individual differences within families but claimed that Sir Frances Galton (Darwin's cousin) had shown, in his book *Hereditary Genius*, that, taken over large numbers of families over several generations, there was an approximation of mental acuity. By careful experiment with plants and animals, Galton had concluded that each offspring derived one-half of their characteristics from each parent, one fourth from each grandparent, one eighth from each of the eight grandparents, and so on to remote ancestry, explaining 'throwbacks'. In other words, one-half of our characteristics were inherited from our two parents, the other half from more remote ancestors. This was similar to the conclusions of Mendel, but not quite the same.

Galton's theory also explained another well-known 'law': the "law of recession towards mediocrity". For example, two tall parents usually gave birth to offspring who were tall, but not as tall as their parents. For short parents, the situation was reversed. Their children tended to be short, but not as short as their parents. The same was true of intellectual and artistic characteristics – either in excess or deficit.

Variation between human beings was greater than that among animals or plants, but variation did exist in nature and it existed in a regular form. This Wallace illustrated by what is today known as the 'Bell' curve: the centre, comprising the majority, formed the 'bell', while a small minority, above and below average, formed the rim. Some 'bells' were tall and thin, some short and wide, but there was always an extension either end. The 'bell' rose slowly, then accelerated to its full height, fell away and petered out, equally slowly.

Wallace gave examples to show that a bird could have, for example, a longer than usual beak yet not a longer than usual tail. Animal and plants were not as uniform as had been thought.

Rapidity of reproduction was also important, especially among plants and smaller animals, lesser able to defend themselves. If numbers fell, the entity was in danger of extinction – which had clearly happened with surprising frequency. If numbers rose too sharply, starvation could ensue, which was just as detrimental. Natural disasters could also reduce numbers unexpectedly.

Wallace concluded that these facts served to rule 'out of court' modern theories of 'mutation' and of 'Mendelism'. "The persistency of Mendelian characters is the very opposite of what is needed amid the ever-changing conditions of nature" (p. 123).

Illustrative Cases of Natural Selection and Adaptation

This was the subject matter of Chapter 8, a fairly long chapter containing much interesting information, such as that the approach of the Northern Hemisphere summer in May caused the snow at the North Pole to melt at the rate of four miles an hour! It was also in this chapter that Wallace discussed *The Uses of Mosquitoes* – so hateful to mankind and so delightful to birds. These insect-pests were found all over the world, from the tropics to the arctic, but their fullest development was "to be found in the icy plains of the Far North, especially within the Arctic circle both in the Eastern and Western hemispheres" (p. 135). At times they swarmed in such abundance that they completely obscured the sun, like a dense thunder-cloud. I have read elsewhere of mosquitoes so dense that they caused the scientist's tent to sway. This same scientist complained that even the simple act of defecation was fraught with peril! I also once saw a sad documentary in which an emaciated deer/elk (I cannot remember which) was shown, emaciated not from lack of food, but lack of blood, which had been sucked out of him by mosquitoes. Apparently, many died. It was the shallow ponds/lakes created by the melting snow which were the perfect breeding ground for the mosquitoes.

In the Arctic spring/summer, birds migrated to the Arctic to breed, not in their thousands, but in their millions. Plenty of food and no predators – why would they not? As the snow melted in the more southern areas, an abundance of cranberries, crowberries and other berries, which had been preserved beneath the winter snow, were revealed; insect eating birds only had to open their mouths to fill then with mosquitoes (p. 136). Both lava and adult were eagerly consumed, the female adult being a rich source of blood, which she had sucked from those poor deer!

However, the interest of its information must not be allowed to obscure the importance of its argument, which was pivotal.

One of the greatest difficulties in the way of acceptance of any theory of evolution by natural means was lack of evidence, at least within the human period, of any new species. New *variations*, whether in nature or under domestication, were readily acknowledged, but the evolution of a distinctly new *species* had been problematic. Naturalists, "having pretty well exhausted the well-defined species" (pp. 124-125) were now turning their attention to varieties. Wallace was following Darwin by blurring the distinction between the two. In their defence, it must be stated that a full understanding of the reproductive process had not yet been reached, the stability of species was still being questioned by some.

All the adaptations cited by Wallace in Chapter 9 were variations. While interesting, they did not advance knowledge in relation to evolution as we understand it today. The following chapter discussed the importance of recognition marks for evolution but, once again, none of the examples progressed the discussion of evolution of species, rather they promoted stability of species.

The Earth's Surface-Changes as the Condition and Motive-Power of Organic Evolution

Wallace now moved to a subject which can be seen to increase in relevance as the book entered its second phase. Attention turned to the inorganic world. The surface of the Earth was constantly changing; the temperature, the weather were constantly changing. These changing conditions had interacted with each other, and with organic matter, to produce the world in which we found ourselves today. Fossils of sea creatures had been found at the top of mountains. Conditions had changed to a degree which our minds had difficulty assimilating. Some changes had been (comparatively) sudden, others had taken untold ages. Much of the material in this chapter recapitulated that written elsewhere (for examples, in *Island Life*) about the effect of climate change, especially the effect of Ice Ages and glaciers.

As the chapter drew to its close, Wallace restated his previous conclusion that there was no other planet in the solar system with conditions suitable for life. These considerations were, for Wallace, powerful arguments in support of the existence of an "overruling MIND, which so ordered the forces at work in the material universe as to render the almost infinitely improbable sequence of events to which I have called attention an actual reality ... the continuous development of the world of life, is hardly to be explained without some Guiding Power over the cosmic forces which have brought about the result" (pp. 186-187).

The Progressive Development of the Life-World as shown by the Geological Record

After a lengthy 'preparation', lasting some nine chapters, Wallace appeared to have arrived at the starting point indicated in Chapter 1, but, No! Wallace felt that his reader needed a firm understanding of the significance of the geological record before he could proceed further.

Earliest geologists had split the rock formations of the Earth into three great divisions: Primary (before life), Secondary (early life), Tertiary (more recent life). These groupings had been amended, but were still in use. 'Primary' formations included early life forms, fish and amphibia, 'Secondary', reptiles of amazing variety and abundance, 'Tertiary', earliest mammals and up until the present.

Opponents of Darwin's theory of gradual evolution had pointed to gaps in the fossil record, which Darwin conceded existed but which Darwin was confident would disappear as the fossil record became perfected. The gaps still existed and Wallace's explanation was even more unsatisfactory than that of Darwin (p. 191):

> Either there is no record of the missing links in the Secondary formation or, what is perhaps more probable, the breaks between the Secondary and Tertiary beds was of such enormous duration as to afford time for the simultaneous dying out of numerous groups of gigantic reptiles and the development in all the large continents of much higher and more varied animals.

This 'explanation' does not explain at all how the 'higher and more varied animals' evolved to replace those becoming extinct without leaving any trace of intermediate forms. This is still the situation today. Some intermediate forms have been found, but it has been said that these finds simply create two (smaller) gaps where only one (larger) gap existed before!

Wallace then conducted his reader through a tour of Primary plant and animal forms, accompanied by some interesting illustrations. He concluded this section (p. 197):

> ... I am endeavouring to show, all life development – all organic forces – are due to mind-action ... guidance; not only such self-acting agencies as are involved in natural selection and adaptation through survival of the fittest, but that far higher mentality which foresees all possible results of the constitution of our cosmos ... co-ordinated forces acting continuously through eons of time, has culminated in the foreseen result.

The section dealing with Secondary life-forms is longer and more profusely illustrated. It includes the dinosaurs, which were, by then, well known. He described several Orders of dinosaur which had been identified. We now believe a comet crashing into our Earth caused the demise of the dinosaurs. This was not known to geologists of Wallace's time and the sudden disappearance of, not only the dinosaurs, but of other Secondary life-forms was a great mystery. Crocodiles and tortoises had survived; snakes and lizards, not previously known, became the dominant form of reptilian life, to be joined by warm-blooded creatures, birds and mammals. Plants, too, underwent similar transformation – flowers making their appearance (p. 216):

> Now here we have a tremendous series of special developments of life-forms, simultaneous in all parts of the earth, affecting both plants and animals, insects and vertebrates, whether living on the land, in the water, or in the air, all contemporaneous in a general sense, and all determining the transition from a lower to a very much higher grade of organisation.

Wallace cited the change in the balance of gases as a contributing factor. Plants absorbed carbon-dioxide, which became 'locked' underground as decaying vegetable matter sank into the ground, eventually becoming coal. Limestone, too, was composed of carbonate of lime, locking up carbon which might otherwise form carbon dioxide in the atmosphere. First amphibians, then other oxygen-breathing animals took advantage of the oxygen released by plant respiration.

Life of the Tertiary Period

The most extraordinary thing about the commencement of the tertiary period was not the disappearance of the dinosaurs and accompanying swimming and flying reptiles, but the appearance *all over the world* of mammals. These may have been small, but their appearance was sudden and universal. The Australian continent evolved marsupials, but these were warm-blooded and suckled their young, thus being a variation of mammal – definitely not reptilian. The only native mammals in Australia were flying bats. Wallace, correctly, assumed the dingo to be a recent human import. Once again, Wallace treated his reader to many illustrations, some of which may well have been new to his readers at that time.

Although found across the globe, there were distinct differences in species between the continents. Evolution had been simultaneous (by geological standards) but varied. Of particular interest were the giant mammals, which seemed to have existed on every continent but which had become extinct following the arrival of humans.

Wallace cited Mr. R. Lydelcker as having suggested that, as individuals have limited life-spans, so do species. This suggestion was later to be made by Niles Eldridge, one of the originators of the theory of 'punctuated evolution' (1972).

Some Extensions of Darwin's Theory

The theory of natural selection, as explained by Darwin in *The Origin of Species* (1859), left many unanswered questions, one of the most persistent being the origin of new organs, which would not have been able to perform their function in the earliest stage of their development and would not, therefore, have been 'selected'. This seemed to annoy Wallace, who felt that on-going criticism was caused by a failure of the criticiser to read printed responses. Wallace reproduced the response of Prof. Poulton (p. 258):

> Organs are rarely formed anew in an animal, but they are formed by modifications of pre-existing organs, so that, instead of having one beginning for each organ, we have to push the beginning further and further back, and find that a single organ accounts for several successive organs, or at any rate several functions instead of one.

This was a truly Darwinian explanation - the simple making of a statement, without any proof. The example offered was the modification of limbs, which are not organs and cannot be compared with, for example, the origin of the heart. Are we not justified in asking of what use was a heart without a circulatory system through which to pump blood, but how did the circulatory system come into being before there was a heart and blood to be circulated?

Wallace stated that our sense organs had evolved from protoplasm - even the most simple organism exhibited reactions, implying rudimentary senses which later evolved into organs of special sense. Rudiments of digestion, distribution of nutrients, etc., were similarly present in the simplest of living organisms. For Wallace, it made no sense to ask how an organ began; each was an integral part of protoplasmic potentiality. Natural selection did not attempt to solve the origin of life, only its evolution, which followed the 'law of perpetual variation'.

If it had been necessary for two or more variations to have happened simultaneously for a change to occur, that could be explained by the large number of individuals (thousands and millions) all varying slightly all the time producing the needed combination of adaptations, indeed, over millions of years, producing a surplus of possible combinations.

Throughout his life, Wallace remained remarkably loyal to Darwin, always attributing the origin of the theory of natural selection to Darwin, even calling the process Darwinism. Could that be, in part, because, the older he grew, the more deficits Wallace found with the theory? Natural selection might 'explain' neutral colours which seemed to have a protective function, but could not explain bright colours, especially those of birds and butterflies, whose intricate markings frequently far exceeded that required to attract a partner. Indeed, birds whose colours were very similar in both the male and female attracted mates just as easily as those in which the colours and markings were strikingly different. Wallace found it difficult to attribute to natural selection *alone* the different shapes and sizes of teeth throughout the whole vertebrate kingdom. Tropical chimpanzees were often clad with fur almost as dense as that of temperate, or even arctic, animals, while many tropical birds had feathers more dense than those of temperate regions, negating the claim that cold determined density of covering (p. 261):

> Neither is it certain that increased gazing improves the eyes, or loud noises the ears, or increased eating the stomach; so that we must conclude that this aid to the powers of natural selection is very partial in its action and that it has no claim to the important position sometimes given to it.

This could almost be seen as a repudiation of natural selection. It certainly placed Wallace in that (large) category of people who attributed simple *variation*, rather than novelty, to natural selection. Although initially appearing to defend Darwinism, Wallace had merely moved the question of the *origin* of organs one step further back; 'selection' only operated on pre-existing functions. Now Wallace specifically denied the role of 'female choice' in determining the development of ornamental colouring, etc., in males. The 'evidence' cited by Darwin in *The Descent of Man* was so scanty "I felt certain that some other cause was at work" (p. 261). Wallace was inclined to attribute to excess of 'energy' the production of 'excessive' features, the most energetic creatures being the most likely to survive and reproduce. In some, this 'excess' of 'energy' eventually became counter-productive, as in the case of excessive horn, tusk or shell growth. Existence of the species may eventually be threatened. Wallace agreed with Dr. Woodward, of the British Museum, that these were indications of 'old age' in a species coming to the end of its existence.

Wallace did not remind his reader that, according to the tenets of Darwinism, favourable changes were retained while unfavourable ones were eliminated. Clearly this had not happened. It seems almost as if Wallace was drawing his reader's attention to Darwinism, not to support it, but to undermine it.

Wallace discussed, with approval, the theories of Weismann regarding germinal selection, whose concept of a three-tiered process, involving *ids, determinants* and *biophors*, surprisingly closely matches today's chromosomes, genes and DNA. Weismann's suggestion that, because every cell in the body was living, *ids, determinants* and *biophors* would not only need nutrition, but would vie for it, some being more successful – and therefore growing stronger – than others, offered a solution for some body parts, such as tusks, growing inordinantly large, while others, such as the pelvis of the whale, would continue to shrink, even though no longer subject to the pressures of selection.

Consideration of the processes of reproduction had confirmed for Wallace that such miraculous events could not have become established without the guidance of a great Mind and that Mind had brought the universe, the earth, its living creatures and Man into being for a Purpose. Earthly life was but preparation for a future life, future development. There was to be no 'Rest in Peace' for all eternity! Knowledge and admiration of Nature would bring our minds into the state necessary for further development in the world beyond.

Birds and Insects: as proofs of an organising and directive Life-Principle

The colours of the wings of birds and insects, such as butterflies and moths, far greater than necessary for any process of selection (as proven by those which were plainly coloured), the structure of wings of birds, the process of metamorphosis of insects, all were marvels beyond explanation. The feathers of birds were particularly extraordinary because, like hair on mammals, the feather is 'dead'; there is no blood circulation. Lack of circulation meant lack of repair. Both hair and feathers were replaced, either constantly and gradually, or by an annual moult, which was completed with extraordinary efficiency in a remarkably short period of time.

Nature of Growth

Protoplasm was composed of cells; cells were composed of carbon, hydrogen, nitrogen and oxygen, along with small amounts of eight other elements: sulphur, phosphorus, chlorine, potassium, sodium, magnesium, calcium and iron. Six others: silicon, fluorine, bromine, iodine, aluminium and manganese, were occasionally found. The idea that the cell, the basic form of life, was simple had had to be abandoned. The more that was discovered about the cell, the more complicated it became. Three basic elements formed both fats and carbohydrates: carbon, hydrogen and oxygen. In animals these three elements combined to form fat, in plants they formed carbohydrate. The addition of nitrogen produced protein in both plants and animals (or proteid, as it was then called). That so small a number of elements should be responsible for such an extraordinary array of results was truly almost beyond comprehension. Not only were there (and had there been) an inestimable number of different forms, but each contained organs/structures, totally different in appearance and properties. In animals, these same elements were the basic constituents of bone, muscle, nerve, etc., and in plants of bark, leaf and flower. How could this be? Identifying the components was an amazing achievement, but did not *explain* how such diversity had come into being.

Hæmoglobin consisted of carbon, hydrogen, nitrogen and oxygen, together with iron and sulphur. Human hæmoglobin contained 1894 atoms while the hæmoglobin of the horse contained 2304. These figures had been drawn from the work of Prof. Max Verworn, who denied the existence of a 'vital force', holding that 'life' resided in the cell, in the protoplasm. Verworn acknowledged that there was a difference between a living cell and a dead one, even though their chemical composition was the same., but he acknowledged no directive or organising power.

Wallace returned to consideration of the wing of a bird, a single one of which consisted of more than a million parts, and, in many cases, of a truly astonishing array of colours. Wallace rejected the 'physiological units' of Herbert Spencer, the 'pangenesis' of Darwin, the 'germ plasm' of Weismann as explanations of these 'mysterious' events. If the feather of a bird was a thing of wonder, even more wonderful was the process of metamorphosis which converted a plain, earth-bound caterpillar into a spectacular, flying butterfly or moth. There were many other insects, which also underwent metamorphosis, if not quite as spectacular, every bit as mystifying. Wallace could not accept these wonders as being simply 'mechanical' or 'chemical'.

General Adaptations of Plants, Animals and Man

Wallace discussed the use in nature of colour, with particular regard to that of flowers to attract insects for cross-pollination. Wallace doubted that small-brained insects were able to perceive the full spectrum of colour that could a large-brained human. Since humans did not need colour vision for reproduction, or even to find food, there must be some other reason we were gifted with this sight. Wallace had come to the conclusion that that purpose was the lifting of our moral and spiritual nature, which occurred when we were awed and inspired by the beauty of nature - a daily vision completely unnecessary for our survival, but preparatory "for a higher and more enduring life of continued progress" (p. 312).

Hæckel, Spencer and most of the followers of Darwin were strongly antagonistic to the idea that the Earth had been created for the advancement of Man. "Darwin himself was quite distressed at my rejection of his own conclusion – that even man's highest qualities and powers had been developed out of those of the lower animals by natural or sexual selection". Wallace had long maintained that man's higher faculties, art and music, for example, had "no survival value in the struggle for existence" (p. 315). He never openly questioned the role of natural selection in the establishment of physical change (variation), although happy (relieved?) to accept Weismann's extension to sub-cellular level to explain over-development.

The Vegetable Kingdom in its Special Relation to Manifestation

Warming to his theme, Wallace drew attention to the many different types of wood provided by the many different types of trees, differences which had been put to different uses by man, but which otherwise served no specific purpose in nature – 'one type fits all' would have been quite sufficient if the evolution of 'trees' was nature's sole purpose. Human's had not only used hard wood to build boats to explore the world, but woods with other characteristics for his habitation and his weapons, such as the flexible yew for his strongest bow. He had used, not only trees, but other vegetation, to provide his pharmacopœpia, oils for cooking and lighting, resins and gums for art, dyes, perfumes, spices for taste, as well as others for gentle medicine, tea, coffee, sugar, wine – so many uses unknown to animals. Were all properties of vegetables provided by nature *solely* for the benefit of the plant – or the animals feeding on them or living in them? Was it not possible that future use by Man had been foreseen by some Directive Mind? (This was not a new idea. The book of *Genesis* described herbs as being 'for the healing of Man'.)

The conditions under which so many variations of life had been formed were remarkably uniform over quite large areas. All alike built their structures from the same elements, yet scientists had been unable to reproduce even the simplest. (To this day, scientists have been unable to produce milk in the laboratory.) Yet nature, starting from the simplest, smallest seed, produced a multitude of vegetable forms, from the smallest of plants growing underfoot to the mightiest of trees in the forest. Was 'blind' nature really that much more clever than the cleverest human? Heredity, as well as nutrition, assimilation and growth, tended to be taken for granted by many scientists, but not by Weismann.

In his early life, Wallace wrote that he had been content to accept this position – but not any more! He quoted Darwin saying that "Natural Selection has been the most important *but not the exclusive* means of modification" (p. 333. Italics added). Even Hæckel had been driven to postulate "mind, soul, or volition" not only in every cell but in each organic molecule or physiological unit (p. 333). I do not believe Hæckel was 'driven' to this conclusion. I believe it was the foundation of his teaching, which Wallace had misunderstood.

Wallace concluded his chapter by once again urging authorities to admit the necessity of some mind, some organising and directive power in nature, some vast intelligence, some pervading spirit, which guided lower forces in accordance with a pre-ordained system of evolution designed to fit humanity for a higher state of existence as spiritual beings.

The Mystery of the Cell

The cell, while acknowledged as being the fundamental basis of all life, had, for many years, been thought to be structureless. Improved microscopes had now shown the cell to consist of three parts: a central, slightly granular, body, a jelly-like mass and another, smaller, transparent, globular portion which looked like an air-bubble, This "contractile vacuole" would expand, then, when it had reached its full size (about a quarter or one-fifth the diameter of the cell), would suddenly disappear, reappearing a short time later, when the process would be repeated. Amœba were single cell organisms, but their shape varied greatly. Most had arm-like processes jutting out in various directions. These simple cells had the power to absorb any particle of organic matter with which they came into contact, which would 'disappear', showing both that they needed nutrition and that they could absorb and 'digest' it. The 'contractile vacuole' was believed to expel carbon dioxide and any other waste products.

Single-celled forms of life were so numerous that they had been classified into five classes. Within the class *Rhizopodia*, were found the beautiful *Foraminifera*, which, despite consisting of only a single cell, were able to make 'shells' of small, inorganic particles. Other *Rhizopodia* were the *Nummilites*, whose coiled shells had contributed to the formation of great masses of limestone. Wallace described others, but space here forbids further extrapolation. They may have no individual organs, but they could digest, respire, reproduce, as could any more complex living creature.

Wallace attributed to Louis Agassiz the concept of the cell as being the basis of life, giving 1840 as the date of this "greatest discovery in the natural sciences in modern times" (p. 337). I have already pointed out that Lamarck had made this discovery towards the end of the eighteenth century.

Different names had been given to the energy which inspired the cell: vital force, cell-soul, organising power. No 'natural' term made clear from whence this energy came and, if 'organised', then organised by whom? Once again, Wallace made his claim that this energy was the expression of a great and powerful Mind – of unknown origin.

Coloured dye had allowed clearer vision of the interior of the cell. The parts of the nucleus most clearly coloured were known as chromosomes. Although their function was not fully understood., they were clearly associated with reproduction and various early stages of this process had been described in some detail. However, since chromosomes occurred in every cell, not merely the reproductive cells, their function was not believed to be *solely* that of reproduction. Explaining *what* happened, no matter how incredible, was not the same thing as explaining *how* or *why* it happened.

Wallace rejected the philosophical position that the Universe was eternal – it had no beginning and, therefore, no Creator. He claimed that ere the first matter came into existence, a 'Being' far higher than man would have needed to initiate and guide the course of its development.

The Elements and Water, in Relation to the Life-World

Microscopic analysis of protein molecules continued to amaze. The estimate of the number of atoms had increased from two thousand to thirty thousand! Carbon, hydrogen, oxygen and nitrogen contributed the majority of these atoms, which produced many different forms of protein molecule, more than seventy combinations already having been identified. The same elements combined in different ways to produce substances with very different properties – cellulose, dextrine and starch being completely different in relation to solubility, for example, despite all containing six atoms of carbon, ten of hydrogen and five of oxygen. The addition of one element of nitrogen to carbon and hydrogen produced either bensonitrile or phenylisocyanide, simply by the reversal of the position of one of the carbon atoms with that of the nitrogen atom. Bensonitrile was harmless, phenylisocyanide was very poisonous.

Even atoms were now known not to be unitary substances, but composed of electrons and 'matter'. What had started out as a search for simplicity – basic unit of life – was becoming more complex with every passing year.

Wallace was puzzled by the fact that, of the more than seventy elements now known, less than a quarter appeared to serve any useful purpose, either in the structure of the earth as a planet or of the living beings developed upon it. Oxygen formed about 47% of the mass of the globe, silicon 25%, aluminium 8% and iron 7%. Calcium, magnesium, sodium and potassium contributed between 2% and 4%, while no other element contributed as much as 1%, many less than 1/50th to 1/100th of 1%. Of what use were these minor elements? Wallace gave no percentage for hydrogen at that point, but stressed its importance as a component of water, without which life would be impossible. In a table, he listed hydrogen and nitrogen each as "0.1%?" (p. 358).

Seven metals have been known to humans from antiquity: gold, silver, copper, iron, tin, lead and mercury. All were widely distributed and easily accessible, but only iron seemed to serve a useful (essential) purpose, either to the earth itself or to the vegetable and animal kingdoms. Gold and silver had called forth Man's creative and artistic abilities. Ornaments, coins, drinking vessels, some of exquisite beauty, had survived from earliest civilisations. Other metals, such as iron, copper and tin, had been utilized in other constructions, yet these metals had existed, untouched and unused, for billions of years before the coming of Man.

Even more striking was the combining of substances to form glass. The silicates of sodium and potassium were soluble in water, those of calcium soluble in acid, yet, combined in certain ways, they produced insoluble, clear, and to some extent, plastic glass. Glass could not only be polished, cut, shaped and blown into a multitude of different shapes, some useful, some ornamental, some both, it could also be coloured. Glass not only formed the windows which provided light for our homes, it rendered possible the microscope, the telescope and the spectroscope which enabled us to study the most minute, as well as the most vast, secrets of the universe. Radium had recently been discovered and was opening up new horizons.

Wallace felt that the 'purpose' of the creation of these elements and the 'purpose' of the creation of humans was inextricably linked.

The mystery of carbon

It seemed that carbon only existed in solid form as a product of vegetation – all animal life being dependent upon vegetable matter for its nutrition, directly or indirectly. It did exist in gaseous form as carbon dioxide, forming 1/2000th of our atmosphere. Today, it is stated to be 0.4%. With the aid of chlorophyll, which the plant manufactured in its leaves, vegetable matter was able to conduct complex chemical actions, which the scientists performed with difficulty, if at all, in their laboratories.

Carbon was the one element never absent from living matter. Carbon dioxide being soluble in water, life could exist in seas, rivers and lakes, as well as upon the earth. Large amounts of carbon were found in limestone rocks, which formed a substantial part of the Earth's surface. This was believed to have been formed by deposition of marine animals, leaving one to marvel at the copiousness of life in the waters of ancient times.

Water's unique properties had long been the subject of wonder, but, in its silent way, carbon was no less incredible as the facilitator of all that made our world so extraordinary.

Is nature cruel? The purpose and limitation of pain

An unwelcome outcome of the increasing acceptance of evolution through the survival of the fittest was the increasing awareness of the universality of destruction, its constant operation seemingly essential to progress. This awareness coincided with an increased compassion extended by humans towards animals, with cruelty to animals having become a criminal offence. How could this cruelty, this destruction, be reconciled with the Christian concept of a God of Love? Yet Christians (or, at least, some of them) allowed this same God of Love to condemn souls, even those of innocent, unbaptised, babies, to suffer the eternity of Hell fire.

Wallace claimed that pain had a purpose, was, indeed, essential to the development of life. It was our inbuilt alarm system, warning us of danger. It was his belief that lower forms of life, which bred rapidly, in great numbers, and whose purpose seemed to be to provide nutrition for higher forms (since many survived for so short a time), felt little, if any, pain. "For why should they? They exist to be devoured" (p. 375). As higher forms evolved, some pain was necessary to teach the young not to try to exceed their powers in climbing, jumping or flying. In Nature, the aim was usually quick death, the quicker the better. Poisonous bites or stings were usually designed to render the victim numb, or unconscious. (Snake bites hurt humans, but snake venom was not designed to kill a creature the size of a human. No snake *seeks* human prey.) Human survivors of attacks by wild animals testified that, at the time of the attack, they experienced little, if any, pain. The same was true of other accidents. A state of dissociation existed for a short time. It was survivors who suffered pain – and in nature there were few survivors!

Wallace suggested that humans may have lost their protective covering of hair to *increase* their sensitivity, that the increased sensitivity of our nervous system was necessary for our mental (and spiritual) advancement. Wallace cited the high tolerance to pain which seemed to be exhibited by native people, such as the Australian aborigine, whose daily lives had not been exposed to the dangers of the needle and the knife - and countless other items in daily use by civilized peoples, some intended for the purpose of causing harm (guns, etc.), others causing pain by accident. In Nature, animals hunt and kill for food, not amusement. Just because (some) humans enjoyed inflicting pain, it must not be assumed that Nature did also.

Wallace stressed that his claim that animals suffered less pain than humans was not to be taken as an endorsement of vivisection. Quite apart from any suffering inflicted upon the animal, the practice also induced callousness in the participant. Much was totally unwarranted, being merely a reproduction of similar 'experiments' carried out by others, solely for educational purposes. Vivisection was brutalising, disgusting and immoral.

Infinite Variety the Law of the Universe – Conclusion

The great diversity of living forms had long been recognized, although never more so than at the time Wallace was writing, thanks to the opening up of the world to travellers from distant lands, who were becoming aware of creatures they had never before known existed. This diversity had come about, over a great expanse of time, due to the constantly changing environment, an environment which had, itself, evolved over time as organic matter started to contribute to, and shape, its form, aided by the raising and lowering of the earth's crust above and below the waters of the sea.

Wonderful as were the modern inventions of man, they paled into insignificance when compared with the bringing into being of the living, moving, self-reproducing structures which populate the Earth, the work, surely, of a Mind many millions of times greater than that of the human?

In a similar way, human understanding of the great

variety of inorganic substances which form our Earth had expanded over the nineteenth century, as more and more elements had been identified, many very rare. Concomitantly, there had been a great increase in our understanding of the complexity of their combinations. Even more incredible was the growing understanding that it was possible for humans to create new combinations, new substances, never before dreamed of.

A host of other discoveries had been made. Electricity, for example. "... the more it was known the less intelligible it became" (p. 387). The more we learned about the world of matter, the more complex it became. Scientists were beginning to understand the complexity of the atom, which had previously been thought to be the simplest of all substances.

Wallace suggested that the antagonism which existed between science and religion was caused by the extreme views held by both parties. The one claimed that there were only blind forces at work, the other that the force (God) was infinite, eternal, omnipotent and that everything which exists, or has ever existed, was the work of this one force alone. Wallace believed that there was an infinite series of graded beings between living beings on this earth and the Deity: "... each successive grade having higher and higher powers in regard to the origination, the development, and the control of the universe" (p. 398). Wallace continued: "... there may have been a vast system of co-operation of such grades of being, from a very high grade of power and intelligence down to those unconscious or almost unconscious 'cell-souls' posited by Hæckel ..." (p. 398). The original thought may have emanated from the Deity, but subordinate beings may have been responsible for its implementation. "The vast whole is therefor a manifestation of his power – perhaps of his very self – but by the agency of his ministering angels through many descending grades of intelligence and power" (pp. 395-396).

Wallace stated that these were the teachings of modern spiritualism. These ideas softened Wallace's insistence that, not only the Earth, but the Universe, had been created for the advancement of humans to another level of existence, since these philosophies postulated gradual advancement from the most basic form of life, through repeated incarnations in a multitude of forms, with gradually increasing complexity, to human existence, the final one on this Earth merely preparatory for greater things to come.

Wallace concluded the penultimate paragraph of his book (p. 400):

> We conclude, therefore, that there are now in the universe infinite grades of power, infinite grades of knowledge and wisdom, infinite grades of influence of higher beings upon lower. Holding this opinion, I have suggested that this vast and wonderful universe, with its almost infinite variety of forms, motions, and reactions of part upon part, from suns and systems up to plant life, animal life, and the human living soul, has ever required and still requires the continuous co-ordinated agency of myriads of such intelligences.

It has not been an easy task, attempting to condense into but a few pages the wealth of information provided by Wallace in four hundred. My aim has been two-fold. Firstly, I have endeavoured to portray something of the immense industry and intellect which Wallace brought to his work - his life's work. Secondly, I hope I have portrayed something of the immense awe and wonder Wallace felt for that Being which he had come to believe cared so much for each and every one of us, for all of Creation.

Chapter 19

Farewell

Wallace had been but forty-nine years old when he returned to England in the Spring of 1862. In the last part of the last chapter of the first book he wrote (*The Malay Archipelago* (1869)), he recorded his 'observations'. These show that this young man, who left school at fourteen, had, in what was little more than half his life-time, acquired a wisdom and understanding not attained by many after years of academic study.

My copy of *The Malay Archipelago* is a *Penguin Classic*, printed in 2016. I have no idea whether Wallace in any way amended his first edition or whether, even, the 'observations' were added later. Did the thoughts here expressed influence his later work or did his later work merely confirm the thoughts here expressed?

Whatever the case may be, there can be no better summary of this man, his life, his work, and the philosophy which drove him than that which he, himself, wrote.

The Malay Archipelago (1869/2016)

Chapter 40: pp.723-726

I have now concluded my task. I have given, in more or less detail, a sketch of my eight years' wanderings among the largest and the most luxuriant islands which adorn our earth's surface. I have endeavoured to convey my impressions of their scenery, their vegetation, their animal productions, and their human inhabitants. I have dwelt at some length on the varied and interesting problems they offer to the student of nature. Before bidding my readers farewell, I wish to make a few observations on a subject of yet higher interest and deeper importance, which the contemplation of savage life has suggested, and on which I believe that the civilized can learn something from the savage man.

We most of us believe that we, the higher races, have progressed and are progressing. If so, there must be some state of perfection, some ultimate goal, which we may never reach, but to which all true progress must bring us nearer. What is this ideally perfect social state towards which mankind ever has been, and still is tending? Our best thinkers maintain, that it is a state of individual freedom and self-government, rendered possible by the equal development and just balance of the intellectual, moral and physical parts of our nature, - a state in which we shall each be so perfectly fitted for a social existence, by knowing what is right, and at the same time feeling an irresistible impulse to do what we know to be right, that all laws and all punishments shall be unnecessary. In such a state every man would have a sufficiently well-balanced intellectual organization, to understand the moral law in all its details, and would require no other motive but the free impulses of his own nature to obey that law.

Now it is very remarkable, that among people in a very low stage of civilization, we find some approach to such a perfect social state. I have lived with communities of savages in South America and in the East, who have no laws or law courts but the public opinion of the village freely expressed. Each man scrupulously respects the rights of his fellow, and any infraction of those rights rarely or never takes place. In such a community, all are nearly equal. There are none of those wide distinctions, of education and ignorance, wealth and poverty, master and servant, which are the product of our civilization; there is none of that wide-spread division of labour, which, while it increases wealth, produces also conflicting interests; there is not that severe competition and struggle for existence, or for wealth, which the dense population of civilized countries inevitably creates. All incitements to great crimes are thus wanting, and petty ones are repressed, partly by the influence of public opinion, but chiefly by that natural sense of justice and of his neighbour's rights, which seems to be, in some degree, inherent in every race of man.

Now, although we have progressed vastly beyond the savage state in intellectual achievements, we have not advanced equally in morals. It is true that among those classes who have no wants that cannot be easily supplied, and among whom public opinion has great influence, the rights of others are fully respected. It is true, also, that we have vastly extended the sphere of those rights, and include within them all the brotherhood of man. But it is not too much to say, that the mass of our populations have not at all advanced beyond the savage code of morals, and have in many cases sunk below it. A deficient morality is the great blot of modern civilization, and the greatest hindrance to true progress.

During the last century, and especially in the last thirty years, our intellectual and material advancement has been too quickly achieved for us to reap the full benefits of it. Our mastery over the forces of nature has led to a rapid growth of population, and a vast accumulation of wealth; but these have brought with them such an amount of poverty and crime, and have fostered the growth of so much sordid feeling and so many fierce passions, that it may well be questioned, whether the mental and moral status of our population has not on the average been lowered, and whether the evil has not overbalanced the good. Compared with our wondrous progress in physical science and its practical applications, our system of government, of administering justice, of national education, and our whole social and moral organization, remains in a state of barbarism. And if we continue to devote our chief energies to the utilizing of our knowledge of the laws of nature with the view of still further extending our commerce and our wealth, the evils which necessarily accompany these when too eagerly pursued, may increase to such gigantic dimensions as to be beyond our power to alleviate.

We should now clearly recognise the fact, that the wealth and knowledge and culture of *the few* do not constitute civilization, and do not of themselves advance us towards the 'perfect social state.' Our vast manufacturing system, our gigantic commerce, our crowded towns and cities, support and continually renew a mass of human misery and crime *absolutely* greater than has ever existed before. They create and maintain in life-long labour an ever-increasing army, whose lot is the more hard to bear, by contrast with the pleasures, the comforts, and the luxury which they see everywhere around them, but which they can never hope to enjoy; and who, in this respect, are worse off than the savage in the midst of his tribe.

This is not a result to boast of, or to be satisfied with; and, until there is a more general recognition of this failure of our civilization - resulting mainly from our neglect to train and develop more thoroughly the sympathetic feelings and moral faculties of our nature, and to allow them a lager share of influence in our legislation, our commerce and our whole social organization – we shall never, as regards the whole community, attain any real or important superiority over the better class of savages.

This is the lesson I have been taught by my observations of uncivilized man. I now bid my readers – Farewell!

Tributes

The Rev. James Marchant finished this, the last of Wallace's published books, with an account of the tributes paid to Wallace's after his death.

An anonymous person sent this verse, with a bunch of Lily-of-the-Valley:

As sets the sun in fine autumnal calm
So dost thou leave us. Thou not least but last
Link with that rare and gallant little band
Of seekers after truth, whose days, though past,
Shed lustre on the hist'ry of their land.
And thou, O Wallace, thine the added charm
Of modesty, thy mem'ry to embalm.

Marchant records the letter, written by Wallace, initially refusing the honorary degree offered by Oxford University, which decision his friends finally persuaded him to reverse. Wallace had written that he hated public ceremonials and only wanted to be left in peaceful obscurity. Wallace similarly rejected proferred membership of the Royal Society, writing that he felt 'almost ashamed of the amount of reputation and honour that has been awarded me' having done so little in the way of what was usually accepted as 'scientific' work. He described his own work as 'amateurish'. He derived more pleasure from contemplation of the leaves and flowers of the plants in his garden but, not wanting to appear ungrateful, he was prepared to accept the Fellowship, if that was what others truly wanted. He did decline offers of honorary degrees from the Universities of Cambridge and Wales.

Wallace took as much care answering letters from correspondents of 'lowly' position as he did that of the most educated. Every sincere enquiry deserved a considered response.

Wallace often referred to himself as 'idle' or 'lazy'. Marchant threw another light upon his behaviour (pp. 463-464):

> ... he had that original insight and creative faculty which enabled him to see, often as by flashlight, the explanation which had remained hidden from the eyes of the man who was most familiar with the particular facts, and he elaborated it with quickening pulse, anxious to put down the whole conception which filled his mind lest some portion of it should escape him ... His idleness was his way of describing his long musings, waiting the bidding of her whom God inspires – Truth, who often hides her face from the clouded eyes of man. For hours, days, weeks, he was disinclined to work ... then, apparently suddenly, whilst in one of his day dreams, or in a fever (as at Ternate, to recall the historical episode when the theory of Natural Selection struck him), an explanation, a theory, a discovery, the plan of a new book, came to him like a flash of light, and with the plan, the material, the arguments, the illustrations; the words came tumbling one over the other in his brain, as suddenly the idleness vanished and work, eager, prolonged, unwearying, filled his days and months and years until the message was written down and the task fully accomplished.

Death came to Wallace in his sleep. It was suggested that he be buried in Westminster Abbey, beside Charles Darwin, but his wife and family expressed the opinion that this was not Wallace's wish. On 10th November, 1913, he was buried in a little cemetery at Broadstone "on a pine-laid hill swept by ocean breezes" (p. 472). It was a simple ceremony, conducted by the Bishop of Salisbury, attended by a number of representatives of various organisations. His monument was a fossil tree-trunk from the Portland beds, erected upon a base of Portland stone, simply engraved with his name and dates of birth and death. The following year, his wife, Annie, was buried in the same grave. It had been a very happy marriage. The two had met because of her father's love of flowers, which she had inherited, thus being able to help Wallace with his botanical work and support him in his many endeavours.

A committee was formed to petition for a memorial plaque in Wallace's honour to be placed next to that of Darwin in Westminster Abbey. On 1st November, 1915, this was done, along with plaques commemorating Sir Joseph Hooker and Lord Lister, who had died in 1911 and 1912, Wallace in 1913. In his address, the Dean stated that small men may need to seek greatness, but such seeking was not needed by those who were truly great. Wallace was one such great man.

November 1st - In Celtic times, this day was the most sacred of the year, known as 'All Hallows' - 'All Holy Day'. The evening before was 'Hallow Evening' - or 'Hallow E'en'. According to the Druids, this was the time when the veil between the two worlds was at its thinnest, when it was easiest for our departed loved ones to make communication with us, when they could sometimes be seen by us, even spoken to.

No better day could have been chosen to honour the memory of that ardent Spiritualist who, I am sure, watched the proceedings, closely, with humble pride.

Epilogue
The Wonder of Wallace

Wallace was a wonderful man – a 'wonder full' man. His 'wonder' started as a child with his curiosity about plants. He specifically mentions his reading of Chamber's *Vestiges of Creation*, but this book was a comprehensive one, covering geology of the Earth and formation of the stars, so to it alone cannot be attributed Wallace's early fascination with plants, with flowers. The English and Welsh countryside in which he grew up would have been awash with flowers, from the tiny violet, almost hidden beneath the grass to the bluebells carpeting the woods and the hillsides awash with daffodils, as immortalized by Wordsworth – not to forget the primroses, the daisies, the dandelions and so, so much more.

It took a certain strength of character for the young man to leave his family, most of his friends, his job, everything he knew, to travel thousands of miles to a little known country, to explore, with his true friend, Bates, land which no white man had explored before. He managed but few such excursions, most of his travels being in a 'little-known' rather than an 'unknown' land.

The quiet strength of Wallace's character – his obstinacy? – was further demonstrated by his decision to travel again, this time to a part of the world where he was virtually guaranteed to be able to visit places yet unexplored by white man. His study had now extended to animals and humans. After his return home, his interest extended from small groups of humans to large, from one planet to many, from one sun to many, from one galaxy to many, from one Universe to many?

Everything which took his interest, he studied as deeply as he could, yet, despite the growing recognition he received, he always remained quiet and humble. He was kind and generous, loyal, with a gentle sense of humour which enabled his expressions of grievances to be made without rancour.

I truly believe Wallace to be among the greatest Englishmen ever to be born. Indeed, in my estimation he is the greatest. He may not have invented the steam engine or recognized the reality of gravity, but for the sheer breadth and depth of his knowledge, of his never ceasing work dedicated, not to the acquisition of personal wealth, but to the welfare of his fellow human beings, I believe he has no equal.

A man full of wonder - a truly wonderful man.

The Grave of Alfred Russel Wallace

Appendix I
Biography of Wallace from
The Revolt of Democracy (1913: pp. 81-119)
(*sic* for spelling and punctuation)

The Life Story of the Author

Like a watchman on a lonely tower, with keen vision and responsive mind and heart, Alfred Russel Wallace has observed more change and development of scientific and social opinion and a higher advance of the tide of knowledge across the shores of human speculation and ignorance than any other scientist.

Yet, unlike that solitary watchman, he himself has been, and is, an active pioneer of scientific revelation. For a long time he has been, and is, an active pioneer of scientific revelation. For a long time he was the voice of a system of truths so far ahead of the attainments of his generation that to his contemporaries much of his teaching seemed rank heresy and almost blasphemy; but, like a true prophet, he has had not only the patience but the opportunity given him to see most of his discoveries and his teachings incorporated into the stately palace of truth.

When he was born in 1823, our world, as we know it to-day (a composite thing of multitudinous energies thirled to the service and utility of mankind) had scarcely come into existence. He has seen the formidable and mysterious powers of electricity enslaved to the service of the ordinary affairs of daily life, and has watched with glowing interest the coming of the motor-car and the flying machine. He has lived under five British sovereigns, has witnessed the spread and development of railways, and the adoption of steam for navigation, the supersession of the wooden walls of the steel bulwarks of Britannia, and other changes beyond record in the practical application of scientific discoveries. When he was a boy, photography was a plaything, the electric telegraph a mere experiment, the penny post unknown, the newspaper a luxury of the few, the material world, as a whole, a vast and impenetrable wilderness, continent separated from continent by wide-stretching seas, traversed only by daring spirits.

He has seen the material world of mere geography shrink till now it can be girdled by the commonest message in a matter of minutes; he has seen the newspaper in every home, the simplest word of love carried the whole empire over for one penny, the criminal and the outcast treated like sinners to be redeemed who are often "more sinned against than sinning".

To have seen so much is to make any man a centre of human interest. To hear the now aged naturalist tell of what his life has been awakens vivid response even in the heart of the most apathetic. But to know that all the while he was no shirker in life's upward march, but himself a profound thinker, a ceaseless searcher, a sagacious discoverer, and that most of his theories and opinions, which had been scouted by thinkers for many years, are now sound and current coin in the treasure house of true science, is gratefully to acknowledge him as one of the greatest sons of his age and a shining benefactor for all time.

His father, Thomas Vere Wallace, a briefless lawyer, was also an experimenter. He had a family of nine children. It was little satisfaction that the number of the Muses was the same, for the Muses were not confronted by the problem of bread-and-butter which perturbs a human family. He was not of a practical turn of mind, and his private income was not sufficient to provide for the necessities of is children. But he was a man of literary taste, and he embarked upon a venture of a very speculative nature, namely the publication of an Art Magazine, which wellnigh exhausted what means he still possessed. He therefore had to leave London, and transferred his household goods and gods to the town of Usk in Monmouthshire, where he tried the new experiment of economy. Here Alfred, the last but one of the nine, was born, and here he spent the first four years of his life, with no need to go outside of his own house for a plentiful supply of playmates. In 1828 the family made another move - to Hertford - and there they remained for about nine years. At the grammar school of that provincial town young Wallace received the only regular education, in the popular acceptance of the term, which was to be the basis of his wider intellectual development.

With him it is different than with most men of note, for his contemporaries, having having all now passed into the greater silence, there is no source of anecdotal reminiscence and estimate of his boyhood left, except his own memory. It is always of pleasing interest to know what a boy's comrades thought of him, what he did or said to make the keen critics of the schoolroom or the playground take note of him, and wherein, if anywhere, he differed from his fellows. One thing, at any rate, is certain: the mode of formal instruction under the shadow of which he passed, in those swift enough years at the Hertford Grammar School, was not of a sort to benefit deeply such a mind as his. Geography was a list of towns and rivers; history little more than tables of dates, all to be learned by rote, without regard to the causal origins of such a thing as a country, a kingdom a river, or the achievement of human effort which gave memorableness to the figures of a calendar. To such a youth, who no doubt from the first looked over the shoulder of to-day back into the misty yesterdays out of which to-day emerges, asking the *Why* as anxiously as the *What* of things, this schooling must have been very unsatisfying. As he himself says: "The labour and mental effort to one who, like myself, has little verbal memory was very painful; and though the result has been a somewhat useful acquisition during life, I cannot but think that the same amount of mental exertion, wisely directed, might have produced far greater and more generally useful results," It was also most natural that the eclectic method of historical study should have most strongly appealed to him, so that he can say, "Whatever little knowledge of history I have ever acquired has been derived more from Shakespeare's plays and from good historical novels than from anything I learned at school."

To watch men and women who thought, toiled and achieved, rough-hewing life's obstacles into instruments of life's victories, is of greater moment than reading tombstone records or having one's name written up on a schoolroom slate. The method of visualised humanities, breathing, living and doing, is ages in advance of that which thinks of history as being mainly great men sitting in their homes in an anatomical museum, labelled "History" Latin grammar, and, in the higher classes, Latin translation - these were the subjects chiefly taught.

But Wallace's life was, fortunately, independent of, and lifted out of such a cramping environment by other circumstances, which such narrow schemes could not control. His father was a book-lover and belonged to a book club, and the soul of the lad was enriched by a constantly flowing stream of suggestive and elevating literature. A bookman's home is the best of universities. His father frequently read aloud in the evenings from such books as Mungo Park's "African Travels," along with those of Denham and Clapperton. Then there was the sunshine that scintillates through Hood's "Comic Annual" and the grave and gay of "Gulliver's Travels" and of "Robinson Crusoe," and the deep-toned gravity and humour, with knowledge of the human heart unparalleled in "The Pilgrim's Progress." Thus the companionship and wisdom of such creations of human genius enlightened the ready mind of the growing youth by the evening fire of that Hertford home. His father for some part of his residence in Hertford was librarian of the town library, and there, in the quickening presence of books, young Wallace spent many of his leisure hours.

When he left school, at the age of fourteen, he stayed for a short time with his elder brother John, who was at that time apprenticed to a builder in London. It was at this period that he first came in contact with people of advanced political and religious opinions, and read such works as Paine's "Age of Reason." He also met followers of Robert Owen, the founder of the Socialist Movement in England. Robert Owen's fundamental principle was that the character of the individual was formed *for* him, and not *by* himself: first, by heredity, which gives him his mental disposition with all its powers and tendencies, its good and bad qualities; and, secondly, by environment, including education and surroundings from earliest infancy, which always modify the original character for better or for worse.

Young Wallace, whose upbringing had been strictly orthodox, was greatly impressed by these doctrines; and the ideas they inspired, though latent for fifty years, no doubt largely influenced his thoughts and his writings when he ultimately turned his attention from purely scientific to social and political subjects.

After a stay of a few months in London he joined his eldest brother William, who was a surveyor; and for the next four years (1837 to 1841) they were occupied together in surveying in the counties of Bedfordshire, Herefordshire, Radnorshire and Brecknockshire. Some of this work was in connection with the various Enclosure Acts by which the landlords obtained powers to enclose waste lands and commons, under the pretext of bringing them into cultivation. The result of these measures was that the cottagers were deprived of the means of keeping their few cattle, pigs, or ponies, while the enclosed land was often not cultivated at all, or, in the course of time was converted into building land or into game reserves, so that the intention of the Acts of Parliament was ignored, and the poor people were driven to the towns, where, unfit to compete, they sank into the deeper poverty of slumdom.

Some of the surveys had to do with new railways which were being projected all over the country at that time, many of them doomed never to come into being, and many being mere clap-trap schemes of the money-sucking adventurers.

It was owing to this open-air life, with plenty of leisure amidst beautiful country, that Wallace's observant mind was drawn into loving observation, which developed into more than companionship with the flowers and insects which everywhere abounded in such vast variety.

From such close interest he soon passed on to a serious study, in pursuit of which he commenced to form a scientific collection of the wild flowers and the insects he met with.

During his residence in Neath in 1841 he began to extend his knowledge in physics, astronomy, and phrenology, that half-blind groping after a greater science, taking advantage of popular lectures on those subjects and of such books as he could obtain.

In 1843 his father died, and in the following year there being then little in the way of surveying to do, Wallace obtained a situation as drawing-master at the Collegiate School at Leicester. His two years' residence in this town was to have an important influence upon his future career, for it was here Principles of Population." This pioneer work, after his long study and observation of tropical fauna, supplied the inspiration which clinched the theory of evolution he originated in 1858.

At this time one other important event happened which was to influence his ideas in later years, namely, a demonstration of the phenomenon of mesmerism, which interested him so much that he practised, and eventually succeeded in mesmerising some of his pupils.

After remaining in Leicester for two years, Wallace returned to Neath, where he and his brother John started in business as architects and builders. Hither they brought their mother and sister to live with them.

He was now twenty-three years of age, and over six feet tall. He had acquired a large store of varied knowledge, and made his first appearance as a lecturer. He delivered a series of expositions of scientific subjects, dealing manly with physics, at the Neath Mechanics' Institute, the building which he and his brother had designed and supervised. He also made his first essays at literature, and wrote papers on botany and on the Welsh peasantry.

His letters of this period throw an interesting light not only upon his own thoughts but upon the problems which were occupying the minds of scientific thinkers. He refers to the writings of Lyell, and to Darwin's 'Journal of a Naturalist", Humboldt's "Personal Narrative," "The Vestiges of Creation," and Lawrence's "Lectures on Man." In a letter to Mr. Bates, dated 1847, he writes:

"I begin to feel rather dissatisfied with a mere local collection; little is to be learnt by it. I should like to take one family, to study thoroughly, principally with a view to the theory of the origin of species. By that means I am strongly of opinion that some definite results might be arrived at." Eleven years later he gave to the world those "definite results" of his study in the theory of "Evolution by the Survival of the Fittest."

Bates and Wallace finally decided to go to the tropics to study the birds and insects, and to support themselves by their collections. They, therefore, sailed from Liverpool in April, 1848, in a barque of one hundred and ninety-two tons, and arrived in Para after a voyage of twenty-nine days.

The four-and-a-half years which Wallace spent in South America have been fully described in his "Travels on the Amazon and Rio Negro." In a letter describing his impressions of the tropics he wrote:

"There is one natural feature of this country the interest and grandeur of which may be fully appreciated in a single walk; it is the 'virgin forest.' Here no one who has any feeling of the magnificent and the sublime can be disappointed; the sombre shade scarce illumined by a singe direct ray even of the tropical sun, the enormous size and height of the trees, most of which rise like huge columns a hundred feet or more without throwing out a single branch, the strange buttresses around the base of some, the spiney or furrowed stems of others, the curious and even extraordinary creepers and climbers which wind around them, hanging in long festoons from branch to branch, sometimes curling and twisting on the ground like great serpents, then mounting to the very tops of the trees, thence throwing down roots and fibres which hang waving in the air or, twisting round each other, form ropes and cables of every variety of size and often of the most perfect regularity. These and many other novel features - the parasitic plants growing on the trunks and branches, the wonderful variety of foliage, the strange fruits and seeds that lie rotting on the ground - taken altogether surpass description and produce feelings in the beholder of admiration and awe. It is here, too, that the rarest birds, the most lovely insects and the most interesting mammals and reptiles are to be found. Here lurk the jaguar and the boa-constrictor, and here amidst the densest shade the bell-bird tolls his peal."

He also relates his "unexpected sensation of surprise and delight" when he first met and lived with man in a state of nature - with absolutely uncontaminated savages. The wild Indians of the Uaupés were different from any he had previously met during two years' wanderings.

"They had nothing that we call clothes; they had peculiar ornaments, tribal marks, etc., they all carried weapons or tools of their own manufacture; they were living in a large house, many families together, quite unlike the hut of the tame Indians; but more than all their whole aspect and manner were different - they were all going about their own work of pleasure which had nothing to do with white man or their ways, they walked with the free step of the forest dweller, and except for the few who were known to my companions, paid no attention whatever to us, mere strangers of an alien race. In every detail they were original and self-sustaining, as are the wild animals of the forests, absolutely independent of civilisation, and who could and did live their own lives in their own way as they had done for countless generations before America was discovered. I could not have believed there could be so much difference in the aspect of the same people in their native state and when living under European supervision. The true denizens of the Amazonian forest, like the forest itself, are unique and not to be forgotten."

Amidst such scenes and among such people Wallace spent four-and-a-half years, often undergoing many hardships, exploring regions not before visited by white men; all the time collecting and studying the varied forms of life with which the forest glades and river banks abounded. He journeyed for many thousand miles in canoes on the great rivers, taking observations with sextant and compass of the courses of the Rio Negro and of the Uaupés which formed the basis for the first reliable map of those hitherto little known waterways,

His voyage home from Para in 1852 was both adventurous and disastrous. After having been at sea a week, the ship caught fire, and all hands had to take to the boats. The vessel, with all its cargo – including Wallace's collections, and most of his notes and journals – was completely destroyed, and the crew, with only their clothes and a small quantity of provisions, were tossed about in the middle of the Atlantic in two small boats for ten days. And when at last they were picked up by a passing vessel their danger and troubles were not yet over, for the ship on which they found themselves was very unseaworthy, and they encountered such violent storms that no one expected to reach land. His companions often wished themselves back in their open boats as being safer than the rotten and overloaded vessel they were on. To add to their discomfort the ship was short of provisions, so that they had to endure semi-starvation during the rest of their tedious journey.

After eighty-two days at sea, Wallace at last landed at Deal, with only the clothes he stood in, and a few sketches of palm trees and of fishes which he had saved out of the wreckage of so many hopes and labours. The valuable collection of four years' toil, the immediate results of patiently acquired knowledge, with the notes and journals of the greater part of his wanderings, were irretrievably lost. One can, without much imagination, picture his feelings under such a crushing blow. Luckily, through the foresight of his agent in London, his collections had been insured for a small amount, so that his losses financially were not so complete as he had feared; yet no monetary recompense could ever make up for the loss of the material and the records of his arduous exploration and research.

Soon after his return, with the aid of such scanty notes as he had saved, and the letters which he had sent home, he commenced to write the story of his travels, which was published in 1853. He also published an account of the palm trees of the Amazon, with illustrations from his own sketches.

In 1854 he again left Britain, and, travelling eastwards, arrived in Singapore, where he was to begin his eight years' wanderings amongst the islands of the Malay Archipelago, an account of which is recorded in his most popular work of that name.

It was while staying at Sarawak, in 1855 – where he became intimately acquainted with the celebrated Rajah Brooke – that he wrote his first article on the question of the Origin of Species. At that time, however, he had not grasped the complete solution to the problem. It was not till 1858, when at Ternate, suffering from an attack of fever, that, pondering over the subject, and recollecting Malthus' writings, the *modus operandi* of evolution flashed with creative vividness upon his mind, resulting in the paper which, together with Darwin's contribution, was to startle the scientific and religious worlds, and set ablaze the fires of a controversy which burned for many years, ere the doctrine of 'survival of the fittest' was finally accepted by the world at large.

Wallace sent his paper to Charles Darwin, with whom he had corresponded about the previous article. Darwin, as the result of long and laborious study, had already arrived at the same conclusion, and had even taken his friends Lyell and Hooker into his confidence; but in spite of their advice and their fears that he might be forestalled, he wished to collect still more evidence to support his theory before making it public. On receiving Wallace's paper he wrote to Sir Charles Lyell: "Your words have come true with a vengeance – that I should be forestalled. I never saw a more striking coincidence."

Darwin who had already written a large part of a book dealing with his conclusions, was naturally much troubled as to what he should do. In another letter to Lyell he wrote: "I would far rather burn my whole book than that Wallace or any other man should think that I had behaved in a paltry spirit."

Ultimately, however, as a result of the advice of friends, who acted on their own responsibility, Mr. Wallace's essay and extracts from Darwin's manuscript were sent to the Linnean Society and read together before that Society in July, 1858.

The interest excited by the papers was intense. Many lingered after the meeting and discussed the subject with bated breath; but it was meanwhile too novel and too ominous to provoke that immediate opposition with which it met when its significance and effect were subsequently realised.

Wallace spent another eight adventurous and arduous years amidst scenes of tropical luxuriance and among the various savage and civilised races of mankind which inhabit the Malay Archipelago, before he returned home in 1862.

The collection he had sent home, comprising many thousands of insects, birds, and other forms of life, many of them previously unknown, together with the scientific papers already mentioned, had made him famous, and secured for him on his return not only his admittance to many of the great learned societies, but the acquaintance and friendship of the scientific leaders of the day with whom he was soon to rank in undisputed parity. Amongst those with whom his intimacy deepened most fruitfully were Sir Charles Lyell and Charles Darwin.

With the former, Wallace had a long, amicable, but controversial discussion on the subject of glacial origin of Alpine lakes, which Lyell was not inclined to accept. At Sir Charles's house, where he was a frequent visitor, Wallace met many interesting people, amongst them being Professor Tyndall, Sir Charles Wheatstone, Mr. Lecky, and the Duke of Argyll, with all of whom he became on friendly terms.

With Charles Darwin, Wallace's relations were still more intimate and friendly, and their rivalry in their great discovery rather enhanced their friendship instead of producing that antagonism which, on smaller minds, would have been the result. Darwin frequently asked Wallace's help on points of difficulty in the application of the new theory, and though on several questions they disagreed, they always maintained the warmest admiration for each other.

In a letter to Wallace written in 1870, Darwin says:

"I hope it is a satisfaction to you to reflect - and very few things in my life have been more satisfactory to me - that we have never felt any jealousy towards each other, though in some sense rivals. I believe I can say his of myself with truth, and I am absolutely sure that it is true of you."

In commenting on this letter Dr. Wallace writes:

"To have thus inspired and retained this friendly feeling, notwithstanding our many differences of opinion, I feel to be one of the greatest honours of my life."

The relations existing between Darwin and Wallace, to which we have already referred are further exemplified by the affectionate love and warm admiration expressed in their letters to each other, and to mutual friends.

Referring to the proposal by Lyell and Hooker that Wallace's paper and an abstract of his own MS should be read together before the Linnean Society, Darwin, in his autobiography, writes:

"I was at first very unwilling to consent, as I thought Mr. Wallace might consider my doing so unjustifiable, for I did not then know how generous and noble was his disposition." ("Life and Letters," I. 85.)

While Wallace was still abroad, and before Darwin and he had met, Darwin wrote to Lyell of having received a letter from Wallace, "very just in his remarks, though too laudatory and too modest; and how admirably free from envy and jealousy. He must be a good fellow."

And in replying to Wallace, Darwin says:

"Before telling you about the progress of opinion on the subject (of 'The Origin of Species') you must let me say how I admire the generous manner in which you speak of my book. Most persons would, in your position, have felt some envy or jealousy. How nobly free you seem to be of this common failing of mankind! But you speak far too modestly of yourself. You would, if you had my leisure, have done the work just as well - perhaps better than I have done it." He ends "with sincere thanks for your letter and with most deeply felt wishes for your success in science, and in every way, believe me, your sincere well wisher."

And in writing to H. W. Bates, Darwin said:

"What a fine philosophical mind your friend Mr. Wallace has, and he has acted in relation to me like a true man with a noble spirit."

Mr. Wallace differed from Darwin in believing that something more than Natural Selection was necessary to produce the higher intellectual qualities of man. This was the 'heresy' to which he refers in a note to Darwin relating to an article by the latter, where he says:

"I have also to thank you for the great tenderness with which you have treated me and my heresies ..."; to which Darwin replied,"Your note has given me very great pleasure, chiefly because I was so anxious not to treat you with the least disrespect, and it is so difficult to speak fairly when differing from anyone. If I had offended you it would have grieved me more than you will readily believe." ("Life and Letters," iii. 134.)

When Darwin heard from Mr. Gladstone that a Government pension had been given to Wallace - in which matter Darwin himself had been largely instrumental - he wrote to a friend, "Good heavens! how pleased I am."

This admirable desire to give each other the credit for the theory of Natural Selection is shown again in their letters, and it should be emphasised here.

"You ought not," Darwin wrote, "to speak of the theory as mine; it is just as much yours as mine. One correspondent has already noticed to me your 'high-minded' conduct on this head." ("More Letters," ii. 32.)

And Wallace, in a long letter, replied:

"As to the theory of Natural Selection itself I shall always maintain it to be actually yours, and yours only. You had worked it out in details I had never thought of years before I had a ray of light on the subject ... All the merit I claim is the having been the means of inducing you to write and publish at once."

Again in a letter referring to colouring of mammals and kindred subjects, Darwin wrote:

"I am surprised at my own stupidity, but I have long recognised how much clearer and deeper your insight into matters is than mine." ("More Letters,' ii. 61.) And, when they differed over Sexual Selection, Darwin wrote: "I grieve to differ from you, and it actually terrifies me, and makes me constantly distrust myself. I fear we shall never quite understand each other," ("More Letters," ii. 85.)

Although Darwin and Wallace worked together so long and assiduously to develop and elucidate the theory they had originated, there were several points in its application in which they differed, and as these, though not in any way affecting the main principles of Natural Selection (on which they entirely agreed), have been seized upon and have been magnified by those who objected to the theory, we should dwell a moment upon them.

The principles differences may be stated thus: Darwin thought that Natural Selection alone was sufficient to explain the development of man, in all his aspects, from some lower form. Wallace, while believing that man, as an animal, was so developed, thought that as an intellectual and moral being some other influence - some spiritual influx - was required to account for his special mental and psychic nature. With regard to many cases of colouration, scent, or power of producing sounds, exhibited by males of numerous animals, Darwin thought they were developed by the choice of the females for the males which were endowed by these qualities in the greatest degree, while those which had them in a less degree were not chosen, and so did not so often produce offspring. Wallace, on the other hand, could find little or no evidence for this form of Sexual Selection. He maintained that all such colours, scents, etc., were produced by some operation of Natural Selection; that with the insects a bright colour was often a warning to insect-eating animals that its possessor was distasteful; that the females required more protection and therefore became coloured to harmonise with their surroundings. The males, owing to their habits and oganisation, require less protection, and would therefore be modified no further than was sufficient to ensure the maintenance of the species.

Darwin explained the presence of Arctic plants by assuming that the tropical lowlands of the whole earth were cooled during the glacial epoch, so that these plants could spread to the localities where they are now found isolated. Wallace, from his study of the floras of oceanic islands, concluded that all these plants were introduced by means of aerial transmission of seeds or by birds, those seeds which were deposited in a suitable soil and climate germinating and in turn producing seeds by which the plant would spread over its new habitat.

The only other important matter on which these two great scientists differed was the question of inheritance of acquired characters. Darwin always believed that the effects of use or disuse, of climate, food, etc., on the individual were transmitted to the offspring; and Wallace himself accepted this theory for many years. But later, after Dr. Weismann had shown how little evidence there was for such inheritance, he became convinced that acquired characters were not inherited.

All this shows in a very clear light the unselfish characters and singleness of purpose of two great minds, who set the dissemination of truth and the illumination of intellect above considerations of personal profit or reputation.

Amongst the celebrities with whom Wallace had frequent intercourse were Herbert Spencer, Thomas Huxley, Sir John Lubbock (afterwards Lord Avebury), Dr. W B. Carpenter, Sir William Crookes, Sir Joseph Hooker, Sir Francis Galton, and many others not less famous.

In 1865 he married the eldest daughter of Mr. William Mitten, of Hurstpierpoint, the greatest living authority on mosses; and for five years lived in St. Mark's Crescent, Regent's Park. Becoming, however, tired of town life, and wishing to return to more congenial rural surroundings, he moved to Grays, in Essex, where he built a house close to an old overgrown chalk pit, which formed part of the garden.

During his residence here he wrote an important book, in two large volumes, with elaborate maps and illustrations, dealing with a subject on which he has always been admitted to be the leading authority, viz. "The Geographical Distribution of Animals." It was published in 1876, and still remains the standard work in the English language on that branch of science. From this time onwards he devoted most of his energies to writing - at first on purely scientific subjects, but later on more general topics, and especially on social and political questions, which gradually assumed a leading place in his thought.

Amongst other scientific works which he produced at this period were "Tropical Nature" and "Australasia" in 1878; "Island Life" in 1880. His most popular book, "The Malay Archipelago," was written while he still lived in London in 1869, and gave an account of his travels and adventures in the East.

In 1876 he found it necessary to give up his house at Grays, and after living a few years at Dorkng and at Croydon, he built a cottage at Godalming, where he remained from 1881 till 1889.

In 1881 a society was formed for advocating for Nationalism of the Land, a subject in which he took a deep interest, and he as elected president, retaining that office until the present time. There is no doubt that his early experience while surveying, and his observations of the life and customs of many civilised and savage races, had left upon his mind those impressions which were to be developed into definite principles and beliefs when he devoted close attention to this and kindred subjects, at the time we are dealing with. With the exception of about eight years, he has spent the whole of his long life in the country, and his powers of keen observation have shown him the inconveniences, the hardship and the injustice often suffered by our rural population on account of the existing system of the private ownership of land, with the privileges which have grown up along with it.

In order to justify the formation of this society, and as a kind of programme of the work it had to do, he wrote a brochure entitled "Land Nationalisation: Its Necessity and Its Aims." This formed the starting point of those political writings of his which have caused such mixed feelings amongst his scientific friends, many of whom deplore his views as unscientific and revolutionary, while others are no less unstinted in their praise and satisfaction.

The beginning of his social views he himself traces to Herbert Spencer's "Social Statics," which he read soon after his return home from the Amazon. That part on *The Right to Use the Earth* especially interested him but under the influence of Mill and Spencer himself, he could not see how to work it out without an excess of bureaucracy. It was twenty-seven years later that the idea suddenly came to him that this difficulty "coiuld be overcome by State tenancy of the bare land, with ownership by the tenant of all that was added to the bare land, so that the State as only *ground landlord,* and need not interfere at all with the tenant who held a perpetual lease"(My Life,"ii 34.)

In the book on "Land Nationalisation," he dealt at length with these subjects. But his objection to Socialism remained for about ten years later, because he could not see he way out of existing things and relations into the practical operation of socialistic principals. Bellamy's book gave him the final impact and, he says, "I have been an absolutely convinced Socialist ever since." He was supported in his step by Spencer's teaching that all classes of society were almost equal morally, and intellectually, in combination with Weissman's proof of the non-heredity of results of education, habit, use of organs, etc. Dr. Wallace has briefly defined Socialism as "the organisation of the labour of all for the equal benefit of all." This implies "the duty of everyone to work for the common good, and the *right* of each to share equally in the benefits so produced, and in those which Nature provides."

An address which he gave at Davos in 1896 on the invitation of Dr. Lunn was the starting point of the three last important works which he has written.

The first of these was "The Wonderful Century," which is an account of the marvellous advances in scientific knowledge and in invention which had taken place during the nineteenth century, of most of which he had been an eye-witness. The astronomical chapters of this book suggested the second namely, "Man's Place in the Universe," which appeared in 1903. This latter work gave a most interesting study of the latest theories and facts with regard to the stellar universe and the solar system and our position therein.

This idea was further developed and extended in his last scientific book "The World of Life," which appeared in 1911, its germ being the lecture which he delivered at the Royal Institution, in the previous year. It was the act of collecting the evidence of this work and "Man's Place in the Universe." from all the best scientific sources to which he had access, that forced upon him the wonderful combination of *conditions* necessary for the possible development of life; and then still more marvellous and ever present manifestations of foreseeing, directing and organising forces, resulting in a World of Life culminating in Man, and in every detail adapted for the development of man's highest mental and moral powers.

"Thus," as he himself writes (letter to the present writer), "the completely materialistic mind of my youth and early manhood has been slowly moulded into the socialistic, spiritualistic, and theistic mind I now exhibit - a mind which is, as my scientific friends think, so weak and credulous in its declining years, as to believe that fruits and flowers, domestic animals, glorious birds and insects wool, cotton, sugar and rubber, metals and gums, were all foreseen and fore-ordained for the education and enjoyment of man."

At a later date, in May, 1913, in another letter to the writer, Dr. Russel Wallace writes upon the possibility of a living organism being some day produced in the laboratory of the chemist from inorganic matter. He declares it to be impossible, because unthinkable while even were it supposable that it should happen, it could not in any way explain Life, with all its inherent forces powers and laws, which necessitate "a constantly acting mind power of almost unimaginable grandeur and prescience, in the co-ordinated motions, actions and forms of the myriad atoms and ions, which cannot be supposed to be all acting in harmonious co-ordination without some superior co-ordinating power.

"Recent discoveries demonstrate the need of co-ordinating power even in the very nature and origin of matter; and something far more than this in the origin and development of mind. The whole cumulative argument of my 'World of Life' is that, *in its every detail*, it calls for the agency of a mind or minds so enormously above and beyond any human minds, as to compel us to look upon it, or them, as 'God or Gods,' and so-called 'Laws of Nature'; as the action by will-power or otherwise of such superhumans or infinite beings. 'Law of Nature' apart from the existence and agency of some such Being or Beings, are more words, that explain nothing- are, in fact, unthinkable. That is my position!

"Whether this 'Unknown Reality' is a single Being and acts everywhere in the universe as direct creator, organiser and director of every minutest motion in the whole of *our* universe, and of all possible universes, or whether it acts through variously conditioned modes, as H. Spencer suggested or through 'infinite grade of beings' as I suggest, comes to much the same thing. Mine seems a more clear and intelligible supposition as stated in the last paragraph of my 'World of Life,' and it is the teaching of the Bible of Swedenborg and of Milton!"

But in the very last paragraph of his "World of Life" he put it as "a speculative suggestion," not as a definite scientific conclusion - "though it does seem to me to be one,"

He concludes (in the letter to the writer) with this definite declaration:

"I write all this to show that to *me*, if the chemist does some day show that living, developing 'life' was, and is now produced from inorganic element, by and through 'natural laws,' it would not alter my argument one iota. 'Natural Laws' of such range and power are unthinkable, except as the manifestation of *Universal Mind.*"

"The World of Life" moved the whole thinking world. It awoke as with the whip-crack of a prophet's word the theological sleepers who had been drowsing in dogmatic ease, and that other loud boasting company of the blind, who confidently thought they were wide awake when they denied the possibility of the very existence of a spiritual world and believed that "matter and force" were sufficient for all things, from cosmic dust to the writing of *Hamlet.*

This book was a revelation of the making of humanity, not starting from any basis of dogmatic preconception, but reasoned out by the clear mind of the trained natural observer, who, turning his searchlight upon the footprint of the long-departed revealed, as the skilled hand drew aside the curtain, the picture of the actual world in process of evolution, this, by a master-stroke, involving the exercise of all his power, displaying eternal Providence, and "justifying the ways of God to man." The earliest result of the evolution theory seemed to be that earth was filled, not with the knowledge but with the terrors of God, and the human heart heard, if it could listen to their agonies and groans, of a struggling and suffering humanity punished for its own blindness and ignorance.

With Wallace, however, pain is the birth-cry of a soul's advance. "The stamp of rank in Nature is capacity for pain." Pain, he holds, is always strictly subordinated to the law of utility, and is never developed beyond what is actually needed for the protection and advance of life. This brings the sensitive soul immense relief. Our susceptibility to the higher agonies is a condition of our advance in life's pageant.

In this volume he summed up and completed his fifty years of brooding thought and long and patient labour on behalf of Darwinian theory of evolution, extending the scope and application of that theory so as to show that it can and does explain many of the phenomena of living things hitherto considered to be outside its range.

Thus Dr. Wallace now believes that to explain life and its manifestations God is a necessary postulate. And he here declares:

"The absolute necessity for an organising and directive Life Principle in order to account for the very possibility of these complex out-growths. I argue that they imply first, Creative Power, which so constituted matter as to render these marvels possible; next a Directive Mind, which is demanded at every step of what we term growth, and often looked upon as so simple and natural a process as to require no explanation; existence of the whole vast life-world in all its long course of evolution through the aeons of geological time. This Purpose, which alone throws light on many of the mysteries of its modes of evolution, I hold to be the Development of Man, the one crowning product of the whole cosmic process of life-development; the only being which can to some extent comprehend Nature; which can perceive and trace out her modes of action; which can appreciate the hidden forces and motions everywhere at work, and can deduce from them a supreme over-ruling Mind as their necessary Cause."

The result of his investigation into spiritualistic manifestations led him to believe in the genuineness of their spiritual origin and he embodied them in his book "miracles and Modern Spiritualism." If his political works produced feelings of regret amongst many of his scientific friends, his advocacy of spiritualism caused them (as Tyndall said) 'feelings of deep-disappointment." He was not, however, without able supporters in his 'heresy,' amongst them being Sir W. Crookes, Sir William Barnett, Lord Lindsay, Robert Chambers, and others.

Through his spiritualistic experiments – of the actuality of which he was entirely convinced – he deduced a system of spiritual media, an angelology whereby the vast Divine Mind operates upon and communicates with "every cell of every living thing that is, or ever has been, upon the earth ... through many descending grades of intelligence and power." He makes therefore his own, that which is, in effect, a summary of his teaching:-

"All nature is but art, unknown to thee,

All chance, direction which thou canst not see;

All discord, harmony not understood;

All partial evil universal good."

And therein he stands to-day the Grand Old Man of British Science, a true Revealer and Prophet in the real sense of being a forthteller of the truth spoken to him.

Dr. Wallace has written many articles and smaller books on diverse subjects, the latest which has aroused deep and widespread interest being his 'Social Environment and Moral

Progress" which was written in his ninety-first year. In it he shows that there is no evidence of any advancement of man's intellectual or ethical manifestation during the whole historical period, and he states his belief that no real improvement is possible until we reorganise society on a rational system of mutual help, instead of our present system of mutual antagonism and degrading competition.

As has been well said - in a review of this work:-

"The author's position as co-discoverer with Darwin of one of the most momentous theories in the history of thought, his venerable age, his wide scientific knowledge and deep philosophic insight, lend to his utterances an authority such as could be claimed by no living writer."

His indictment of the present school environment as the worst in history constitutes a challenge to civilisation, and demands the closest scrutiny of the most impartial minds He shows that it is well established that the essential character of man - intellectual, emotional and mental - is inherent in him from birth; that it is subject to great variation from individual to individual, and that its manifestations in conduct can be modified in a very high degree by the influence of public opinion and by education These latter changes, however, are *not* hereditary, and it follows that no definite advance in morals can occur in any race *unless there is some selection or segregation agency at work*. He declares that history shows that the increase of wealth and luxury has been distributed with gross injustice, no provision having been made for the overflow of those being utilised for the greater happiness and comfort of the producers, or the improvement of the conditions of the struggling millions.

He finds the "selective agency" which is to work for the amelioration which he desires in sexual selection, which will be the prerogative of the woman; and therefore woman's position in the not distant future "will be far higher and more important than any which has been claimed for or by her in the past." When political and social rights are conceded to her on equality with men, her free choice in marriage no longer influenced by economic and social considerations, will guide the future moral progress of the race, restore the lost equality of opportunity to every child born in our country, and secure the balance between the sexes. "It will be their (women's) special duty so to mould public opinion through home training and social influence, as to render the women of the future the regenerators of the entire human race."

But before this can effectively operate much has to be faced, and Dr. Wallace summarises the matter into one general conclusion, namely, that a civilised government must, as its prime duty, "organise the labour of the whole community for the equal good of all," but it is also bound immediately to take steps to "abolish *death by starvation and by preventable disease* due to insanitary dwellings and dangerous employments, while carefully elaborating the *permanent* remedy for want in the midst of wealth." The laws of evolution are all in favour of such a revolution, but the present system of competition must become one of brotherly co-operation and co-ordination for the equal good of all. Apart from this there is no hope for advance towards true, living freedom, and this present volume on "The Revolt of Democracy" emphasises and illustrates this tremendous indictment.

And now we must bring to a close this very imperfect sketch, in the writing of which we have received great assistance, which we gratefully knowledge, from Dr. Wallace himself, his son, Mr. W. G. Wallace, and a generous friend who desires to remain unknown.

In 1889 Dr. Wallace removed to Parkstone Dorset, where he resided till 1902, when he again built himself a house - this time at Broadstone overlooking Poole Harbour and the

350

Purbeck Hills. Here he lived until his death on November 7, 1913, finding real interest and delight in his greenhouse and garden, which were always such a pleasurable source of recreation in his time of leisure.

He was always an omnivorous reader, and his mind was stored with facts in relation to a very wide range of knowledge, while he was seldom without a novel by his side for his hours of relaxation.

Dr. Wallace's optimism was one of his more striking traits, and he looked back upon whatever misfortunes and hardships had fallen to his lot as blessings in disguise, which strengthened his character and stimulated him to fresh endeavour.

At the memorable meeting of the British Association at Oxford, in 1894, Lord Salisbury, recalling the historic reception of the Darwinian hypothesis in the same place half a century previously, and in paying a just tribute to Charles Darwin, said that "The equity of his judgment, the single-minded love of truth, and patient devotion to the pursuit of it through years of toil and other conditions the most unpropitious – these things endeared to numbers of men everything that came from Charles Darwin, apart from his scientific merit and literary charm and whatever final value may be assigned to his doctrine, nothing can ever detract from the lustre shed upon it by the wealth of his knowledge and the infinite ingenuity of his resource."

This tribute might be, with equal justice, applied to Wallace. In his charming modesty, his unselfishness, his instinct for truth – which, said Darwin to Henslow, "was something of the same nature as the instinct for virtue" – in his constant and singularly patient consideration of every opinion which differed from his own, and in his inventive imagination, Wallace was the worthy companion of Darwin.

But, as we have seen, he had other claims to be

remembered by posterity. He was also a fearless social reformer who vigorously laid the axe to the root of great evils which flourish in our midst some of which present-day society cherishes. He struck what he believed to be hard blow at vaccination - still an almost heaven-sent weapon against smallpox in the armoury of many doctors; and he dared boldly to accept a spiritualistic interpretation of Nature which is still treated as charlatanism.

He was not the recluse calmly spinning theories from a bewildering chaos of observations, and building up isolated facts into the unity of a great and illuminating conception in the silence and solitude of his library, unmindful of the great world of sin and sorrow without. He could say with Darwin "I was born a naturalist" but we can also add, his heart was on fire with love of discovering a vast and splendid generalisation, which not only worked a complete revolution in biological science, but also illuminated the vast field of human knowledge. Yet his greatest ambition was to improve the cruel conditions under which thousands of his fellow-creatures suffer and die, and to make their lives sweeter and happier. His mind was great enough to encompass all that lies between the visible horizons of human thought and activity, and in his old age he lived upon the topmost peaks eagerly looking for the horizon beyond In the words of the late Mr. Gladstone's own precept, "He has been inspired with the belief that life is a great and noble calling not a mean and grovelling thing that we are to shuffle through as we can, but an advanced and lofty destiny"

John Marchant

Appendix II
LISTS OF WALLACE'S WRITINGS

Alfred Russel Wallace; Letters and Reminiscences (Vol. 2)

I.—BOOKS

Date	Title
1853	"Palm Trees on the Amazon"
1853	"A Narrative of Travels on the Amazon and Rio Negro." New Edition in "The Minerva Library," 1889
1866	"The Scientific Aspect of the Supernatural"
1869	"The Malay Archipelago," 2 vols. Tenth Edition, 1 vol., 1890
1870	"Contributions to the Theory of Natural Selection." Republished, with "Tropical Nature," 1891
1874	"Miracles and Modern Spiritualism." Revised Edition, 1896
1876	"The Geographical Distribution of Animals," 2 vols.
1878	"Tropical Nature and other Essays." Printed in 1 vol. with "Natural Selection," 1891
1879	"Australasia." "Stanford's Compendium of Geography and Travel." (New issue, 1893)
1880	"Island Life." Revised Edition, 1895
1882	"Land Nationalisation"
1885	"Bad Times"
1889	"Darwinism." 3rd Edition, 1901
1898	"The Wonderful Century." New Edition, 1903
1900	"Studies, Scientific and Social"
1901	"The Wonderful Century Reader"
1901	"Vaccination a Delusion"
1903	"Man's Place in the Universe." New Edition, 1904. Cheap 1s. Edition, 1912
1905	"My Life," 2 vols. New Edition, 1 vol., 1908
1907	"Is Mars Habitable?"
1908	"Notes of a Botanist on the Amazon and Andes," by Richard Spruce. Edited by A.R. Wallace
1910	"The World of Life"
1913	"Social Environment and Moral Progress"
1913	"The Revolt of Democracy"

II.—ARTICLES, PAPERS, REVIEWS, ETC.

The articles marked with an asterisk were republished in Wallace's "Studies, Scientific and Social."

	DATE	PERIODICAL OR SOCIETY	SUBJECT
	1850	Proc. Zool. Soc., Lond.	On the Umbrella Bird
	1852	" "	Monkeys of the Amazon
	1852-3	Trans. Entomol. Soc.	On the Habits of the Butterflies of the Amazon Valley
	1853	Zoologist	On the Habits of the Hesperidæ
	1853	Proc. Zool. Soc., Lond.	On some Fishes allied to Gymnotus
June 6	1853	Entomolog. Soc.	On the Insects used for Food by the Indians of the Amazon
June 13	1853	Royal Geograph. Soc.	The Rio Negro
	1854-5	Zoologist	Letters from Singapore and Borneo
	1854-6	Trans. Entomol. Soc.	Description of a New Species of Ornithoptera
	1855	Annals and Mag. of Nat. Hist.	On the Ornithology of Malacca
	1855	Journ. Bot.	Botany of Malacca
	1855	Zoologist	The Entomology of Malacca
Sept.	1855	Annals and Mag. of Nat. Hist.	On the Law which has regulated the Introduction of New Species
	1856	" "	Some Account of an Infant Orang-Outang
	1856	" "	On the Orang-Outang or Mias of Borneo
Dec.	1856	" "	On the Habits of the Orang-Outang of Borneo
	1856	" "	Attempts at a Natural Arrangement of Birds
Nov. 22	1856	Chambers's Journ.	A New Kind of Baby
	1856	Journ. Bot.	On the Bamboo and Durian of Borneo
	1856	Zoologist	Observations on the Zoology of Borneo
	1856-8	Trans. Entomol. Soc.	On the Habits, etc., of a Species of Ornithoptera inhabiting the Aru Islands
	1856-9	" "	Letters from Aru Islands and from Batchian
Dec.	1857	Annals and Mag. of Nat. Hist.	Natural History of the Aru Islands
	1857	" "	On the Great Bird of Paradise

	1857	Proc. Geograph. Soc.	Notes of a Journey up the Sadong River
	1858	" "	On the Aru Islands
	1858	Zoologist " "	Note on the Theory of Permanent and Geographical Varieties
	1858	" "	On the Entomology of the Aru Islands
	1858-61	Trans. Entomol. Soc.	Note on the Sexual Differences in the Genus Lomaptera
	1859	Annals and Mag. of Nat. Hist.	Correction of an Important Error affecting the Classification of the _Psittacidæ_
	1859	Proc, Linn. Soc. (iii. 45)	On the Tendency of Varieties to Depart Indefinitely from the Original Type73
Oct.	1859	Ibis	Geographical Distribution of Birds
Dec.	1859	Entomolog. Soc.	Note on the Habits of Scolytidæ and Bostrichidæ
	1860	Journ. Geograph. Soc.	Notes of a Voyage to New Guinea
	1860	Ibis	The Ornithology of North Celebes
	1860	Proc. Zool, Soc., Lond.	Notes on Semioptera wallacii
	1860	Proc. Linn. Soc. (iv. 172)	Zoological Geography of Malay Archipelago
	1861	Ibis	On the Ornithology of Ceram and Waigiou
	1861	"	Notes on the Ornithology of Timor
	1862	Proc. and Journ. Geogr. Soc.	On the Trade between the Eastern Archipelago and New Guinea and its Islands
	1862	Proc. Zool. Soc., Lond.	List of Birds from the Sula Islands
	1862	Ibis	On some New Birds from the Northern Moluccas
	1862	Proc. Zool. Soc., Lond.	Narrative of Search after Birds of Paradise
	1862	"	On some New and Rare Birds from New Guinea
	1862	"	Description of Three New Species of _Pitta_ from the Moluccas
	1863	Annals and Mag. of Nat. Hist.	On the Proposed Change in Name of _Gracula pectoralis_
	1863	Entomol. Journ.	Notes on the Genus _Iphias_
	1863	Ibis	Note on _Corvus senex _and _Corvus fuscicapillus_

	1863	"	Notes on the Fruit-Pigeons of Genus _Treron_
	1863	Intellectual Observer	The Bucerotidæ, or Hornbills
	1863	Proc. Zool. Soc. Lond.	List of Birds collected on Island of Bouru
April	1863	Zoologist	Who are the Humming-Bird's Relations?
June	1863	Royal Geograph. Soc.	Physical Geography of the Malay Archipelago
	1863	Proc, Zool. Soc., Lond.	On the Identification of _Hirundo esculenta_, Linn.
	1863	"	List of Birds inhabiting the Islands of Timor, Flores and Lombok
	1863	Annals and Mag. of Nat. Hist.	On the Rev. S. Haughton's Paper on the Bee's Cell and the Origin of Species
Jan. 1		Nat. Hist. Rev.	Some Anomalies in Zoological and Botanical Geography
Jan. 7	1864	Edinburgh New Journ. (Philos.)	Ditto
	1864	Proc. Zool. Soc., Lond.	Parrots of the Malayan Region
	1864	Anthropol. Soc. Journ.	The Origin of Human Races and the Antiquity of Man deduced from Natural Selection
	1864	Proc. Entom. Soc. and Zoologist	Effect of Locality in producing Change of Form in Insects
	1864	Proc. Entom. Soc.	Views on Polymorphism
	1864	Ibis	Remarks on the Value of Osteological Characters in the Classification of Birds
	1864	"	Remarks on the Habits, Distribution, etc., of the Genus _Pitta_
	1864	"	Note on _Astur griseiceps_
	1864	Nat. Hist. Rev.	Bone Caves in Borneo
	1865	Proc. Zool. Soc., Lond.	List of the Land Shells collected by Mr. Wallace in the Malay Archipelago
Jan.	1865	Trans. Ethnolog. Soc.	On the Progress of Civilisation in North Celebes
Jan.	1865	"	On the Varieties of Man in the Malay Archipelago
	1865	Proc. Zool. Soc., Lond.	Descriptions of New Birds from the Malay Archipelago

June 17	1865	Reader	How to Civilise Savages*
Oct.	1865	Ibis	Pigeons of the Malay Archipelago
	1866	Trans. Linn. Soc. (xxv.) (Abstract in Reader, April, 1864)	On the Phenomena of Variation and Geographical Distribution as illustrated by Papilionidæ of the Malayan Region
	1866	Proc. Zoo. Soc., Lond.	List of Lepidoptera collected by Swinton at Takow, Formosa
	1866	Proc. Entomol. } Soc. }	Exposition of the Theory of Mimicry as explaining Anomalies
	1867	Zoologist }	of Sexual Variation
	1867	Intellectual Observer	The Philosophy of Birds' Nests
Jan.	1867	Quarterly Journ. of Sci.	Ice-Marks in North Wales
April	1867	"	The Polynesians and their Migrations*
July	1867	Westminster Rev.	Mimicry and other Protective Resemblances among Animals
Sept.	1867	Science Gossip	Disguises of Insects
Oct.	1867	Quarterly Journ. of Sci.	Creation by Law
	1867	Proc. Entomol. } Soc. }	A Catalogue of the Cetoniidæ of
	1868	Trans. Entomol. } Soc. }	the Malayan Archipelago, etc.
Jan. 7	1868	Ibis	Raptorial Birds of the Malay Archipelago
	1868	Trans. Entomol. Soc.	On the Pieridæ of the Indian and Australian Regions
	1868	--	The Limits of Natural Selection applied to Man*
	1869	Trans. Entomol. Soc.	Note on the Localities given in the "Longicornia Malayana"
	1869	Journ. of Travel and Nat. Hist.	A Theory of Birds' Nests
April	1869	Quarterly Rev.	Reviews of Lyell's "Principles of Geology" (entitled "Geological Climates and Origin of Species")
	1869	Macmillan's Mag.	Museums for the People*
	1869	Trans. Entomol. Soc.	Notes on Eastern Butterflies (3 Parts)
	1870	Brit. Association Report	On a Diagram of the Earth's Eccentricity, etc.

March	1871	Academny	Review of Darwin's "Descent of Man"
May 23	1871	Entomolog. Soc.	Address on Insular Faunas, etc.
	1871	"	The Beetles of Madeira and their Teachings*
Nov.	1871	--	Reply to Mr. Hampden's Charges
	1873	Journ. Linnean Soc.	Introduction to F. Smith's Catalogue of Aculeate Hymenoptera, etc.
Jan. 4	1873	Times	Spiritualism and Science
April	1873	Macmillan's Mag.	Disestablishment and Disendowment, with a Proposal for a really National Church of England*
Sept. 16	1873	Daily News	Coal a National Trust*
Dec.	1873	Contemp. Rev.	Limitation of State Functions in the Administration of Justice*
Jan. 17	1874	Academy	Reviews of Mivart's "Man and Apes" and A.J. Mott's "Origin of Savage Life"
April	1874	--	Review of W. Marshall's "Phrenologist amongst the Todas"
April	1874	--	Review of G. St. Clair's "Darwinism and Design"
	1874	Ibis	On the Arrangement of the Families constituting the Order Passeres
May	1876	Academy	Review of Mivart's "Lessons from Nature"
	1877	Proc. Geograph. Soc.	The Comparative Antiquity of Continents
July	1877	Quarterly Journ. of Sci.	Review of Carpenter's "Mesmerism and Spiritualism," etc.
Sept. and Oct.	1877	Macmillan's Mag.	The Colours of Animals and Plants
Nov.	1877	Fraser's Mag.	The Curiosities of Credulity
Dec.	1877	Fortnightly Rev.	Humming-Birds
Dec.	1877}	Athenæum	{Correspondence with W.B.
Jan.	1878}	"	{ Carpenter on Spiritualism
Nov.	1878	Fortnightly Rev.	Epping Forest, and How to Deal with it
Feb.	1879	Contemp. Rev.	New Guinea and its Inhabitants

April	1879	Academy	Review of Haeckel's "Evolution of Man"
July	1879	Nineteenth Cent.	Reciprocity: A Few Words in Reply to Mr. Lowe*
July	1879	Quarterly Rev.	Glacial Epochs and Warm Polar Climates
Jan.	1880	Nineteenth Cent.	The Origin of Species and Genera*
Oct.	1880	Academy	Review of A.H. Swinton's "Insect Variety"
Nov.	1880	Contemp. Rev.	How to Nationalise the Land*
Dec. 4	1880	Academy	Review of Seebohm's "Siberia In Europe"
	1881	Rugby Nat. Hist. Soc. Rept.	Abstract of Four Lectures on the Natural History of Islands
Dec.	1881	Contemp. Rev.	Monkeys: Their Affinities and Distribution*
Aug. and Sept.	1883	Macmillan's Mag.	The Why and How of Land Nationalisation*
March	1884	Christn. Socialist	The Morality of Interest–The Tyranny of Capital
	1886	Claims of Labour Lectures	The Depression of Trade*
Mar. 5	1887	Banner of Light	Letter "_In re_ Mrs. Ross (Washington, D.C.)"
Mar. 17	1887	Independ. Rev.	Review of E.D. Cope's "Origin of the Fittest"
	1887	Nation "	
Oct.	1887	Fortnightly Rev.	American Museums*
	1888	– –	The Action of Natural Selection in producing Old Age, Decay and Death
June	1889	Land Nationalisation Soc.	Address
Sept.	1890	Fortnightly Rev.	Progress without Poverty (Human Selection)*
Oct.	1891	"	English and American Flowers*
Dec.	1891	"	Flowers and Forests of the Far West*
Jan.	1892	Arena	Human Progress, Past and Future*
	1892	Address to L.N.S.	Herbert Spencer on the Land Question*
Aug.	1892	Nineteenth Cent.	Why I Voted for Mr. Gladstone

Aug. and Dec.	1892	Natural Sci.	The Permanence of Great Ocean Basins*
Nov.	1892	Fortnightly Rev.	Our Molten Globe*
Dec.	1892	Natural Sci.	Note on Sexual Selection
Feb.	1893	Nineteenth Cent.	Inaccessible Valleys*
Mar. and Apr.	1893	Arena	The Social Quagmire and the Way Out of it*
Apr. and May	1893	Fortnightly Rev.	Are Individually Acquired Characters Inherited?*
Nov.	1893	"	The Ice Age and its Work*
Dec.	1893	"	Erratic Blocks, etc. Lake Basins*
	1893	Arena	The Bacon-Shakespeare Case
April 9	1894	Land Nationalisation Soc.	Address on Parish Councils
June	1894	Natural Sci.	The Palearctic and Nearctic Regions compared as regards Families and Genera of Mammalia and Birds
June	1894	Contemp. Rev.	How to Preserve the House of Lords*
July	1894	Land and Labour	Review of F.W. Hayes' "Great Revolution of 1905"
Sept.	1894	Natural Sci.	The Rev. G. Henslow on Natural Selection*
	1894	Smithsonian Rep.	Method of Organic Evolution
Oct.	1894	Nineteenth Cent.	A Counsel of Perfection for Sabbatarians*
	1894	Vox Clamantium	Economic and Social Justice*
Feb. and March	1895	Fortnightly Rev.	Method of Organic Evolution*
Oct.	1895	"	Expressiveness of Speech or Mouth-Gesture as a Factor in the Origin of Language*
	1895	Agnostic Annual	Why Live a Moral Life?*
May	1896	Contemp. Rev.	How Best to Model the Earth*
July 25	1896	Labour Leader	Letter on International Labour Congress
Aug.	1896	Fortnightly Rev.	The Gorge of the Aar and its Teaching*
Dec.	1896	Journ. Linn. Soc. (v. 25)	The Problem of Utility: Are Specific Characters always or generally Useful?
March	1897	Natural Sci.	Problem of Instinct*
	1897	"Forecasts of Coming Century"	Re-occupation of Land, Solution of the Unemployed Problem*

March 20	1898	Lancet	Letter on Vaccination
May 9	1898	Shrewsbury Chron.	Letter to Dr. Bond and A.K.W. on Vaccination
June 16, 21, 25, Aug. 15	1898	Echo	"
Sept. 1	1898	The Eagle and the Serpent	Darwinism and Nietzscheism in Sociology
	1898	Printed for private circulation	Justice not Charity (Address to International Congress of Spiritualists, London, June, 1898)*
Dec. 31	1898	Academy	Paper Money as a Standard of Value*
Feb., March, April	1899	Journ. Soc. Psychical Res.	Letters on Mr. Podmore _re_ Clairvoyance, etc.
May	1899	L' Humanité Nouvelle	The Causes of War and the Remedies*
Nov. 18	1899	Clarion	Letter on the Transvaal War
	1899	N.Y. Independent	White Men in the Tropics*
	1900	N.Y. Sun	Evolution
Nov.	1900	N.Y. Journ.	Social Evolution in the Twentieth Century: An Anticipation
	1900	--	Ralahine and its Teachings*
		--	True Individualism the Essential Preliminary of a Real Social Advance*
	1901	Morning Leader	An Appreciation of the Past Century
Jan. 17	1903	Black and White	Relations with Darwin
March	1903	Fortnightly Rev.	Man's Place in the Universe
Sept.	1903	"	Man's Place in the Universe. Reply to Critics
Oct.	1903	Academy	The Wonderful Century. Reply to Dr. Saleeby
Nov. 12	1903	Daily Mail	Does Man Exist in Other Worlds? Reply to Critics
Jan. 1	1904	Clarion	Anticipations for the Immediate Future, Written for the _Berliner Lokalanzeiger_, and refused

Feb., April	1904	Fortnightly Rev.	An Unpublished Poem by E.A. Poe, "Leonainie"
Apr., May	1904	Independent Rev.	Birds of Paradise in the Arabian Nights
	1904	Anti-Vaccination League	Summary of the Proofs that Vaccination does not Prevent Small-pox, but really Increases it
	1904	Labour Annual	Inefficiency of Strikes
	1904	Clarion	Letter on Opposition to Military Expenditure
		Vaccination Inquirer	Letter on Inconsistency of the Government on Vaccination
Oct. 27	1906	Daily News	Why Not British Guiana? Five Acres for 2s. 6d.
Nov.	1906	Independent Rev.	The Native Problem in South Africa and Elsewhere
Jan.	1907	Fortnightly Rev.	Personal Suffrage, a Rational System of Representation and Election
Feb.	1907	"	A New House of Lords
	1907	Harmsworth's "History of the World"	How Life became Possible on the Earth
Sept. 13	1907	Public Opinion	Letter on Sir W. Ramsay's Theory: Did Man reach his Highest Development in the Past?
Jan. 1	1908	N.Y. World	Cable on Advance in Science in 1907
Jan. 18	1908	Outlook	Letter on Woman
Jan.	1908	Fortnightly Rev.	Evolution and Character
June and July	1908	Socialist Rev.	The Remedy for Unemployment
July	1908	Times	Letter on the First Paper on Natural Selection
July	1908	Delineator	Are the Dead Alive?
Aug. 14	1908	Public Opinion	Is it Peace or War? A Reply
Aug.	1908	Contemp. Rev.	Present Position of Darwinism
Sept.	1908	New Age	Letter on Nationalisation, not Purchase, of Railways
Dec.	1908	Contemp. Rev.	Darwinism _v._ Wallaceism
Christ-mas	1908	Christian Commonwealth	On the Abolition of Want
Jan. 22	1909	Royal Institution	The World of Life, as Visualised, etc., by Darwinism

Feb.	1909	Clarion pamphlet (? Socialist Rev.)	The Remedy for Unemployment
Feb. 6	1909	Daily News	Flying Machines in War
Feb. 12	1909	Daily Mail	Charles Darwin (Centenary)
Feb. 12	1909	Clarion	The Centenary of Darwin
March	1909	Fortnightly Rev.	The World of Life (revised Lecture)
April 8	1909	Daily News	Letter on Aerial Fleets
April 8	1910	"	Man in the Universe
Oct. 14	1910	Public Opinion	A New Era in Public Opinion
Jan. 25	1912	Daily Chronicle	Letter on the Insurance Act
Aug. 9	1912	Daily News	A Policy of Defence
Sept.	1912	--	The Nature and Origin of Life

III.—LETTERS, REVIEWS, ETC., IN "NATURE"

VOL.	PAGE	DATE	SUBJECT
I.	105	1869	Origin of Species Controversy
"	132	"	" " "
"	288, 315	1870	Government Aid to Science
"	399, 452	"	Measurement of Geological Time
"	501	"	Hereditary Genius
II.	82	"	Pettigrew's "Handy Book of Bees"
"	234	"	A Twelve-wired Bird of Paradise
"	350	"	Early History of Mankind
"	465	"	Speech on the Arrangement of Specimens in a Natural History Museum (British Association)
"	510	"	Glaciation of Brazil
III.	8, 49	"	Man and Natural Selection
"	85, 107	"	" " "
"	165	"	Mimicry versus Hybridity
"	182	1871	Leroy's "Intelligence and Perfectibility of Animals"
"	309	"	Theory of Glacial Motion
"	329	"	Duncan's "Metamorphoses of Insects"
"	385	"	Dr. Bevan's "Honey Bee"
"	435	"	Anniversary Address at the Entomological Society
"	466	"	Sharpe's Monograph of the Alcedinidæ
IV.	22	"	Staveley's "British Insects"
"	178	"	Dr. Bastian's Work on the Origin of Life
"	181	"	H. Howorth's Views on Darwinism
"	221	"	" " "

References

Breummer, F.E. (1993) *Arctic Memories.* Toronto: Key Porter Books

Chambers, R. (1844) *Vestiges of the Natural History of Creation.* Chicago: University of Chicago Press

Cuvier, G. (1798/1817) *Essay on the Theory of the Earth.* (3rd edn.) New York: Arno Press

Lamarck, J. B. (1809) *Zoological Philosophy.* New York: Hafner Publishing Co.

Lyell, C. (1830-1833) *Principles of Geology.* (Vols. 1-3) London: Penguin

Malthus, T. (1816) *An Essay on the Principle of Population.* London: Ward, Loch & Co.

Paley, W. (1785/1833) *The Works of William Paley.* Edinburgh: Peter Brown & Thomas Nelson

Roth, J. L. (1899) *The Aborigines of Tasmania.* Halifax: F. King & Sons

Wallace, A. R. (1866) *The Scientific Aspect of the Supernatural: Indicating the Desirableness of an Experimental Enquiry by Men of Science into the Alleged Powers of Clairvoyants and Mediums.* No publication details given. Reproduction: Red Books Ltd.

Wallace, A. R. (1869) *The Malay Archipelago.* No publication details given. Re-issued: London: Penguin Classics

Wallace, A. R. (1889) *Vaccination.* London: E. W. Allen. Reproduction: hanse

Wallace, A. R. (1895) *Island Life.* London: ? Reproduction: The Perfect Library

Wallace, A. R. (1896) *Miracles and Modern Spiritualism.* London: George Redway

Wallace, A. R. (1898) *The Wonderful Century.* Toronto: George N. Morang. Reproduction: Forgotten Books

Wallace, A. R. (1900) *Studies Scientific & Social (2 vols.)* London: Macmillan & Co. Reproduction: Nabu Public Domain Reprints

Wallace, A. R. (1905) *Man's Place in the Universe: A Study of the Results of Scientific Research in Relation to the Unity Or Plurality of Wolds.* No publication details given. Reproduction: Scholar Select

Wallace, A. R. (1905) *My Life: A Record of Events and Opinions.* (2 vols.) London: Chapman & Hall. Download.

Wallace, A. R. (1906) *Land Nationalisation: Its Necessity and Its Aims.* London: Swan Sonnenschein & Co. Reproduction: Trieste

Wallace, A. R. (1907) *Is Mars Habitable? A Critical Examination of Professor Percival Lowell's book "Mars and Its Canals" with an Alternative Explanation.* London: Macmillan & Co. Reproduction: Bibliobazar

Wallace, A. R. (1913) *The Revolt of Democracy.* London: Cassel & Co. Reproduction: Scholar Select

Wallace, A. R. (1914) *Social Environment and Moral Progress.* London: Cassel & Co. Facsimile Reproduction: Scholar Select

Wallace, A. R. (1914) *The World of Life: A Manifestation of Creative Power, Directive Mind and Ultimate Purpose.* London: Chapman and Hall. Facsimile Reproduction: Scholar Select

Wallace, A. R. (1916). *Alfred Russel Wallace: Letters and Reminiscences* (Vol. 1). Read Books Ltd.

Wallace, A. R., & Marchant, J. (1916). *Alfred Russel Wallace; Letters and Reminiscences* (Vol. 2). Harper.

About the Author

Denise Carrington-Smith was born in 1937. She spent her childhood in London, migrating to Australia with her young family in 1967.

Having trained in yoga, which she taught for some years, Denise qualified as a Natural Therapist, specializing in homoeopathy. She lectured in herbalism, Bach Flower Remedies and homoeopathy before establishing the Victorian College of Classical Homoeopathy, of which she was Principal for a number of years. She also served as both State and Federal President of the Australian Federation of Homoeopaths.

Recognizing the need for profressional training in counselling, Denise qualified as a psychologist and also a hypnotherapist.

Denise retired to Far North Queensland at the end of 1995, returning to University, where she took up the study of archaeology, receiving her doctorate in 2013. Denise has seven children, eighteen grandchildren and a smattering of great-grandchildren.